LAW
for
PROFESSIONAL ENGINEERS
Second Edition

D. L. Marston, B.Sc., P.Eng., LL.B.

of Osler, Hoskin & Harcourt
Barristers & Solicitors
Toronto
and
Special Lecturer in Engineering Law
Faculty of Applied Science and Engineering
University of Toronto

McGraw-Hill Ryerson Limited

Toronto   Montreal   New York   Auckland   Bogotá
Cairo   Guatemala   Hamburg   Johannesburg   Lisbon
London   Madrid   Mexico   New Delhi   Panama   Paris
San Juan   São Paulo   Singapore   Sydney   Tokyo

LAW
for
PROFESSIONAL
ENGINEERS
Second Edition

ISBN: 0-07-548840-X

2 3 4 5 6 7 8 9 0   D   4 3 2 1 0 9 8 7 6

Printed and bound in Canada

Care has been taken to trace ownership of copyright material contained in this text. The publishers will gladly take any information that will enable them to rectify any reference or credit in subsequent editions.

Canadian Cataloguing in Publication Data

Marston, D. L. (Donald L.), date
    Law for professional engineers

Includes index.

ISBN 0-07-548840-X.

1. Engineering law — Canada. 2. Engineers — Legal status, laws, etc. — Canada. I. Title.

KE2730.M37 1985   349.71'02462   C85-098231-6

TABLE
OF
CONTENTS

Preface ix
Table of Cases xi

1 THE CANADIAN LEGAL SYSTEM 1
Historical Basis 1
The Theory of Precedent 2
The Common Law 2
Legislation 2
Federal and Provincial Powers 3
The Federal and Provincial Court Systems 7
Public and Private Law 8
The Law of Quebec 8
Basic Terminology 9

2 BUSINESS ORGANIZATIONS 11
Basic Forms 11
The Independence of the Corporate Entity 11
Duration of Partnerships and Corporations 14
Effect of Personal Guarantees 14
Basic Tax Considerations 15
Summation of Exceptions to Salomon Principle 16
The Engineering Corporation 16
The Partnership Agreement 17
Limiting Partnership Liability 17
Registration of Partnerships 18
Incorporation 19
Objects 20
"Private" and "Public" Corporations 20
Shareholders, Directors and Officers 21
Shareholders' Agreements 21
The Director's Standard of Care 22
Disclosure of Conflicts 25
The Joint Venture 25

3 TORT LIABILITY 27

Principles of Tort Law 28
The Engineer's Standard of Care 28
Development of Tort Law 30
Strict Liability 36
Vicarious Liability 37
Concurrent Tortfeasors 39
Products Liability 40
Standard of Care and Duty to Warn 41
Economic Loss 45
Limitation Periods 48
Other Relevant Torts 53

4 PROOF 57
The Burden of Proof 57
Engineers as Expert Witnesses 57

5 CONTRACTS 59
Assignment of Rights 60

6 OFFER AND ACCEPTANCE 61
Irrevocable Offers 61
The Option Contract 62
Manner of Communication 63
   (a) Timing 63
      Accepting an Offer
      Revoking an Offer
   (b) Governing Law 63
The Battle of the Forms 64

7 INTENT 67
Mutual Intent 67
Letters of Intent 67

8 CONSIDERATION 69
Equitable Estoppel 70

9 CAPACITY 75
Minors 75
Drunks and Lunatics 75
Corporations 76

10 LEGALITY 77
Contrary to Statute Law 77
Contrary to Common Law 79

11 THE STATUTE OF FRAUDS 81
Deprivation of Statute 82
Unenforceable Contracts Not Void 83
Desirability of Written Form 83

iv

12 MISREPRESENTATION, DURESS, AND UNDUE INFLUENCE 85
Misrepresentation 85
Misrepresentations in Engineering Specifications 86
Duress 87
Undue Influence 87

13 MISTAKE 89
Rectification 89
Unilateral Mistake 89

14 CONTRACT INTERPRETATION 97
Parol Evidence Rule 97
Implied Terms 98

15 DISCHARGE OF CONTRACTS 101
Performance as a Means of Discharge 101
Agreement to Discharge 101
Discharge Pursuant to Express Terms 101
Discharge by Frustration 102

16 BREACH OF CONTRACT 105
Repudiation 107
Remedies 107
Duty to Mitigate 109
Penalty Clauses 109
Quantum Meruit 109
Substantial Compliance 110
Specific Performance and Injunction 111
    Specific Performance 111
    Injunction 112

17 FUNDAMENTAL BREACH 113

18 THE AGREEMENT BETWEEN CLIENT AND ENGINEER 119
The Agency Relationship 119
The Engineer's Remuneration 120
Estimated Fee 120
Standard-Form Engineering Agreements 122
Limiting Liability by Contract 123
Engineer's Compliance with the Law 123

19 THE QUESTION OF CONCURRENT LIABILITY IN TORT AND CONTRACT 127

20 THE DUTY OF HONESTY 131

v

21 CONSTRUCTION CONTRACTS 133
Certificates Fraudulently Prepared 136
Inspection Services 136
The Engineer's Advice to the Contractor 138
Contract Administration 139
Drawings and Specifications 140
The Tendering Process 142
Types and Forms of Construction Contracts 143
    1. Stipulated-Price or Lump-Sum Contract 144
    2. Unit-Price Contract 144
    3. Cost-Plus Contracts 144
        (i) Cost plus Percentage 144
        (ii) Cost plus Lump-Sum Fee 145
        (iii) Cost plus Lump-Sum Fee plus Bonus ... 145
    4. Guaranteed Maximum Price plus Bonus 145
    5. Design-Build Contracts 146
Project Management 146
Prime Contract and Subcontracts 147
Emerging Trends in Contracting 148
Delay and Interference Claims 149
Bonds 149
   Bid Bond 150
   Performance Bond 150
   Labour and Material-Payment Bond 150
Letters of Credit 151

22 ARBITRATION 153
Appointment of Arbitrator 154
The Arbitrations Act 154
Appeals 155

23 LIEN LEGISLATION 157
Differences in Provincial Lien Acts 157
Persons Entitled to Lien Rights 159
Rights Against Owner Where No Contract Exists 159
Effect of Lien 160
The New Ontario Construction Lien Act, 1983 161
The Trust Fund 167
Engineers' Rights to Lien Claims 167
Lien Statutes 169

24 THE COMBINES INVESTIGATION ACT 171
Misleading Advertising 171
Bid-rigging 172
Conspiracy 173
Trade Associations 174

25 STATUTES GOVERNING THE ENGINEERING PROFESSION 177
Purpose of Legislation 177
Definition of Professional Engineering 178
Professional Engineer's Seal 179
Partnerships and Corporations 180
Disciplinary Hearings 180
Penalties 183
Certificates of Authorization 183
Overlapping in the Scope of Engineering and Architectural Practices 184
Background to Changes in Ontario Legislation 184
Code of Ethics 187

26 INDUSTRIAL PROPERTY 191
PATENTS OF INVENTION 191
  Definition and Purpose 191
  What May Be Patented 191
  Term of Patent 193
  Assignment and Licensing of Patent Rights 193
  Infringement of Patents 193
  Assignment of Patent Rights by Employee Engineer 194
TRADE-MARKS 196
  Definition 196
  When Trade-Marks Are Registrable 196
  Registered-User Agreements 197
  Duration of Registration 197
  Infringement 197
COPYRIGHT 197
  Definition 197
  Term of Copyright 198
  Assignment of Copyright 198
  Registration of Copyright 198
  Engineering Plans 198
INDUSTRIAL DESIGNS 198
  Definition 198
  Term 199
  Assignment 199
  Employees 199
  Registration 199
TRADE SECRETS 200
  The Nature of a Trade Secret 200
  When a Duty of Confidence Arises 202

27 LAWS RELATING TO LABOUR 205
Federal Laws 205
Provincial Laws 206
Provincial Statutes — Ontario 206
   The Employment Standards Act 206
   The Workers' Compensation Act 208
   The Health Insurance Act 208
   The Human Rights Code, 1981 209
   The Occupational Health and Safety Act 209
   The Ontario Labour Relations Act 210
STATUTES RELATING TO LABOUR 211

APPENDIX 217

THE PROFESSIONAL ENGINEERS ACT, 1984 of
Ontario 217

THE ENGINEERING, GEOLOGICAL AND
GEOPHYSICAL PROFESSIONS ACT of Alberta 264

TABLE OF ABBREVIATIONS 309

SELECTED REFERENCES 310

SAMPLE CASE STUDIES 311

INDEX 318

PREFACE

As stated in the first edition, the purpose of this book is to provide a current common-law text to serve the engineering profession in Canada, the practice of professional engineering having been complicated by the number and complexities of applicable statutes and court decisions and the aggressive pursuit of claims against professionals. Every professional engineer needs to be aware of the law relevant to his or her practice for the protection of both the engineer's interests and those of the client or employer. The professional engineer should also be aware of the importance of seeking legal advice when appropriate, both in anticipation of problems and after problems arise.

Important developments in the law since the first edition in 1980 have made this second edition necessary, particularly the enactment in Ontario of the new Professional Engineers Act, 1984, and the Construction Lien Act, 1983. Selected case law developments of significance are also reported, especially those dealing with limitation periods and professional liability for negligence. In response to requests and enquiries from engineers, descriptive summaries have been added relating to bonding, to letters of credit, and to certain aspects of land law, particularly subdivision control and Planning Act considerations.

Additional commentary has also been provided on the advisability of careful construction project structuring and early attention to contract documentation, especially in circumstances such as those involving construction managers, design-builders or multiple prime contractors where projects proceed otherwise than on traditional contractual arrangements.

Comments have been added on the Canadian Charter of Rights and Freedoms, part of the Constitution Act of 1982, a major development since the first edition.

For ease of reference, a Table of Cases has also been included. Statute citations throughout the text have been updated.

The approach taken throughout the text has been to summarize and simplify the subject matter. The book focuses on fundamentals and areas of business law of relevance and interest to engineers. Recognizing traditional problems with legal terminology, the use of technical legal terms has been minimized, as have references to extensive procedural details and complex legal arguments that are more appropriately the concern of lawyers. The analytical nature of our legal system is illustrated by emphasizing the courts' application of established legal principles in deciding cases. The analytical nature of the law usually makes it particularly appealing to the engineer.

Although broad in scope, this is not an exhaustive law text; it deals with selected areas of the law, and it is for engineers practising within the common-law jurisdictions of Canada. Certain statutory examples place emphasis on Ontario legislation, but similar statutes of other provinces are generally referenced. The scope of this text does not extend to civil-law matters of the Province of Quebec.

I am grateful for the many positive comments received on the first edition of this text and, in embarking upon this second edition, for the encouragement of Professor A.H. H. Corrie, P. Eng. and other representatives of The Association of Professional Engineers of the Province of Ontario. I also wish to thank those of my partners who assisted with comments on certain aspects of the second edition. I am particularly grateful for the assistance of Terence S. Dobbin who, during his articling year with my firm, contributed enthusiastically to the preparation of this second edition.

Don Marston
October, 1984

TABLE
OF
CASES

Alkok v. Grymek, [1968] S.C.R. 452 110

Amber Size & Chemical Co., Ltd. v. Menzel, [1913] 2 Ch. 239 201

Ambro Materials and Construction Ltd. v. 230056 Investments Limited et al, 9 O.R. (2d) 226 168

Attorney-General of Canada v. Libling et al, 29 O.R. (2d) 44 48

Bahamaconsult Ltd. v. Kellogg Salada Canada Ltd., 75 D.L.R. (3d) 522 67

Beaufort Realties (1964) Inc. and Belcourt Construction (Ottawa) Limited and Chomedey Aluminum Co. Ltd., [1980] 2 S.C.R. 718 116

Belle River Community Arena Inc. v. W.J.C. Kaufman Co. et al (1977), 15 O.R. (2d) 738 90

Belle River Community Arena Inc. v. W.J.C. Kaufman Co. et al (1978), 20 O.R. (2d) 447 (Ont. C.A.) 92

Bethlehem Steel Corporation v. St. Lawrence Seaway Authority, 79 D.L.R. (3d) 522 46

Blakely v. Victaulic Company of Canada, [1979] 1 A.C.W.S. 351 207

Brennan Paving Co. Ltd. v. Oshawa, [1953] 3 D.L.R. 16 134

British Reinforced Concrete Engineering Co. Limited v. Lind, [1917] 34 R.P.C. 101 194

Brown & Huston Ltd. v. The Corporation of the City of York et al, 5 C.L.R. 240 33

John Burrows Ltd. v. Subsurface Surveys Ltd. et al, 68 D.L.R. (2d) 354 71

Calax Construction Inc. v. Lepofsky, (1974), 5 O.R. (2d) 259 78

Calgary v. Northern Construction Company Division of Morrison-Knudsen Company Inc. (1982), 23 Alta. L.R. (2d) 388 94

Canama Contracting Ltd. v. Huffman et al, 5 C.L.R. 149 34

City of Kamloops v. Nielsen et al, [1984] 29 C.C.L.T. 97 52

Coco v. Clark, [1969] R.P.C. 41 203

Conwest Exploration Co. Ltd. et al v. Letain, 41 D.L.R. (2d) 198 70

Corporation of District of Surrey v. Carroll-Hatch et al, [1979] 6 W.W.R. 289 39

Croft Construction Co. v. Terminal Construction Company, 20 D.L.R. (2d) 247 135

Dabous v. Zuliani et al, 68 D.L.R. (3d) 414 137

Davis Contractors Ltd. v. Fareham Urban District Council, [1956] A.C. 696 103

Demers v. Dufresne Engineering et al, [1979] 1 S.C.R. 146 138

Derry v. Peek, [1889] 14 App. Cas. 337 85

Dominion Chain Co. Ltd. v. Eastern Construction et al (1974), 3 O.R. (2d) 481 29

Dominion Chain Co. Ltd. v. Eastern Construction et al, 68 D.L.R. (3d) 385 (Ont. C.A.) 50, 127

Dominion Chain Co. Ltd. v. Eastern Construction et al, [1978] 2 S.C.R. 1346 (S.C.C.) 129

Donoghue v. Stevenson, [1932] A.C. 562 .... 30, 41

Dutton v. Bognor Regis United Building Co. Ltd., [1972] 1 All E.R. 462 37

Englewood Plumbing & Gas Fitting Ltd. v. Northgate Development Ltd. et al, [1966] 54 W.W.R. 225 168

Re Application of Erickson/Massey, [1971] 2 W.W.R. 767 168

Fairbanks Soap Co. Ltd. v. Sheppard, [1952] 1 D.L.R. 417 110

Fern Brand Waxes Ltd. v. Pearl, [1972] 3 O.R. 829 ... 12

G. Ford Homes Ltd. v. Draft Masonry (York) Co. Ltd., 43 O.R. (2d) 401 99

General Electric Company Limited v. Fada Radio, Limited, [1930] A.C. 97 192

George Ho Lem v. Barotts Sports Ltd. and Ponsness-Warren, Inc. 41

Grant, Smith & Co. v. The King, [1920] 19 Ex. C.R. 404 136

Re Thomas Hackett, [1939] 2 D.L.R. 332 155

Hadley v. Baxendale (1854), 9 Exch. 341 107

Halvorson Inc. v. Robert McLellan & Co. et al, [1973]
S.C.R. 65 129

*Harbutt's Plasticine Ltd. v. Wayne Tank and Pump Co.
Ltd.*, [1970] 1 All E.R. 255 113

Hedley Byrne & Co. Ltd. v. Heller & Partners Ltd., [1964]
A.C. 465 30

Imperial Glass Ltd. v. Consolidated Supplies Ltd., 22
D.L.R. (2d) 759 89

Jackson et al v. Drury Construction Co. Ltd., 4 O.R. (2d)
735 54

John Burrows Ltd. v. Subsurface Surveys Ltd. et al, 68
D.L.R. (2d) 354 71

Junior Books Ltd. v. Veitchi Co. Ltd., [1982] 3 All ER
201 47

Kamlee Construction Ltd. v. Town of Oakville, [1961] 26
D.L.R. (2d) 166 135

City of Kamloops v. Nielsen et al (1984), 29 C.C.L.T.
97 .... 52, 127

Kidd v. Mississauga Hydro-Electric Commission et al., 97
D.L.R. (3d) 535 120

Kocotis v. D'Angelo, [1958] O.R. 104 78

Lambert v. Lastoplex Chemicals Co. Limited et al, [1972]
S.C.R. 569 42

Lazarowicz v. Orenda Engines Limited, 26 D.L.R. (2d)
433 207

*George Ho Lem v. Barotto Sports Ltd. and Ponsness-
Warren, Inc.* (1976), 1 C.C.L.T. 180 41

MacMillan Bloedel Ltd. v. Foundation Co. (1977), 1
C.C.L.T. 358 46

Markland Associates Ltd. v. Lohnes, [1973] 33 D.L.R. (3d)
493 99

Township of McKillop v. Pidgeon and Foley, [1908]
O.W.R. 401 86

*Metropolitan Water Board v. Dick, Kerr and Company,
Limited*, [1918] A.C. 119 102

Monticchio v. Torcema Construction Ltd. et al, 26 O.R.
(2d) 305 79

"The Moorcock", [1889] 14 P.D. 64 99

Murray v. Sperry Rand Corporation et al, 23 O.R. (2d)
457 116

Mutual Finance Co. Ltd. v. John Wetton & Sons Ltd.,

[1937] 2 K.B. 389 87

Nedco Ltd. v. Clark et al, 43 D.L.R. (3d) 714 13

Newman et al v. Conair Aviation Ltd. et al, 4 O.R. (2d) 731-5. 54

Northwestern Mutual Insurance Co. v. J. T. O'Bryan & Co., 51 D.L.R. (3d) 693 39

J. Nunes Diamonds Ltd. v. Dominion Electric Protection Co., [1972] S.C.R. 769 129

Owen Sound Public Library Board v. Mial Developments Ltd. et al, 26 O.R. (2d) 459 73

Permutit Co. v. Borrowman, [1926] 43 R.P.C. 356 .. 192

Photo Production Ltd. v. Securicor Transport Ltd., [1980] 1 All E.R. 556 114

Pigott Construction Co. Ltd. v. W. J. Crowe Ltd., 27 D.L.R. (2d) 258 .... 99, 105

Pirelli General Cable Works Ltd. v. Oscar Faber and Partners, [1983] 1 All E.R. 65 51

Pym v. Campbell, [1856] 119 E.R. 903 98

The Queen et al v. Commercial Credit Corp. Ltd., 4 D.L.R. (4th) 31 64

Ramsay and Penno v. The King, [1952] 2 D.L.R. 819 . 30

Regina v. Margison and Associates Limited, [1955] O.W.N. 705 184

Rex v. Bentall, [1939] 3 W.W.R. 39 184

Rivtow Marine Ltd. v. Washington Iron Works et al (1974), 40 D.L.R. (3d) 530 45

Ron Engineering et al v. The Queen in right of Ontario et al (1979), 24 O.R. (2d) 332 92

The Queen in Right of Ontario et al v. Ron Engineering et al., 119 D.L.R. (3d) 267 (SCC) 93

Salomon v. Salomon & Co. Ltd., [1987] A.C. 22 12

Saltman v. Campbell, [1948] 65 R.P.C. 203 202

Schwebel v. Telekes, [1974] 3 O.R. (2d) 481 127

Schwebel v. Telekes, (1967), 1 O.R. 541 50

Seager v. Copydex Ltd., [1967] R.P.C. 349 200

Sealand of the Pacific Ltd. v. R. C. McHaffie Ltd., [1974] 6 W.W.R. 724 129

Robert Simpson Co. Ltd. v. Foundation Co., (1981) 34 O.R. (2d) 1 50

Robert Simpson Co. Ltd. v. Foundation Co. (1982), 36 O.R. (2d) 97 (Ont. C.A.) 51

Sparham Souter et al v. Town & Country Developments

(Essex) Ltd. et al, (1976) C.A. 858 49

Corporation of District of Surrey v. Carol Hatch et al, [1979] 6 W.W.R. 289 39

Sutcliffe v. Thackrah et al, [1974] All E.R. 859 136

Swanson Construction Company Ltd. v. Government of Manitoba; Dominion Structural Steel Ltd., Third Party, 40 D.L.R. (2d) 162 104

Township of McKillop v. Pidgeon and Foley, (1908) 11 O.W.R. 401 86

Trident Construction Ltd. v. W. L. Wardrop and Assoc. et al, [1979] 6 W.W.R. 481 .... 32, 141

Unit Farm Concrete Products Ltd. v. Eckerlea Acres Ltd. et al.; Canama Contracting Ltd. v. Huffman et al, 5 C.L.R. 149 34

Viscount Machine and Tool Ltd. v. Clarke, 126 D.L.R. (3d) 160 51

Willard's Chocolates Ltd. v. Bardsley, [1928-29] 35 O.W.N. 92 194

CHAPTER ONE

THE CANADIAN
LEGAL SYSTEM

HISTORICAL BASIS

The legal system of the nine common-law provinces and the
territories of Canada is based upon the English common-
law system. It is important to understand something of the
evolution of the English system in order to appreciate how
the Canadian system operates.

At one of its early stages of development, the English
legal system was very rigid. Certain specific remedies were
available in only certain circumstances. This system of
specific remedies was called the "common law." As time
passed, it became evident that the specific remedies provided by the common-law courts were not sufficient. Where
relief beyond the scope of the common law was sought,
special appeals were made to the English Monarch; if the
Monarch saw fit to exercise his or her discretion, a remedy
more "equitable" than that provided by the common law
was declared. Eventually, the English "courts of equity"
were developed as a separate court system, providing more
reasonable remedies as circumstances required. As pointed
out in Black's Law Dictionary, the term "equity," in its
broadest and most general sense, denotes a spirit of fairness, justness and right dealing . . . grounded in the precepts
of conscience.

Eventually, the two systems — the old common-law
system and the courts of equity — were combined, and an
improved system was developed to provide remedies premised on both common-law precedents and on equitable
principles. This improved system continued to be called the
"common law," and is the system from which the present
Canadian common-law system evolved.

THE THEORY OF PRECEDENT

In deciding cases, the courts apply legal principles established in previous court decisions which involved similar or analogous fact situations; this is called "the theory of precedent." But the courts also dispense equitable relief and thus there is flexibility in the courts' decision-making process. At times, to slavishly follow precedent would not reflect society's values: hence a court can exercise its equitable discretion to reach a policy decision that may represent a departure from case precedents.

Factual distinctions between cases may also provide the basis for flexibility. A court may see fit to dismiss the application of a precedent on the basis of relatively minor factual distinctions between the precedent and the facts of the case before the court, provided the end result is justified.

However, departures from established precedents are often very slow to evolve. This slow evolution is a characteristic of our legal system that may, at times, be criticized; nevertheless, the theory of precedent is of major importance and is the basis of predictability in the legal system.

THE COMMON LAW

A major source of law is "judge-made law" — court decisions establishing legal principles.

LEGISLATION

In addition to the "common law" or judge-made law," an extremely important source of law is legislation: statutes enacted by elected legislatures. A statute is a codification of the law as the legislature determines at the time of enactment; it may be codification of existing common law or the enactment of new law.

Applicability of a statute can be questioned in a lawsuit; if so, it is up to the court to determine whether the statute does apply to the facts of the case. The court must apply the statute appropriately. At times, the wording of a statute must be interpreted by the court.

Some statutes provide for regulations as a further source

of law. The Professional Engineers Act, 1984 of Ontario[1] (and similar statutes of other common-law provinces, for example) provides that an elected and appointed council may prescribe the scope and conduct of examinations of candidates for registration; and may regulate other matters, such as the designation of specialists.

When made in accordance with an authorizing statute, regulations are another source of law.

Many statutes are relevant to the professional engineer. It is important that the engineer complies with federal and provincial statutes of relevance to his or her practice and that he or she is aware of amendments and new statutes.

FEDERAL AND PROVINCIAL POWERS

Under the Canadian Constitution, the British North America Act, 1867 (renamed the Constitution Act, 1867 by the Constitution Act, 1982), the federal government and the provinces have authority to enact legislation. The division of powers between the federal government and the provinces is expressed in Sections 91 and 92 of the Constitution Act, 1867, excerpts from which are reproduced, for illustrative purposes, as follows:

91. It shall be lawful for the Queen, by and with the Advice and Consent of the Senate and House of Commons, to make Laws for the Peace, Order, and good Government of Canada, in relation to all Matters not coming within the Classes of Subjects by this Act assigned exclusively to the Legislatures of the Provinces; and for greater Certainty, but not so as to restrict the Generality of the foregoing Terms of this Section, it is hereby declared that (notwithstanding anything in this Act) the exclusive Legislative Authority of the Parliament of Canada extends to all Matters coming within the Classes of Subjects next herein-after enumerated; that is to say, —

Legislative Authority of Parliament of Canada

---

[1] S.O. 1984, c. 13

(Note that, in the interests of brevity, statute citations throughout the text do not include amendments.)

2. The Regulation of Trade and Commerce. . . .
3. The raising of Money by any Mode or System of Taxation. . . .
10. Navigation and Shipping. . . .
15. Banking, Incorporation of Banks, and the Issue of Paper Money. . . .
21. Bankruptcy and Insolvency.
22. Patents of Invention and Discovery.
23. Copyrights. . . .
27. The Criminal Law...
29. Such Classes of Subjects as are expressly excepted in the Enumeration of the Classes of Subjects by this Act assigned exclusively to the Legislatures of the Provinces.

And any Matter coming within any of the Classes of Subjects enumerated in this Section shall not be deemed to come within the Class of Matters of a local or private Nature comprised in the Enumeration of the Classes of Subjects by this Act assigned exclusively to the Legislatures of the Provinces.

Exclusive Powers of Provincial Legislatures.

Subjects of exclusive Provincial Legislation.

92. In each Province the Legislature may exclusively make Laws in relation to Matters coming within the Classes of Subject next herein-after enumerated; that is to say, —. . . .

2. Direct Taxation within the Province in order to the raising of a Revenue for Provincial Purposes. . . .
5. The Management and Sale of the Public Lands belonging to the Province and of the Timber and Wood thereon. . . .
10. Local Works and Undertakings other than such as are of the following Classes: —

   (*a*) Lines of Steam or other Ships, Railways, Canals, Telegraphs, and other Works and Undertakings connecting the Province with any other or others of the Provinces, or extending beyond the Limits of the Province;

      (*b*)   Lines of Steam Ships between the Province and any British or Foreign Country;

      (*c*)   Such Works as, although wholly situate within the Province, are before or after their Execution declared by the Parliament of Canada to be for the general Advantage of Canada or for the Advantage of Two or more of the Provinces.

11. The Incorporation of Companies with Provincial Objects. . . .

13. Property and Civil Rights in the Province.

14. The Administration of Justice in the Province, including the Constitution, Maintenance, and Organization of Provincial Courts, both of Civil and of Criminal Jurisdiction, and uncluding Procedure in Civil Matters in those Courts. . . .

16. Generally all Matters of a merely local or private Nature in the Province.

Note that Section 92 of the Constitution Act, 1867 grants to the provinces certain exclusive powers. Section 91, on the other hand, enumerates specific matters that fall within the exclusive legislative authority of the Parliament of Canada. It also provides that the federal parliament shall have authority ''to make laws for the Peace, Order, and good Government of Canada'' with respect to matters that are not within the exclusive authority of the provinces. This general reference to ''Peace, Order, and good Government'' is open to broad interpretation, providing a basis for extensive federal legislative powers where circumstances may raise concerns of national importance.

The provincial legislatures are generally empowered to enact statutes dealing with matters of a provincial nature, including property rights. Mechanics', construction or builders' lien legislation is an example of provincial statute law that may be of particular importance to the engineer.

At times, a dispute may arise as to who has the authority to enact a statute — the federal government or a provincial legislature. Traditionally, if a party sought to challenge the ''constitutionality'' of a statute, the party had to convince a court that the statute was beyond the authority of the government that enacted it. Provincial statutes would be challenged on the basis that they dealt with a matter assigned to

5

the federal Parliament in section 91 of the Constitution Act, 1867 (for example, the regulation of trade and commerce, criminal law). Federal statutes would be attacked on the grounds that they dealt with a matter within a province's jurisdiction (for example, local works, property and civil rights in a province). If a court could be convinced that the statute was beyond such authority, or "ultra vires," that statute would be effectively rendered void.

Before the Canadian Charter of Rights and Freedoms was enacted as part of the Constitution Act, 1982, courts could strike down legislation on the basis that it was beyond the authority of the government that passed it. But the courts could not void a law because it offended civil liberties. Canadian courts had adopted the British "doctrine of Parliamentary Supremacy." This meant that, theoretically, the Courts could not question the wisdom of any statute, even one that offended civil liberties. Although a court might find that a particularly offensive piece of legislation was beyond the authority of one level of government, that same legislation would be within the authority of another level of government. Theoretically, then, all the rights of the citizens of Canada could be removed by the government if it so desired. The only question would be which of the governments, federal or provincial, would have the ability to remove each right.

This has been dramatically changed through the enactment of the Canadian Charter of Rights and Freedoms as part of the Constitution Act, 1982. The Charter provides that everyone has certain rights. For example, section 2 provides that:

> Everyone has the following fundamental freedoms:
> (a) freedom of conscience and religion;
> (b) freedom of thought, belief, opinion and expression, including freedom of the press and other media of communication;
> (c) freedom of association.

The Charter is particularly significant because section 52(1) provides:

> The Constitution of Canada is the supreme law of Canada, and any law that is inconsistent with the provi-

sions of the Constitution is, to the extent of the inconsistency, of no force or effect.

Courts now have the power to rule that statutes are invalid because they violate rights guaranteed by the Charter. The Charter has reduced the effect of the doctrine of Parliamentary Supremacy by placing some limits on the powers of Parliament and the provincial legislatures.

However, it is important to realize that the Charter does not completely eliminate the concept of Parliamentary Supremacy. Section 1 provides, in effect, that governments may, through statutes, place "reasonable limits" on the rights outlined in the Charter. However, if called upon, the government will have to show that such limits are necessary.

Further, Section 33 of the Charter provides that a government may expressly override certain provisions of the Charter. That is, the government may declare that a statute is valid even if the statute violates certain Charter rights. The theory is that a government will be reluctant to announce to its citizens that it believes it is violating the rights of the people. Accordingly, it is assumed that the Section 33 override power will be used sparingly.

THE FEDERAL AND PROVINCIAL COURT SYSTEMS

The most persuasive precedent is usually the decision of most recent date from the highest court. Decisions of the Supreme Court of Canada rank highest, followed by decisions of the Court of Appeal of the province in which a case is commenced. Precedents from other common-law jurisdictions may also be followed. For example, where a provincial court cannot follow a precedent from a higher court within the province or from the Supreme Court of Canada, it may follow a precedent set by the courts of another province, or by a court in another common-law jurisdiction. England and the United States provide common-law precedents; Canadian courts have more often preferred to follow English case precedents than U.S. common law.

The court system within each of the common-law provinces is generally the same; our system was modelled on the

English system, and consists of a number of different province-wide courts responsible for a variety of matters. For example, the Surrogate Court handles estates; Provincial Court (Family Division) deals with domestic matters (except divorce), and Provincial Court (Criminal Division, at one time referred to as Magistrate's Court in Ontario) handles criminal matters. Small Claims Court deals with disputes involving relatively small amounts of money. As of January 1, 1985, Provincial County Courts are to be replaced by a province-wide District Court which will deal with larger claims and also with criminal matters. The Supreme Court of Ontario, comprised of both a Trial Division (The High Court of Justice) and an Appeal Division (The Court of Appeal) deals with both large claims and criminal matters. The highest provincial appeal court is the Court of Appeal, which hears appeals from courts such as the District Court and the High Court of Justice.

Federal courts include The Federal Court of Canada, which has jurisdiction over federal matters such as patents, trade-marks and copyright, and the Supreme Court of Canada, Canada's final appeal court.

PUBLIC AND PRIVATE LAW

Certain areas of the law are often classified as either public or private law.

Public law deals with the rights and obligations of government, on the one hand, and individuals and private organizations, on the other. Examples of public law are criminal law and constitutional law. Private law deals with rights and obligations of individuals or private organizations. Examples of private law which will be discussed in this text are contracts and torts.

THE LAW OF QUEBEC

Quebec's legal system is not founded upon the English common-law system. The civil law or Civil Code of Quebec has evolved from the Napoleonic Code, and is different from the common-law system. It is most important that engineers doing business in the Province of Quebec seek legal advice from Quebec counsel.

Reference to the civil law of Quebec can create confusion, as the term "civil" is also used in our common-law system. In the common-law system, "civil" usually means "private." "Civil litigation," for example, refers to a dispute under *private* law, rather than a *criminal* law dispute. In this text, "civil" means "private."

BASIC TERMINOLOGY

In order to appreciate references in this text, an understanding of some basic terminology is important.

(a) Litigation — a lawsuit

(b) Plaintiff — In civil litigation: the party bringing the action or making the claim in the lawsuit. In criminal matters, the "plaintiff" is usually the Crown.

(c) Defendant — The party defending the action, or the party against whom the claim has been made. In criminal matters, the "defendant" is called the "accused."

(d) Appellant — The party appealing the decision of a lower Court, in either civil litigation or criminal matters.

(e) Respondent — The party seeking to uphold a decision of the lower Court that is being appealed. The term applies in both civil litigation and criminal matters.

(f) Privity of contract — Describes the legal relationship between parties to a contract.

(g) Creditor — A party to whom an amount is owing.

(h) Debtor — A party that owes an amount to a creditor.

(i) Indemnification — A promise to directly compensate or reimburse another party for a loss or cost incurred. An indemnification, or "indemnity," is similar to a guarantee; the essential difference is that indemnity rights can be exercised directly. For example, a guarantee works as follows: suppose Jason Smith promises John Doe that Smith will guarantee the debts of ABC Corporation.

Enforcement of the guarantee requires that ABC Corporation defaults in making its payment to John Doe and that John Doe first looks to ABC Corporation for such payment. Only then may Doe require payment from the guarantor, Jason Smith. An indemnification, however, works as follows: suppose Jason Smith had indemnified John Doe on account of ABC Corporation's indebtedness to him. As soon as any such debt is incurred, John Doe can require payment directly from Jason Smith without first pursuing ABC Corporation for payment. (As a practical matter, it is often very difficult to distinguish a guarantee from an indemnity, as the guarantee may, for example, by its terms cover the essential difference as described above. That is, a guarantee may expressly provide that the creditor need not exhaust his remedies against a debtor before pursuing the guarantor for payment.)

CHAPTER TWO

BUSINESS ORGANIZATIONS

BASIC FORMS

An awareness of the three basic forms of business organizations — sole proprietorships, partnerships and corporations — is essential to the engineer's appreciation of legal rights and liabilities.

In a sole proprietorship, as the name suggests, an individual carries on business by and for himself. The proprietor personally enjoys the profits of his enterprise and personally incurs any business losses of the enterprise.

A partnership is an association of persons who conduct a business in common with a view to profit. Individuals or organizations carrying on business in partnership share profits and losses personally. One presumed advantage of partnership is that there is strength in numbers, and the combining of energies and talents of individuals may well be advantageous. The essential risk of partnership, however, is that the partnership may incur substantial debts, which the partnership business is unable to pay, with the result that the partnership's creditors may obtain judgments against the partners personally. Such judgments are sometimes satisfied only by seizure and sale of the partners' personal assets — a grim possibility.

Unlike the sole proprietorship and the partnership, the corporation is an entity unto itself, distinct from its shareholder owners. The corporation as an entity has been described as a "fictitious person." The corporation itself owns its assets and incurs its own liabilities; it can sue or be sued in its own name. In fact, a shareholder of a corporation can contract with or sue that corporation.

THE INDEPENDENCE OF THE CORPORATE ENTITY

The existence of a corporation as separate and apart from

its shareholder-owners, and the basic premise that a corporation's liabilities are its own and not those of its shareholders, has long been recognized by our Courts. This separate existence provides a strong incentive for individuals to incorporate rather than carry on as sole proprietors or as partners, as the personal assets of sole proprietors and partners remain vulnerable to business creditors. The courts' recognition of the separate status of the corporation was confirmed in the 1897 decision of the English House of Lords in *Salomon* v. *Salomon & Co. Ltd.*[1] Salomon had, for many years, carried on business as a leather merchant and wholesale boot manufacturer. Eventually he incorporated a company, to which he sold his business. The shareholders of the company consisted of himself and his family, and Salomon held the majority of the shares personally. As part payment of the purchase price for the sale of his business to the corporation, shares of the corporation were issued to Salomon; in addition, debentures constituting security, to evidence the corporation's indebtedness, were also issued to him. All of the requirements of the governing corporate statute were complied with, and at the date of the sale the business was solvent. Eventually, however, the business experienced difficult times and went into insolvency. A lawsuit resulted. The issue was whether Salomon ranked before the general unsecured creditors of the corporation by virtue of being a secured debenture holder. The English Court of Appeal was of the opinion that the incorporation and the sale of the business was a scheme to enable Salomon to carry on business in the name of the corporation with limited liability. The Court of Appeal also thought that Salomon had been trying to obtain a preference over unsecured creditors of the company. However, on appeal, the House of Lords recognized Salomon's corporation as a separate and distinct entity from himself. The House of Lords emphasized that there was no evidence of intent by Salomon to deceive or defraud.

But where it can be established that the limited-liability characteristic of a corporation is being used for the protection of an individual in perpetrating a fraud, the courts will refuse to recognize the separate identities of the individual and the corporation. To illustrate: in the 1972 decision in

[1] [1897] A.C.22.

Fern Brand Waxes Ltd. v. *Pearl*[2], the Ontario Court of Appeal determined that the defendant, who was a director, officer and accountant of the plaintiff, Fern Brand Waxes Ltd., had used his position to transfer unauthorized funds. He used the funds as a loan, which was made by the plaintiff to two companies controlled by the defendant. Part of those transferred funds were used to pay for shares in Fern Brand Waxes Ltd. The court determined that such payment for the shares of Fern Brand Waxes Ltd. did not constitute a proper payment for such shares. The court stated that the defendant should not be allowed to profit from his breach of trust. In such circumstances, the corporate character of his two companies was no shield for his conduct, because each company was his instrument and was used to divert funds for his own purposes.

There are other exceptional circumstances, short of fraud, where the courts will intervene to "lift the corporate veil." One such case was *Nedco Ltd.* v. *Clark et al*[3], a 1973 decision of the Saskatchewan Court of Appeal. Nedco Ltd. was a wholly owned subsidiary of Northern Electric Company Limited. Employees of Northern Electric Company Limited went on strike and picketed the premises of Nedco Ltd. In an action to restrain the Northern Electric employees from picketing Nedco, the court had to decide whether to consider Northern Electric Company Limited and Nedco Ltd. as separate corporate entities. In concluding its judgment, and stressing the exceptional nature of the facts of the case, the court stated, in part:

> After reviewing the foregoing, and many other cases, the only conclusion I can reach is this: while the principle laid down in *Salomon* v. *A. Salomon & Co., Ltd.,* supra, is and continues to be a fundamental feature of Canadian law, there are instances in which the Court can and should lift the corporate veil, but whether it does so depends upon the facts in each particular case. Moreover, the fact that the Court does lift the corporate veil for a specific purpose in no way destroys the recognition of the corporation as an

[2] [1972] 3 O.R.829
[3] 43 D.L.R. (3d) 714

(Note that certain case name references are abbreviated throughout this text.)

independent and autonomous entity for all other purposes.

In the present case Nedco Ltd. is a wholly-owned subsidiary of Northern Electric Company Limited. It was organized and incorporated to take over what was formerly a division of Northern Electric Company Limited. As such wholly-owned subsidiary, it is controlled, directed and dominated by Northern Electric Company Limited. Thus, viewing it from a realistic standpoint, rather than its legal form, I am of the opinion that it constitutes an integral component of Northern Electric Company Limited in the carrying on of its business. That being so, I can see no grounds upon which lawful picketing of Nedco Ltd., pursuant to a lawful strike against Northern Electric Company Limited, should be restrained.

I want to make it perfectly clear that, in reaching this conclusion, I have not attempted to lay down any general principle. It is only because of the special circumstances prevalent in this case that I have reached the conclusion which I have. While Nedco Ltd. is, for the purposes of this application, an integral component of Northern Electric Company Limited, for all other purposes it remains an autonomous and independent entity.

DURATION OF PARTNERSHIPS AND CORPORATIONS

Unless otherwise provided by the terms of a partnership agreement, pursuant to The Partnership Act of Ontario and similar statutes in other common-law provinces, a partnership is dissolved by the death or bankruptcy or insolvency of one of its partners. A corporation, on the other hand, has perpetual existence as long as the corporation complies with its governing statute, and as long as no procedural steps are taken to dissolve the corporation. The death of a shareholder does not have the effect of dissolving a corporation.

EFFECT OF PERSONAL GUARANTEES

14   As noted, a shareholder is not theoretically liable for the

corporation's debts. However, the limited-liability characteristic of a corporation is often substantially reduced or nonexistent, as a practical matter. For example, when setting up the banking arrangements for the corporation, the incorporator is often required to sign a personal guarantee in return for satisfactory credit terms. The incorporator shareholder who signs a guarantee becomes personally obligated to the lending institution for the debts of the corporation to the extent of the guarantee. He therefore loses the advantage of the limited-liability concept of the corporation's indebtedness in relation to that creditor.

BASIC TAX CONSIDERATIONS

The basic combined federal and provincial corporate income tax rate is approximately fifty per cent. However, for a ''Canadian-controlled private corporation'' that carries on only an active business (such as manufacturing, processing, mining or construction) and does not carry on any non-qualifying business, the effective rate of tax is reduced to approximately thirty-three per cent, of which approximately eight per cent is deferred until dividends are paid (the precise rate will vary from province to province). This reduction is commonly referred to as ''the small-business deduction,'' and was enacted as an incentive to encourage small businesses by reducing their tax burden. The rate is further reduced for manufacturing and processing income.

The small-business deduction applies only to the first $200,000 of income per year.

When the corporation distributes its after-tax income to its shareholder or shareholders by way of dividends, each shareholder who is an individual must pay a tax on such dividend income, and is entitled to a dividend tax credit.

In some cases, the effect of the small-business deduction is that the aggregate of the tax paid by the corporation entitled to such deduction on the income earned by it and the tax paid by the individual shareholder receiving the dividend is less than the tax that would have been paid had the business been carried on through a sole proprietorship. In other words, dividend income from a corporation can result in less tax payable than does income derived from a sole proprietorship or partnership.

15

In addition, there is a timing advantage available. The taxes paid by shareholders on corporate dividends are payable only when dividends are paid by the corporation. If the board of directors of the corporation chooses to defer the payment of dividends to a subsequent taxation year, then the tax payable on that dividend is deferred.

Corporations that are controlled by the same person or group of persons are deemed to be "associated corporations" for the purpose of the Income Tax Act of Canada. Associated corporations are permitted to claim the lower tax rate only on the first $200,000 per year of the combined taxable incomes of such associated corporations.

An in-depth examination of tax law is beyond the scope of this text. However, the engineer should appreciate the need for specialized tax advice in business planning.

SUMMATION OF EXCEPTIONS TO SALOMON PRINCIPLE

"Associating" corporations controlled by the same person or group of persons for tax purposes is an example of the dilution of the concept of separate and distinct corporate entities dictated by the economic realities of the business world. There are several other examples of such departures from the general concept of the distinctiveness of the corporate entity: the willingness of the courts to "pierce the corporate veil" in exceptional circumstances; the courts' disregard for the distinction between the individual and the corporate entity where fraud has been involved; the courts' "association" of corporations for certain tax purposes. Nevertheless, it is important to bear in mind that such departures are the exceptions.

THE ENGINEERING CORPORATION

The Professional Engineers Act of Ontario[4] and similar statutes governing engineering in the other common-law provinces recognize that engineers may incorporate and carry on the business of engineering as a corporation.

[4] R.S.O. 1980, c. 394

Incorporation may provide both limited liability and tax advantages.

THE PARTNERSHIP AGREEMENT

If a decision is made to enter into a partnership, it is important to define the basis of that partnership and to execute a partnership agreement. Because of the very personal nature of the obligations that partnership creates, it is advisable to retain legal counsel for the preparation of the partnership agreement. Indeed, each partner should ideally obtain independent legal advice about the partnership agreement. Important aspects of the agreement will include: a description of the management responsibilities of each of the partners; the basis for calculating each partner's share of the profits or losses and contributions to working capital; provisions for dissolution of the partnership; and the basis for the withdrawal or expulsion of partners.

Partnership agreements are usually between individuals. But organizations, such as corporations, may enter into a partnership. Partnerships of corporations are not uncommon business vehicles today. When corporate partners enter into a partnership, each corporate partner's assets are at risk. The scope of each proposed partnership agreement should be closely examined to determine if the purpose of the partnership justifies that risk.

LIMITING PARTNERSHIP LIABILITY

Most of the common-law provinces have passed statutes that allow a partner to limit his or her liability. For example, The Limited Partnerships Act of Ontario[5] provides for the formation of limited partnerships, which consist of one or more general partners and one or more limited partners. Like the partners in an ordinary partnership, general partners in a limited partnership remain responsible for the

---

[5] R.S.O. 1980, c. 241

debts of the firm. On the other hand, the limited partner's liability is normally limited to the amount the limited partner has contributed or has agreed to contribute. The Limited Partnerships Act of Ontario requires each limited partnership to file a certificate disclosing basic information about the partnership. The information includes the names of all general and limited partners and the amount of capital that each limited partner has contributed. A limited partner should ensure that his name is not used in the name of the partnership. If it is used, section 5(2) of the Limited Partnerships Act states:

> . . . the limited partner is liable as a general partner to any creditor of the limited partnership who has extended credit without actual knowledge that the limited partner is not a general partner.

In effect, the limited partner may be responsible, along with the general partners, for a debt that exceeds his contribution to the firm.

Only general partners are authorized to transact business on behalf of the limited partnership. Pursuant to section 11 of The Limited Partnerships Act of Ontario, a limited partner may from time to time examine into the state and progress of the partnership business and may advise as to its management. But he must be cautious, and limit his involvement. If he takes part in the control of the business, he can become liable as a general partner pursuant to section 12 of that Act.

REGISTRATION OF PARTNERSHIPS

Most provincial jurisdictions require certain partnerships to file basic information identifying the partnership. For example, The Partnerships Registration Act of Ontario[6] provides that trading, manufacturing or mining partnerships must file a declaration. The declaration must contain basic information such as names of partners and the name and nature of the partnership. Failure to file the declaration renders the partnership incapable of maintaining any action or other proceeding in any Court in Ontario in respect of any contract made in connection with the partnership business.

[6] R.S.O. 1980, c. 371

"private" company is generally defined as a company in which:

(i) the right to transfer shares is restricted. (For example, such transfer may be subject to the approval of its board of directors);

(ii) the number of its shareholders, exclusive of present and former employees, is not more than fifty; and

(iii) any invitation to the public to subscribe for its securities is prohibited.

Most engineering corporations begin as private or closely held companies. A corporation might decide to "go public" and to thereby distribute its securities to the public. Such a decision will necessitate continuing compliance with extensive disclosure and reporting requirements of provincial securities legislation.

SHAREHOLDERS, DIRECTORS AND OFFICERS

The shareholders are the "owners" of the corporation. They receive share certificates as evidence of such ownership, usually in return for invested capital.

As its owners, the shareholders elect the directors of the corporation. The board of directors of the corporation supervises the management of the corporation's affairs and business.

The officers of a corporation are elected or appointed by its directors. The officers of the corporation usually provide for the day-to-day business management. The duties of particular officers are normally set out in the by-laws of the corporation.

SHAREHOLDERS' AGREEMENTS

It is advisable for the shareholders of a closely held corporation to enter into a shareholders' agreement. An agreement commonly covers such matters as who is entitled to nominate members of the board of directors of the company; the obligations of the shareholders with respect to

21

guarantees of the company's indebtedness; and the basis upon which issued shares of the company may be sold by a shareholder. It may also contain agreements not to communicate trade secrets of the company; or provisions to ensure that future share issuances do not dilute the respective percentage holdings of the company's shareholders.

The importance of a shareholders' agreement can be illustrated by considering the potential consequences of three individuals incorporating a company. Assume each individual takes one-third of the issued shares of the company without entering into a shareholders' agreement. Now suppose there is a "falling out" between the parties; suppose also that two of the shareholders join forces. The third shareholder may find himself unable to elect a representative to the board of directors of the company. He may also find himself ousted from his former position as an officer. And he might lose his status as an employee of the company. The board of directors controls the declaration of dividends by the company. In our example, the board may choose not to declare dividends. Hence, the minority shareholder may find himself left with very little to show for his one-third shareholder interest. And he might be unable to dispose of such shares. The shareholder in our example might be able to get some legal help — remedies may be available to dissenting shareholders, particularly where a "fraud on the minority" has been committed. However, it is preferable for shareholders to protect their respective interests by entering into an appropriate shareholders' agreement.

THE DIRECTOR'S STANDARD OF CARE

Directors and officers are expected to comply with a certain standard of care in carrying out their respective responsibilities. For example, Section 134(1) of the Business Corporations Act of Ontario provides:

> Every director and officer of a corporation in exercising his powers and discharging his duties shall,
> (a) act honestly and in good faith with a view to the best interests of the corporation; and
> (b) exercise the care, diligence and skill that a reason-

ably prudent person would exercise in comparable circumstances.

Any individual who consents to act as a director of a corporation must take such responsibilities seriously. An engineer who agrees to act as a director of a corporation engaged in the business of engineering must realize that the position of director has potential liabilities. The engineer must be willing to act in good faith and in the best interests of the corporation.

In addition, there are a number of statutory provisions imposing responsibilities on directors of corporations. To illustrate:

1. Pursuant to section 131 of the Business Corporations Act of Ontario, a director of a corporation is potentially personally liable for up to six months' unpaid wages of employees of the corporation, provided action is commenced against the corporation and the director in accordance with section 131.

> 131.(1) *Director's liability to employees for wages* — The directors of a corporation are jointly and severally liable to the employees of the corporation for all debts not exceeding six months' wages that become payable while they are directors for services performed for the corporation and for the vacation pay accrued while they are directors for not more than twelve months under The Employment Standards Act, and the regulations thereunder, or under any collective agreement made by the corporation.
>
> (2) Limitation — A director is liable under subsection (1) only if,
>
> (a) he is sued while he is a director or within six months after he ceased to be a director; and
>
> (b) the action against the director is commenced within six months after the debts became payable, and
>
>   (i) the corporation is sued in the action against the director and execution against the corporation is returned unsatisfied in whole or in part, or
>
>   (ii) before or after the action is commenced the corporation goes into liquidation, is ordered to be wound up or makes an authorized assignment under the Bankruptcy Act (Canada), or a receiving

23

order under the Bankruptcy Act (Canada) is made against it, and in any such case, the claim for the debts is proved.

2. Section 242 of the Income Tax Act (Canada) provides that directors who personally participate in the commission of offences against that Act are personally liable together with the corporation.

> 242. Where a corporation is guilty of an offence under this Act, an officer, director or agent of the corporation who directed, authorized, assented to, acquiesced in, or participated in, the commission of the offence is a party to and guilty of the offence and is liable on conviction to the punishment provided for the offence whether or not the corporation has been prosecuted or convicted.

3. Subsection 42(3) of the Combines Investigation Act (Canada) is also relevant. It provides that, if a corporation does not properly submit certain returns, which can be required in connection with an enquiry under the Act, any director or officer of that corporation who assents to or acquiesces in the offence committed by the corporation in not filing the returns is guilty of that offence personally. The penalty for each offence is a fine of not more than $5,000, or imprisonment for not more than two years, or both.

4. Pursuant to the Corporations Information Act, R.S.O. 1980, c. 96, of Ontario a corporation may not carry on business in Ontario — or identify itself to the public in Ontario — by a name or style other than its own, unless the assumed name and style are first registered under the Act. Corporations that do use assumed names must include their full corporate names on all contracts, invoices, negotiable instruments and orders for goods and services issued or made by them or on their behalf. Contravention of the Act or its regulations is an offence. If a corporation is guilty of such an offence, every director or officer of the corporation who authorized, permitted or acquiesced in the offence is also guilty of an offence, and is liable to a fine of not more than $2,000.

5. Section 243 of the Canada Business Corporations Act is also relevant. It is an offence to file a report, return, notice

or other document required by the Act or its regulations that contains an untrue statement. As well, documents cannot omit a material fact required by the Act. Where an offence is committed by a corporation, any director or officer of the corporation who knowingly authorized, permitted or acquiesced in the offence is liable to a fine of up to $5,000, or to imprisonment for a term of up to six months, or both.

DISCLOSURE OF CONFLICTS

As noted, a director must act in good faith and in the best interests of the corporation. As well, each director is required, by statute governing the corporation, to disclose any personal interest in any material contract or transaction to which the corporation is a party. The director must not vote in approval of any such contract or transaction. If the director does not disclose interest in the contract, he or she is potentially accountable to the corporation or to its shareholders for any profit or gain realized from the contract or transaction.

THE JOINT VENTURE

The joint venture as a form of business organization has become increasingly popular amongst contractors, engineers and architects in connection with large-scale projects, where it makes sense to join forces. A joint venture is often essentially a partnership limited to one particular project; and joint venturers should ensure that the scope of the joint venture is limited to the single project, in order to protect the assets of the joint venturers as partners in the project. It is also advisable for each of the joint venturers to indemnify each of the other joint venturers for liabilities that may arise as a result of respective services and contract obligations negligently performed. The joint-venture agreement should include a clear definition of the scope of the venture; it should also define obligations of the parties to the agreement, and the manner in which revenues and costs are to be shared.

CHAPTER THREE

TORT LIABILITY

The term "tort" has become more familiar to the engineering community as a result of the increasing frequency of claims against professionals in the past fifteen years or so. But its meaning may not be readily appreciated. Legal writers have not yet achieved agreement on a satisfactory precise definition of tort. The term generally refers to a private or civil wrong or injury, one that exists independently of contract. Torts are best understood by looking at some examples, and by examining the principles the courts apply to determine if tort liability exists.

Tort liability may, for example, arise from automobile accidents, from the transportation of hazardous cargoes, from the sale of unsafe products and from the negligent performance of professional services. No privity of contract is required for tort liability to exist. Obviously, no contract exists between a negligent driver and the victim of an automobile accident, or between a company transporting dangerous explosives and a victim who sustains injuries as a result of such transportation. Even services performed gratuitously — without a contract — can give rise to liability in tort if the services are performed negligently.

The fundamental purpose of tort law is to compensate victims of torts. Punishment of negligent wrongdoers is not a purpose of tort law. If the circumstances of the tort also constitute criminal activity, punishment of the criminal would be governed by the Criminal Code of Canada[1]. Criminal proceedings are independent of civil proceedings.

In order to ensure that funds are available to provide compensation to tort victims, engineers should obtain appropriate professional liability insurance coverage. Professional liability insurance should provide protection if an engineer's negligence results in damage arising in tort.

[1] R.S.C. 1970, c. C-34

PRINCIPLES OF TORT LAW

The essential principles applicable in a tort action can be isolated to provide a basis, or formula approach, for analyzing whether tort liability arises in a given situation. In order to satisfy the court that compensation should be made, the plaintiff in a tort action must substantiate that:

    (a) the defendant owed the plaintiff a duty of care;

    (b) the defendant breached that duty by his or her conduct; and

    (c) the defendant's conduct caused the injury to the plaintiff.

If any one of these three essential aspects of a tort action is not substantiated to the satisfaction of the court, the plaintiff will not succeed.

When tort principles are applied to a particular situation, reasonableness plays a major role.

For example: for tort liability to be established to the satisfaction of the court in a negligence action, the court must be persuaded that three things are true. First, that the defendant owed the plaintiff a duty to use a reasonable degree of care. "Reasonable" is measured by the conduct expected of a reasonable person in the circumstances. Second, that the defendant ought, reasonably, to have foreseen that his failure to exercise a reasonable degree of care would likely result in injury or damage to the plaintiff. Third, that, as a result of fault on the part of the defendant (and not because of some other intervening act by a third party) the plaintiff sustained the injury. Note that reasonableness may also be a factor in determining the third item. Was the fault of the defendant the reasonable proximate cause of the damage? Or was the damage claimed too remote or not reasonably forseeable to the defendant in the circumstances?

THE ENGINEER'S STANDARD OF CARE

A significant factor in a tort action is the establishment of the standard of care required of the defendant. For example, suppose a court is to determine whether an engineer has been negligent in the performance of engineering services. The court must apply some standard to determine whether the engineer's conduct was negligent. The standard applied is based on the premise that engineers have a duty to use the reasonable care and skill of engineers of ordinary competence. The "reasonable care" is measured by applicable professional standards of the engineering profession at the time the services are performed. In 1974, the High Court of Justice of Ontario decided *Dominion Chain Co. Ltd.* v. *Eastern Construction Co. Ltd. et al.*[2] The case concerned an action for damages arising out of the alleged faulty construction of a large factory roof. The court made the following statements (and references to Halsbury's text) relating to the duty of the engineer:

Liability of engineer

It is trite law that an engineer is liable for incompetence, carelessness or negligence which results in damages to his employer and he is in the same position as any other professional or skilled person who undertakes his professional work for reward and is therefore responsible if he does or omits to do his professional undertakings with an ordinary and reasonable degree of care and skill.

In 3 Hals., 3rd ed., p. 528, para. 1050, it is stated:

Architects and engineers are bound to possess a reasonable amount of skill in the art or profession they exercise for reward, and to use a reasonable amount of care and diligence in the carrying out of work which they undertake, including the preparation of plans and specifications. Every person who enters into a profession undertakes to bring to the exercise of it a reasonable degree of care of skill, and represents himself as understanding the subject and qualified to act in the business in which he professes to act. The employer buys both skill and judgment, and the architect ought not to undertake the work if it cannot succeed, and he should know whether it will or not.

And in para. 1051 of the same volume of Halsbury, it is stated:

As to the amount of skill required, the architect or engineer need not necessarily exercise an extra ordinary degree of skill. It is not enough to make him responsible that others of greater experience or ability might have used a greater degree of skill, or even that he might have used some greater degree. The question is whether there has been such a want of competent care and skill, leading to the bad result, as to amount to negligence.

And in paragraph 1056, pp. 530-1, it is stated:

In addition to this, if the negligence or want of skill of the architect or engineer has occasioned loss to his employer, he will be liable to the latter in damages. These are not limited to the amount of remuneration which under the agreement the architect or engineer was to receive, but are measured by the actual loss occasioned. . . .

The terms "negligence" and "mistake" are not necessarily synonymous. *Ramsay and Penno* v. *The King*[3] was an action against the Crown involving flooding of lands, alleging negligence in the design and construction of certain dams. The court stated, in part:

Whether or not there was negligence in regard to design and construction of the dam is a question of fact. Engineers are expected to be possessed of reasonably competent skill in the exercise of their particular calling, but not infallible, nor is perfection expected, and the most that can be required of them is the exercise of reasonable care and prudence in the light of scientific knowledge at the time, of which they should be aware. . . .

DEVELOPMENT OF TORT LAW

There have been many significant tort case decisions. Two of the most significant cases to date have been the 1932 decision in *Donoghue* v. *Stevenson*[4], and the 1963 decision in *Hedley Byrne & Co. Ltd.* v. *Heller & Partners Ltd*[5]. Both cases were decided by England's highest court, the House of Lords.

Donoghue v. Stevenson was a very important decision in the evolving field of products liability. The plaintiff had become ill after consuming the contents of a bottle of ginger

[3] [1952] 2 D.L.R. 819
[4] [1932] A.C. 562
[5] [1964] A.C. 465

beer, which had been given to the plaintiff by a friend. The bottle of ginger beer reportedly contained a decomposed snail. The House of Lords determined that the manufacturer was under a legal duty to the ultimate consumer to take reasonable care that the ginger beer was free from any defect likely to cause injury to health. (Note that no privity of contract existed between the plaintiff-consumer and the manufacturer.)

Hedley Byrne is probably the most significant case to date, as far as professionals are concerned generally. In Hedley Byrne, the plaintiffs were advertising agents who asked their bankers to inquire into the credit rating of a company with which the plaintiffs had business dealings. The plaintiff's bankers then made inquiries of the defendants, who were bankers for the company about whom credit information was being sought. The defendant bankers negligently reported that the company's financial position was favourable, but expressly stipulated that such advice on credit-worthiness was "without responsibility." The plaintiff proceeded to do business with the company, relying on the advice of the bankers. As a result, the plaintiff eventually lost £17,000. The House of Lords held that, had there not been an express disclaimer of responsibility from the defendant bank, the defendant bank would have been liable to provide compensation to the plaintiff for the financial loss that resulted from the defendant bank's negligent misrepresentation. Implicit in the decision of the House of Lords was the belief that, where one person relied on the special skill and judgment of another, and when the second person knew of that reliance, the second person was duty bound to take reasonable care in exercising the special skill.

Prior to the Hedley Byrne decision, tort law provided relief where damages to person or property had been incurred. Hedley Byrne expanded the scope of damages to include financial loss that resulted from advice negligently given — where the person giving the advice knew, or ought to have known, that reliance was being placed on his skill and judgment. The case is significant for two reasons. First, it expanded the scope of damages that may be recovered in a tort action. Second, it focussed attention on services performed by professionals who possessed special skills. 31

The principles enunciated in the Hedley Byrne decision have since been applied in cases involving engineers. One example is the 1979 decision of the Manitoba Queen's Bench, in the case of *Trident Construction Ltd.* v. *W.L. Wardrop and Assoc. et al*[6]. An engineer provided services on a project that involved the construction of a sewage disposal plant. The engineer was held liable to the contractor on the project because of his unsuitable design. No privity of contract existed between the contractor and the engineer. In applying the Hedley Byrne decision, the Manitoba court made reference to the summary given by the authors of *Charlesworth on Negligence* (5th ed., p. 32, para 49):

> The House of Lords has thus expressed the opinion that if in the ordinary course of business including professional affairs a person seeks advice or information from another who is not under any contractual or fiduciary obligation to give it, in circumstances in which a reasonable man so asked would know he was being trusted or that his skill or judgment was being relied on, and such person then chooses to give the requested advice or information without clearly disclaiming any responsibility for it, then he accepts a legal duty to exercise such care as the circumstances require in making his reply; for a failure to exercise that care, an account for negligence will lie if damage or loss results.

Subsequently, the Manitoba court concluded:

> Why should it be otherwise, as to the responsibility of the professional engineer or architect whose plans the builder is required to follow, in the event a mistake in those plans proves costly to the builder? Surely, the party whose design it is may be taken to have in contemplation the party invited to build the project as designed, and who by his contract will have to abide by the plans in question, as forming an integral part of his undertaking with the owner. I have no difficulty in fixing the professional engineer with a duty of care towards the person who is to follow the engineer's design, to ensure that the plans are workable, for

32   [6] [1979] 6 W.W.R. 481

breach of which duty the engineer may be made accountable.

A similar example of the application of the Hedley Byrne decision is the 1983 judgment of the Ontario High Court in *Brown & Huston Ltd.* v. *The Corporation of the City of York et al*,[7] another case in which the contractor succeeded against consulting engineers who had omitted certain important information relating to a soils report and ground-water levels. The contract involved the construction of an underground pumping station and required the contractor to satisfy himself, by a personal examination, as to the conditions he would encounter during construction. The court found that, because the engineers omitted information, the contractor bid on the job assuming there was no water problem. The court concluded that the contractor plaintiff was partly negligent because he did not ask about the soils report, and he did not learn the precise meaning of the information the engineers provided. But the court held the consulting engineers liable and apportioned responsibility for damages seventy-five percent against the engineers and twenty-five percent against the contractor. In considering the specific nature of the negligence of the consulting engineers, the court stated, in part:

> . . . The engineers must have known that tenderers would rely on the tender package; particularly when the contract documents did not require the contractor to satisfy itself about the sub-surface conditions.
>
> Was the lack of reference to the soils reports and the change of the sketch and plan a negligent omission to convey necessary information? Information concerning the water and sub-surface conditions was of great significance to any tenderer. I can think of no good reason why the engineers did not refer to the soils reports in the tender package and no reason for this omission was advanced at trial.
>
> I am satisfied that the plaintiff company relied on the tender package in preparing its bid and bid the job on the basis that there was not a water problem. Mr. Leonardelli saw the inverted triangle and recognized it

as a water mark but thought it could well be surface water. Having concluded that there was no water problem, or more properly, not having recognized a water problem, the proposed method of excavation was reasonable. I am also satisfied that had the plaintiff recognized the water problem the bid would have been different or the plaintiff would not have made a bid at all.

The main defence is that the information given in the tender package and particularly SK-1 and SK-2 and the description of work in the Schedule of Unit Prices which required close timber sheeting should have made it clear to the plaintiff that there was a water problem. In this connection I do not accept the evidence of Mr. Mitchell that the inverted triangle would be understood by a reasonable contractor to be the stabilized ground water level. His evidence in this connection is not in accord with the evidence of Mr. Cummings and Mr. King. It is also contrary to the CSA standard (Ex. 27) above referred to.

I also accept the evidence adduced on behalf of the plaintiff that the term ''close timber sheeting'' from the description of work means ''close timber sheeting as required''. I have come to the conclusion that there was reasonable reliance on the lack of information concerning a water condition so as to bring the case within the principles enunciated in *Hedley Byrne & Co.* v. *Heller & Partners Ltd.*

At time of writing this second edition, the Brown & Huston case is being appealed.

Principles from Hedley Byrne were also applied at the Ontario Supreme Court level in a November, 1983 decision, *Unit Farm Concrete Products Ltd.* v. *Eckerlea Acres Ltd. et al.*; *Canama Contracting Ltd.* v. *Huffman et al.*[8]. In this case, a contractor was engaged by an owner to design and construct a barn to be placed over a manure pit. The contractor succeeded in bringing an action against an engineer who was employed by the Department of Agriculture of Ontario. The court decided that the plaintiff contractor was entitled to rely on the advice of the defendant engineer,

[8] 5 C.L.R. 149

a government employee and not a consulting engineer. From time to time over the years, the plaintiff contractor had relied upon advice given by the defendant engineer, who was employed by the government to assist farmers and contractors to work out their plans. The judgment also indicates that the contractor and the engineer had never met to discuss the plans, but had discussed the matter by telephone. A copy of the plans had been left on the engineer's desk by the contractor. The engineer acknowledged at trial that he did not carefully review the plans. However, he did look through the plans and he forwarded the following written message to the contractor:

> Good set of plans. I like the detail. Wish I could spend that amount of time on each project. Keep up the good work.

The court noted that the plans had two particular deficiencies. One: the plans showed the reinforcing rod to be in the middle of the wall. The rebar should have been closer to the inside of the wall for maximum support. Two: there was a complete absence of any rebar schedule on the plans. Hence the structural-steel components and requirements vital to the integrity of the cement wall were missing. Expert evidence established, to the court's satisfaction, that it would be part of the duty of the engineer to note the deficiencies in the plans. The court concluded that the engineer failed in his duty by giving wrong advice with respect to the rebar schedule and by not reading the plans carefully and not noting the deficiencies. Also, as the court noted, the engineer was negligent in referring to the plans as "good plans," the effect of which "would be to lull the plaintiff into thinking the plans were adequate." As a result of the deficiencies, portions of the manure-tank walls failed.

The defendant engineer argued that he did not know he was being consulted. The court pointed out that, when "being held to account for negligence, it is not what we subjectively feel or think but what our conduct objectively makes the other person believe we feel or think."

In the Canama case, the court was also critical of the performance of the contractor. The court concluded that the engineer had failed to comply to the standard of care of a reasonable engineer, but also concluded that the contractor had failed to comply to the standard of care of a reasonable designer and builder in the circumstances. The court particularly noted the manner in which the contractor placed the plans on the engineer's desk, pointing out that the contractor had a duty, as a designer, to make it clear to the engineer that the engineer was being asked for advice. The contractor failed in that duty. The contractor and the engineer were each found to be fifty percent at fault in causing the damage to the walls of the manure tank.

In the Canama case, the court also pointed out that, had the defendant engineer clearly disclaimed responsibility for his words, as occurred in Hedley Byrne, the engineer could have avoided responsibility. Although the contractor was partly responsible, the court judged for the plaintiff against the defendant engineer and his employer, Her Majesty The Queen, because the defendant engineer was a crown servant and an employee of the Province of Ontario at the time.

The Canama case was appealed by the contractor to the Ontario Court of Appeal. The Court of Appeal noted the circumstances in which the engineer had provided the advice, but nevertheless increased the engineer's liability, reapportioning responsibility and holding the engineer seventy-five percent, and the contractor twenty-five percent, responsible for the damage.

STRICT LIABILITY

The discussion of torts to this point has emphasized the concept of fault; we have concentrated on cases where the conduct of the party that caused the injury was unsatisfactory in terms of duty owed. However, our legislators have sometimes found the application of the concept of fault inadequate for the purpose of compensating injured parties. For example, workmen's compensation legislation recognizes that fault is not necessary if compensation is to be provided. All employers are expected to make contributions on behalf of employees and if an employee negligently injures himself, compensation is provided according to provincial workmen's compensation legislation.

In products liability cases in the United States, a manufacturer may be strictly liable for any damage that results from the use of his product even though the manufacturer was not negligent in producing it. Canadian products liability law has not yet adopted this "strict liability" concept, but the law appears to be developing in that direction.

VICARIOUS LIABILITY

Our courts have long recognized the concept that the employer is vicariously liable for the negligent performance of an employee. If an employee commits a tort in the course of employment, the employer will be vicariously liable for the damage caused. This concept may appear onerous as far as the employer is concerned, but it is consistent with the basic premise of tort law; its purpose is to compensate the injured party. The employer provides compensation because he is presumed to be in a better financial position than the employee.

In 1972, England's Court of Appeal decided the case of *Dutton* v. *Bognor Regis United Building Co. Ltd.*[9] Foundations laid by the builder of a house were discovered to be inadequate to carry the load of the building, and damage resulted. The house had been built on a rubbish deposit and the foundations should have been deeper to withstand the pressure of settling. Building by-laws required that the building's foundations be approved by a local building inspector before construction continued. The inspector failed to make proper inspection before giving approval. The local building authority that employed the inspector was held liable to a subsequent purchaser of the house for the inspector's negligence. In his reasons for judgment, Lord Denning examined the question of the liability of the inspector:

> It is at this point that I must draw a distinction between the several categories of professional men. I can well see that in the case of a professional man who gives advice on financial or property matters — such as a banker, a lawyer or an accountant — his duty is only to those who rely on him and suffer financial loss in consequence. But, in the case of a professional man who gives advice on the safety of buildings, or machines, or material, his duty is to all those who may suffer injury in case his advice is bad. In *Candler* v.

---

[9] [1972], 1 All E.R. 462

Crane, Christmas & Co., I put the case of an analyst who negligently certifies to a manufacturer of food that a particular ingredient is harmless, whereas it is in fact poisonous; or the case of an inspector of lifts who negligently reports that a particular lift is safe, whereas it is in fact dangerous. It was accepted that the analyst and the lift inspector would be liable to any person who was injured by consuming the food or using the lift. Since that case the courts have had the instance of an architect or engineer. If he designs a house or a bridge so negligently that it falls down, he is liable to everyone of those who are injured in the fall: see *Clay* v. *A.J. Crump & Sons Ltd.* None of those injured would have relied on the architect or the engineer. None of them would have known whether an architect or engineer was employed, or not. But beyond doubt, the architect and engineer would be liable. The reason is not because those injured relied on him, but because he knew, or ought to have known, that such persons might be injured if he did his work badly.

The action was framed against the local building authority and not against the inspector in his personal capacity. Nevertheless, the Court of Appeal made it clear that the inspector was one of those responsible:

First, Mrs. Dutton has suffered a grevious loss. The house fell down without any fault of hers. She is in no position herself to bear the loss. Who ought in justice to bear it? I should think those who were responsible. Who are they? In the first place, the builder was responsible. It was he who laid the foundations so badly that the house fell down. In the second place, the council's inspector was responsible. It was his job to examine the foundations to see if they would take the load of the house. He failed to do it properly. In the third place, the council should answer for his failure. They were entrusted by Parliament with the task of seeing that houses were properly built. They received public funds for the purpose. The very object was to protect purchasers and occupiers of houses. Yet, they failed to protect them. Their shoulders are broad enough to bear the loss.

Employees are also potentially liable in tort. An example is the case of *Northwestern Mutual Insurance Co.* v. *J.T. O'Bryan & Co.*[10], decided in 1974 by the British Columbia Court of Appeal. Northwestern asked its agent to delete a certain risk from a policy. This was a standard practice in the insurance industry. The employee of the agency negligently assured Northwestern that the risk had been deleted. The company relied on that assurance. Subsequently, however, Northwestern was required to pay on the risk. On the basis of Hedley Byrne, the British Columbia Court of Appeal held both the agency and its employee liable for negligence. The court found that the employee owed a duty of care towards the insurance company, Northwestern, which he breached by his total lack of care. That lack of care was the sole cause of the damage.

Hence tort liability can apply vicariously to the employer, and the employee will also be personally liable for the tort the employee has committed. To protect its employee engineers, therefore, a corporation providing engineering services should ensure that its professional liability insurance policy extends to cover the liability of both the corporation and its employee engineers.

CONCURRENT TORTFEASORS

At times, torts concur to produce the same damage. It is possible for more than one party to be liable in such a tort action. The defendants are said to be "concurrent tortfeasors."

An example is the 1979 decision of the British Columbia Court of Appeal in *Corporation of District of Surrey* v. *Carrol-Hatch et al*[11]. An architect had designed a new police station, and had engaged a firm of engineers to perform structural design services. The building eventually underwent "extensive structural change" because of settlement problems The problems could have been avoided had proper soils tests been conducted. After examining two shallow test pits, the engineers had recommended to the architect that deep soils tests be taken. But the architect had rejected the recommendation, and the engineers had submit-

[10] 51 D.L.R. (3d) 693
[11] [1979] 6 W.W.R. 289

ted a ''soils report'' to the owner on the basis of a superficial examination of the shallow test pits only. Both the architect and the engineers were held liable to the owner. The Appeal Court agreed with the trial judge's apportionment of fault — 60% to the architect and 40% to the engineers — in the circumstances. The court held that the architect and engineers were concurrent tortfeasors; they had breached their duty to warn the owner that additional soils tests should be taken.

PRODUCTS LIABILITY

Products liability in Canada is not yet premised on strict liability, as it is in some jurisdictions in the United States. Canadian courts continue to apply principles of negligence in products-liability matters. Generally, where the plaintiff can establish that damage has clearly resulted from appropriate use of a product, the defendant manufacturer must then persuade the court that, considering the state of the particular industry's technological advance at the time, the manufacturer could not have foreseen the defective nature of the goods manufactured. Otherwise liability will arise.

Products liability has developed through considerations of both contract law and tort principles. The tort concept of fault has been applied to extend the limits of the scope of products liability; the development has also been premised on implied contractual warranties. This is a logical overlap between contracts and torts: a contract of sale is essential, at some point, for products liability to arise. For example, The Sale of Goods Act in Ontario[12] and similar statutes in the other common-law provinces imply various conditions and warranties in a sale-of-goods contract. One condition is that the goods will be merchantable and reasonably fit for the purpose for which they are sold. (Where a vendor attempts to limit his warranty obligation by contract, consumers may have the benefit of provincial consumer protection statutes requiring manufacturers to provide warranty protection to the consuming public.)

An awareness of products liability matters is important to engineers as professionals who may be engaged in manufacturing or sales, as well as to engineers as consumers.

[12] R.S.O. 1980, c. 462

The scope of products liability has substantially increased since the following principles were enunciated in the *Donoghue* v. *Stevenson* case[13]:

> A manufacturer of products which he sells in such a form as to show that he intends them to reach the ultimate consumer in the form in which they left him, with no reasonable possibility of intermediate examination, and with the knowledge that the absence of reasonable care in the preparation or putting up of the products will result in injury to the consumer's life or property, owes a duty to the consumer to take that reasonable care.

The Donoghue v. Stevenson case referred to the "manufacturer of products." Our courts have now extended the duty of care to others, for example, assemblers, installers, sub-manufacturers, importers, wholesalers, retailers, distributers, repairers and business suppliers. Wherever it can be established that injury ought reasonably to have been foreseen in any particular circumstances, a potential for products liability arises.

STANDARD OF CARE AND DUTY TO WARN

Risk of injury is inherent in some products. A manufacturer must warn the consumer of any dangerous potential of the product by appropriate labelling.

For example, in 1976 the Alberta Supreme Court (Appellate Division) decided the case of *George Ho Lem* v. *Barotto Sports Ltd. and Ponsness-Warren, Inc.*[14] The plaintiff, an experienced hunter, purchased a shot-shell reloading machine that was in no way defective; if operated in accordance with its clear instructions, the machine would produce only normal shot-shells. The plaintiff received personal instruction on the use of the machine, but he did not follow instructions; nor did he follow the instruction manual. He did not realize the consequences of not following the instructions. The machine mismanufactured some shot-

---

[13] *Supra*, at page 30
[14] (1976) 1 C.C.L.T. 180

shells, the chamber of the plaintiff's gun burst on firing, and the plaintiff was injured.

The shot-shell reloading machine was manufactured by one defendant and sold to the plaintiff by another defendant. The plaintiff's claim was that the defendants had failed in their duty to warn him adequately of the possibility of mismanufacture of a shot-shell which would nevertheless be normal in appearance.

The Appellate Court held that adequate instructions for the use of the machine had, in fact, been given. The plaintiff lost his case because he had not followed clear and simple instructions. The manufacturer's responsibility was to warn of dangers related to its product; this warning was given. The damage suffered by the plaintiff was not caused by failure in a duty owed to him by either of the defendants. Rather, the court held that damage was caused by the plaintiff's own fault. The manufacturer had met the very high standard of care expected of manufacturers of potentially dangerous products.

Not all manufacturers succeed in meeting that high standard of care, in the court's opinion. An example is the 1971 decision of the Supreme Court of Canada in *Lambert* v. *Lastoplex Chemicals Co. Limited et al*[15]. The male plaintiff was a consulting engineer who had graduated in mechanical engineering. He and his wife, the co-plaintiff, jointly owned a home, to which the plaintiff was doing some repairs. He purchased two one-gallon cans of a fast-drying lacquer sealer manufactured by one of the defendants. The plaintiff proposed to use it to seal a parquet floor, which he was installing in the recreation room of his home. The recreation room was located in the basement of the house; it was separated from the furnace and utility room by a plywood wall and by a fireplace. There was a door opening at the northerly end between the two rooms, but there was no door. In the furnace and utility room there was a natural-gas furnace and a natural-gas water heater, both of which had pilot lights.

The cans of lacquer sealer bore certain caution notices on the labels. The plaintiff read the labels before starting to apply the lacquer sealer. However, during the application, one or both of the pilot lights in the furnace and utility room

[15] [1972] S.C.R. 569

came in contact with the fumes or vapours of the lacquer sealer. There was an explosion and consequent damage when fire reached one of the half-full cans of lacquer sealer, which was open.

The product containers bore three separate warnings that the product was inflammable. But such warnings were inadequate, in the court's view. As stated by the court:

> The three labels on the cans of the respondent's product contained, respectively, the following cautions: (1) The largest label, rectangular in shape, which bore the name and description of the product, contained on its end panel, in addition to drying time information, the words "Caution inflammable! Keep away from open flame!" Along the side of this panel vertically and in small type, were the words "Danger— harmful if swallowed, avoid prolonged skin contact, use with adequate ventilation, keep out of reach of children". (2) A diamond-shaped red label with black lettering, issued in conformity with packing and marking regulations of the then Board of Transport Commissioners for Canada and having shipping in view, had on it in large letters the following: "KEEP AWAY FROM FIRE, HEAT AND OPEN-FLAME LIGHTS", "CAUTION", "LEAKING Packages Must be Removed to a Safe Place", "DO NOT DROP". (3) A third label, rectangular in shape, contained a four-language caution, which was in the following English version: "CAUTION, INFLAMMABLE — Do not use near open flame or while smoking. Ventilate room while using".

The evidence disclosed that a lacquer sealer sold by a competitor of the respondent contained on its label a more explicit warning of danger in the following terms: "DANGER—FLAMMABLE", "DO NOT SMOKE. ADEQUATE VENTILATION TO THE OUTSIDE MUST BE PROVIDED. ALL SPARK PRODUCING DEVICES AND OPEN FLAMES (FURNACES, ALL PILOT LIGHTS, SPARK-PRODUCING SWITCHES, ETC.) MUST BE ELIMINATED, IN OR NEAR WORKING AREA."

On appeal, the Supreme Court of Canada found in favour of the plaintiff. According to the court, in labelling

43

the product, the manufacturer had failed to warn a reasonable user of the danger of the pilot lights. The case emphasizes the need for extreme caution on the part of manufacturers in labelling products.

In its decision, the Supreme Court of Canada also made the following statements:

> Manufacturers owe a duty to consumers of their products to see that there are no defects in manufacture which are likely to give rise to injury in the ordinary course of use. Their duty does not, however, end if the product, although suitable for the purpose for which it is manufactured and marketed, is at the same time dangerous to use; and if they are aware of its dangerous character they cannot, without more, pass the risk of injury to the consumer.
>
> The applicable principle of law according to which the positions of the parties in this case should be assessed may be stated as follows. Where manufactured products are put on the market for ultimate purchase and use by the general public and carry danger (in this case, by reason of high inflammability), although put to the use for which they are intended, the manufacturer, knowing of their hazardous nature, has a duty to specify the attendant dangers, which it must be taken to appreciate in a detail not known to the ordinary consumer or user. A general warning, as for example, that the product is inflammable, will not suffice where the likelihood of fire may be increased according to the surroundings in which it may reasonably be expected that the product will be used. The required explicitness of the warning will, of course, vary with the danger likely to be encountered in the ordinary use of the product.

In the *Lambert* v. *Lastoplex Chemicals* case, Justice Laskin made an additional comment that points out the high standard of care imposed on the manufacturer and may be of interest to the engineer-consumer. The manufacturer was unable to avoid liability although he emphasized that the injured party was a qualified engineer:

> The question of special knowledge of the male appellant was argued in this Court as going to the duty of the

respondent to him and not to his contributory negligence. What was relied on by the respondent as special knowledge was the fact that the male appellant had qualified as a professional engineer, he knew from his experience that a lacquer sealer was inflammable and gave off vapours, and hence knew that it was dangerous to work with the product near a flame. This, however, does not go far enough to warrant a conclusion that the respondent, having regard to the cautions on the labels, had discharged its duty to the male appellant.

ECONOMIC LOSS

In the *Hedley Byrne*[16] decision, a tort matter, economic losses resulted from advice negligently given. In products-liability matters, however, there was a reluctance to extend liability for negligence to economic losses in the absence of actual physical injury until the 1973 decision of the Supreme Court of Canada in *Rivtow Marine Ltd.* v. *Washington Iron Works et al*[17]. The court decided that economic losses caused by the use of a defective product may, in some circumstances, be recoverable. In the Rivtow Marine case, the plaintiff chartered a logging barge, which was fitted with a crane manufactured by one defendant — Washington Iron Works, an American corporation — and distributed in Canada by another defendant. Washington Iron Works had also manufactured a second crane, virtually identical to the one on the logging barge chartered by the plaintiff. The second crane had been installed on a similar barge and had collapsed. The crane operator was killed, and there was an investigation by the Workmen's Compensation Board of British Columbia. Very serious structural defects were found in the crane chartered by the plaintiff. The defects were similar to those that were later found to have caused the death of the crane operator. It was established, from the evidence, that the defendants had both been aware for some time that the cranes were subject to cracking as a result of negligence in design. But neither of the defendants had taken steps to warn the plaintiff of the potential danger

[16] *Supra* at page 30
[17] (1974) 40 D.L.R. (3d) 530

and necessity for repair. The Supreme Court of Canada held that the defendants were under a duty to warn the plaintiff of the necessity for repairs as soon as they became aware of the defects and the potential danger. Thus the manufacturers were liable to the plaintiff in negligence for the economic loss attributable to their failure to warn. In other words, they were liable for lost profits while the crane was out of service for repairs.

The potential for liability for economic loss in products-liability matters was established in the Rivtow Marine decision. In 1977 the British Columbia Supreme Court decided the case of *MacMillan Bloedel Ltd.* v. *Foundation Co.*[18]. In the MacMillan Bloedel case, the defendant's workmen negligently damaged an electric cable that supplied electricity to the office building of MacMillan Bloedel. This damage interrupted the supply of electricity. As a result, the plaintiff was unable to continue its operations and was forced to send its employees home for the day. The plaintiff sought to recover the amount of the salaries and wages paid to its staff ($48,841.00). The court concluded that the defendant ought to have foreseen the economic harm caused to the plaintiff. The loss was a direct result of the defendant's negligence — the damage to the electrical cable. The court indicated that if economic loss was suffered by the plaintiff as a result of the defendant's negligent act, such loss was not too remote to be compensated. However, the court was not satisfied that the employees' salaries constituted an economic loss that resulted from the defendant's negligence. As the court pointed out, the salary payments were payable to the employees in any event. The court had no other evidence before it of economic loss that resulted from negligence, so the plaintiff's action was dismissed. But the court did indicate that it was willing to award damages for economic loss, if such economic loss could be properly accounted for.

However, the courts have imposed limitations on when economic loss may be compensated. In 1977, the Federal Court, Trial Division, decided the case of *Bethlehem Steel Corporation* v. *St. Lawrence Seaway Authority*[19]. The court asserted that, where there has been no damage to person or property in which the claimant might have some interest,

[18] (1977) 1 C.C.L.T. 358
[19] 79 D.L.R. (3d) 522

the right to recovery for pure economic loss remains very limited.

In the Bethlehem Steel Corporation case, a ship ran into a lift bridge over a canal, destroying the bridge and obstructing the canal. As a result, shipping through the canal was delayed for several days. The court found that the owner of the ship that struck the bridge was legally responsible. When the time came to distribute funds that had been paid into court, the validity of two particular claims became an issue. One of the claimants asked for loss of profits for two of its ships, which had been delayed for about two weeks. The other claimant asked for the cost of shipping certain cargo overland to Toronto, where it could be loaded for shipment to Europe. Neither claim was allowed.

The court stated that the Rivtow Marine case did not change the law. At best, the court suggested the Rivtow Marine case only extended liability to economic loss where there had been physical harm to the property of the claimant, or where such physical harm had been threatened. As there was no harm or threat of harm to the claimants' property in the Bethlehem Steel case, recovery for purely economic loss was denied.

However, a 1982 decision of the English House of Lords in *Junior Books Ltd.* v. *Veitchi Co. Ltd.*[20] may well influence future Canadian court decisions. The decision actually extended liability for consequential economic loss to a negligent subcontractor. A negligently laid floor was defective but had not caused danger to the health or safety of any person, or risk of damage to any other property belonging to the owner. The House of Lords pointed out that the defendant subcontractor was a specialist whose skill and knowledge was relied upon. No direct contractual relationship existed between the owner and the subcontractor, but the House of Lords noted that the relationship fell only just short of a direct contractual relationship. The damage caused to the owner was a direct and foreseeable result of the subcontractor's negligence in laying the defective floor. The subcontractors were in breach of a duty owed to take reasonable care. The subcontractor was held liable for the foreseeable consequences of the breach, including such items as the costs of replacing the floor, storage of books

[20] [1982] 3 All ER 201

during the carrying out of remedial work and removal of machinery to enable the remedial work to be carried out; lost profits due to business disturbance; lost wages; and overhead costs.

LIMITATION PERIODS

Limitations statutes of the common-law provinces generally provide that tort actions and actions for breach of contract must be commenced within prescribed time periods after the time the cause of action "arose." An action may be commenced at any time within the prescribed period. Should the action be commenced at a later date, it will fail. For tort actions in Ontario, the prescribed period generally is six years from the "time the cause of action arose." In contract, unless the contract expressly limits the time period (as is often the case), the prescribed period is generally six years but is extended to twenty years where the contract is signed under seal. An action commencing after the prescribed period is said to be "statute barred." There are, however, a number of statutes that expressly provide for other limitation periods, and such statutes will govern where applicable. Note that Section 47 of the Professional Engineers Act, 1984 of Ontario provides that an action against a member, licensee or holder of a certificate of authorization for damages that arise when the member provides a service within the practice of professional engineering must be commenced no later than twelve months after the service was, or ought to have been, performed. The court can, however, extend the time limitation if it is satisfied there are reasonable grounds.

In 1980, the Ontario Divisional Court considered the time limitation in *Attorney-General of Canada* v. *Libling et al.*[21] The court pointed out that it had to consider all the circumstances of the particular case, including the reason for the delay; the extent to which the plaintiff acted properly and reasonably once he knew whether the act or omission of the defendant engineer might give rise to a lawsuit; the increase in difficulty of proof that accompanies the passage of time; and any prejudice to either the plaintiff or the defendant engineer if the extension of the limitation period

[21] 29 O.R. (2d) 44

was or was not granted. In the Libling case, the defendant engineers said another engineer was responsible for certain roof-design problems. The court noted that attempts had been made to correct the problem with the roof, but the engineer in question had not been told of the problem for almost eleven years. He had no records of the roof design. The court was not prepared to extend the limitation period.

However, engineers should appreciate that the courts are empowered by the Professional Engineers Act, 1984 (as they were by its predecessor statute) to extend the limitation period. They may do so if circumstances are appropriate.

The Professional Engineers Act, 1984 does not use the more general reference found in limitation statutes: "from the time the cause of action arose." Instead, the Act refers, as indicated, to the date of performance of services. But contractors generally still need to understand the phrase "from the time the cause of action arose. The "time the cause of action arose" might not be when the contractor performs the work; it might be many years later, when deficiencies that resulted from the contractor's negligence start to appear. And the claim might conceivably be made in tort by someone who was not even a party to the original contract — a subsequent purchaser of a house, for example. Thus the contractor's potential liability may be extended for a remarkable period of time. In circumstances when both contractor and engineer are responsible for any deficiencies, a court might extend the limitation period against the engineer pursuant to section 47 of the Professional Engineers Act, 1984. The question of extended limitation periods is a matter of considerable controversy amongst contractors and professionals engaged in the construction industry. A review of certain case decisions is important to an understanding of the law.

The English courts have accepted the principle that the limitation period starts only when the damage manifests itself and the plaintiff first discovers it, or ought, with reasonable diligence, to have discovered it. An example is the 1976 English Court of Appeal decision in *Sparham Souter et al* v. *Town & Country Developments (Essex) Ltd. et al*[22]. The case involved negligence in the erection of a building.

[22] (1976) C.A. 858

The Court of Appeal considered the question of the time when the cause arises and stated:

> The cause of action accrues when the damage caused by the negligent act is suffered by the plaintiff and that cannot be before that damage is first detected, or could by the exercise of reasonable skill or diligence have been detected.

In 1976, the Ontario Court of Appeal heard the case of Dominion Chain Ltd.[23] The trial judge found that a roof failure was caused by the negligent construction procedures of the contractor and by the negligent performance of professional skills by the engineering firm on the project. The Court of Appeal considered the question of when a cause of action arises in tort and referred to the Sparham Souter decision as establishing the legal principle; that the cause of action arises when the damage is first detected, or ought to be detected. The reference by the Ontario Court of Appeal to the Sparham Souter decision represented a departure: in previous Canadian case decisions, the "time the cause of action arises" was held to be when the services were negligently performed[24]. It therefore became arguable that the principle enunciated in the Sparham Souter decision was applicable in Canada; the design professional could conceivably find himself liable for negligent design services performed more than six years before the defect is discovered.

The Ontario High Court of Justice, however, rejected the application of the Sparham Souter decision in its 1981 decision in *Robert Simpson Co. Ltd.* v. *Foundation Co.*[25] The case involved alleged negligence in the design, manufacture and installation of certain ceiling anchors, as well as alleged negligent misrepresentation that materials and method of construction were adequate. Justice Holland stated, in part:

> In the present case I am of the view that the damage occurred when the inadequate anchors were incorporated in the building, but, in any event, no later than the date at which the building was turned over to Simpsons. In

---

[23] 68 D.L.R. (3d) 385
[24] Schwebel v. Telekes (1967) 1 O.R. 541
[25] (1981) 34 O.R. 2d (1)

my opinion the law of Ontario has not yet adopted the test which found favour in *Sparham Souter* v. *Town and Country Developments (Essex) Ltd.* . . .

As more than six years had elapsed since the damage had so occurred, the Ontario High Court held that the limitation period had expired and the plaintiff could not succeed.

However, the decision of the Ontario High Court in the Robert Simpson case was reversed on appeal. In its 1981 decision in the case,[26] the Ontario Court of Appeal applied the concept endorsed by the English courts: in tort, the cause of action against the contractor arose not necessarily when the work was performed, but rather at such time as the damage was first detected or ought reasonably to have been detected.

In fact, in another case in 1981, the Ontario High Court of Justice reached the same conclusion. In *Viscount Machine and Tool Ltd.* v. *Clarke*,[27] Justice Henry held that the six-year limitation period during which an action in tort could be commenced against a negligent land surveyor commenced not when the negligent act was done but when the damage was discovered, more than six years after the survey had been negligently performed.

The decision of the Ontario Court of Appeal in the Robert Simpson case confirmed the application of the English precedent, the Sparham-Souter case, but the matter was further complicated by a subsequent English House of Lords decision. In 1982, the House of Lords heard *Pirelli General Cable Works Ltd.* v. *Oscar Faber and Partners.*[28] In the Pirelli case, the House of Lords expressly overruled the decision of the English Court of Appeal in Sparham-Souter, holding that the limitation period commences when physical damage occurred to the building whether or not the damage could have been detected by the exercise of reasonable skill or diligence at the date the physical damage occurred. The Pirelli case involved the construction of a chimney about one hundred sixty feet high. The chimney was made of pre-cast concrete. Unfortunately, the concrete used for the re-

---

[26] (1982) 360 O.R. (2d) 97
[27] 126 D.L.R. (3d) 160
[28] [1983] 1 All ER 65

fractory inner lining was partly made of a relatively new material, called Lytag, which was unsuitable for the purpose. Cracks developed, and eventually the chimney had to be taken down and replaced. The House of Lords acknowledged that it was difficult to determine when the damage actually occurred. But they pointed out that that is, in any event, a matter of evidence. In Pirelli, the House of Lords indicated that new legislation would be desirable, to ''remedy the unsatisfactory state of the law on this subject.'' In overruling the Sparham-Souter decision, the House pointed out that the concept endorsed in Sparham-Souter − of a ''date of discoverability'' − could lead to the investigation of facts many years after their occurrence. This might be unfair to a defendant unless a ''final longstop date'' could be prescribed, perhaps by statute.

However, the Supreme Court of Canada considered and decided not to adopt the Pirelli case in a significant 1984 decision in *City of Kamloops* v. *Nielsen et al.*[29] The Supreme Court confirmed that the municipality was liable to a house purchaser for the negligence of its building inspector, who failed to enforce a stop-work order during construction. The inspector had issued the stop-work order because the foundations had not been constructed in accordance with the approved plans. At the time of construction, the owner did not want to comply with the stop-work order. The construction was completed without complying with the order; eventually, the foundations subsided (the trial judge found the owner seventy-five per cent responsible and the municipality twenty-five per cent responsible for causing damages). No occupancy permit was issued. However, a plumbing permit was issued about eight months after the stop-work order was issued. About two years after the house was finished, it was sold to the plaintiff, who discovered that the foundations had subsided. The municipality was held to be liable for twenty-five per cent of the ''economic loss'' to the plaintiff. The ''loss'' was the cost of reconstruction plus ancillary expenses (the Supreme Court of Canada distinguishing *Kamloops* v. *Nielson* from the Rivtow Marine case).

In deciding not to follow the Pirelli case but to confirm the application, in Canada, of the Sparham-Souter principle in a tort action − that the limitation period commences

[29] [1984] 29 C.C.L.T. 97

when the damage is first discovered, or ought with reasonable diligence to have been discovered by the plaintiff – the Supreme Court concluded:

> There are obvious problems in applying Pirelli. To what extent does physical damage have to have manifested itself? Is a hair-line crack enough or does there have to be a more substantial manifestation? And what of an owner who discovers that his building is constructed of materials which will cause it to collapse in 5 years' time? According to Pirelli he has no cause of action until it starts to crumble. But perhaps the most serious concern is the injustice of a law which statute-bars a claim before the plaintiff is even aware of its existence. . . . Lord Fraser and Lord Scarman were clearly concerned over this. . . . The only solution in their eyes was the intervention of the Legislature.
>
> This Court is in the happy position of being free to adopt or reject Pirelli. I would reject it. This is not to say that Sparham-Souter, supra, presents no problem. As Lord Fraser pointed out in Pirelli the postponement of the accrual of the cause of action until the date of discoverability may involve the Courts in the investigation of facts many years after their occurrence. Dennis v. Charnwood Borough Council, [1982] 3 All E.R. 486 (C.A.) is a classic illustration of this. It seems to me, however, to be much the lesser of two evils.

OTHER RELEVANT TORTS

There are many different classifications of torts. Some of the other torts that may be relevant to engineers include:

(1) the tort of defamation, which is further divided into two classifications: libel and slander. In essence, the reputation of the plaintiff is damaged by untrue statements publicly made by the defendant. If the statements are made in writing, the tort is referred to as libel; if the statements are verbal, the tort is referred to as slander. If statements that damage a reputation are true, no liability arises.

(2) occupiers' liability. The occupier of property must exercise the required standard of care to ensure the safety of individuals coming onto that property. A duty of care extends to trespassers, although trespassers are not accorded a standard of care as are those coming onto the property for business reasons or as guests. Guests must be safeguarded against dangers the occupier is aware of. A higher duty is owed to those who come onto the property for business reasons; business visitors must be safeguarded against damages the occupier is aware of or ought to be aware of as a reasonable person. The occupier is under an obligation not to deliberately harm a trespasser; for example, he cannot set traps. In Ontario, The Occupiers' Liability Act of 1980 supersedes the common law. Liability is now governed by the Act, which specifies duties of care generally consistent with common-law principles. But the Act does not recognize the previous general common-law distinction between business and social guests.

(3) the tort of nuisance, designed to alleviate undue interference with the comfortable and convenient enjoyment of the plaintiff's land. For example, in 1972, the British Columbia Supreme Court decided *Newman et al.* v. *Conair Aviation Ltd. et al.*[30] The defendant aviation company's insecticide spray drifted onto lands for which the spray was not intended, and nominal damages were awarded. Another example is the 1974 decision of the Ontario Court of Appeal in *Jackson et al* v. *Drury Construction Co. Ltd.*[31] Blasting operations by a contractor resulted in fissures opening up in the granite bedrock. The fissures allowed material in a barnyard to escape into the percolating

[30] 33 D.L.R. (3d) 475

[31] 4 O.R. (2d) 735

waters feeding the plaintiff's well. The Court of Appeal concluded that the contractor should be liable. The following excerpt from the judgment of the Court of Appeal is of interest:

"It is to be observed that a blasting operation such as this cannot be viewed as a natural use of the land. It is inherently a dangerous operation. As long as the percolating waters found their way to the plaintiffs' premises, the plaintiffs ought not to have been deprived of its beneficial properties. Surely if, in the course of excavation, deleterious materials flow from the equipment onto the plaintiffs' lands or are placed directly on the plaintiffs' premises as a result of the dynamiting, it can scarcely be argued that the plaintiffs would not have a cause of action. In my view, the same principle should govern where the plaintiffs' percolating waters are polluted as a direct result of the defendant's blasting operations, even though the pollution comes from a source other than the defendant's property or premises."

CHAPTER FOUR

PROOF

THE BURDEN OF PROOF

In civil proceedings, such as actions in tort or contract, the plaintiff must generally prove his case against the defendant by persuading the court on a "balance of probabilities" that the facts are as the plaintiff alleges them, and that the defendant should be held liable. In certain criminal proceedings, an accused person must be proven guilty "beyond a reasonable doubt"; proof "on the balance of probabilities" is obviously different. Much has been written about these two degrees of proof. The degree of proof implied by the term "on the balance of probabilities" is obviously less than the degree of proving guilt "beyond a reasonable doubt."

In hearing a particular case, a court may be faced with conflicting testimony from witnesses; the court must decide which of the witnesses is more credible. A judge may have to accept one man's word rather than another's. As difficult as that may seem, it is not an unusual experience for a judge.

ENGINEERS AS EXPERT WITNESSES

Engineers often find themselves making appearances as expert witnesses in court. As an expert witness, the engineer often plays a vital and persuasive role. The expert is permitted to express opinions with respect to his or her area of expertise; the witness should be cautious, and restrict testimony to such areas. Non-expert witnesses are not usually permitted to express opinions; they are restricted to establishing the facts of the case.

The expert witness is usually enlisted by one of the disputants, and is thus allied with one "side" of a case. An engineer who acts as an expert witness must take his duties seriously. He can expect to be subjected to cross-examination by counsel for the other party. The engineer should not undertake to appear as an expert witness unless he is confident that he can handle cross-examination. It is likely that counsel for the other side will attempt, during cross-examination, to dissuade the court from accepting the engineer's opinions.

Preparation is of the utmost importance in litigation. The expert witness should clearly understand the issues in the lawsuit; he should be aware of the scope of questions that can be reasonably expected.

CHAPTER FIVE

CONTRACTS

It is important for the engineer in business to understand the essential elements of a contract. For a contract to be binding and enforceable, five elements must be present:

1. an offer made and accepted;
2. mutual intent to enter into the contract;
3. consideration;
4. capacity to contract;
5. lawful purpose.

Within the framework of these essential elements and in accordance with the contract rules the courts have developed, parties choose terms and conditions to define the nature of the agreement between them. The private nature of the law of contracts thus becomes most evident.

Contracts consist of benefits to and obligations of the contracting parties. Agreements are generally arrived at by choice or through negotiation. The law will enforce the provisions of a valid contract; the law will not intervene to impose contract terms more favourable than those negotiated between the parties.

In certain circumstances the law may intervene to declare a contract void, voidable or unenforceable; some of these circumstances will be discussed later in this text. However, the engineer must be aware of one basic premise: if a "bad business deal" is negotiated, the courts will not impose more favourable terms.

Parties can, however, always alter an existing contractual arrangement by mutual agreement, provided the amendment is effected within the framework of the essential contract elements.

ASSIGNMENT OF RIGHTS

Contractual benefits (i.e. rights arising pursuant to the contract; for example, the right to receive payment for services rendered) can be assigned to a third party by one of the contracting parties without the consent of the other party to the contract. For example, book debts or accounts receivable can be assigned. If contracting parties wish to limit such assignment rights, they should expressly provide that no rights under the contract are assignable to a third party without the written consent of the other contracting party.

CHAPTER SIX

OFFER AND ACCEPTANCE

An offer is a promise made by one person — the offeror — to another — the offeree. It may involve a promise to supply certain goods or services on certain terms, for example.

Not all contracts must be in writing. The offer may be communicated orally. For the purpose of evidence, however, it is preferable to effect communications in writing.

Until it is accepted, the offer may be withdrawn by the offeror unless it is made expressly and effectively irrevocable by its terms. The offer will lapse if it is not accepted within a reasonable period of time.

If the offeree does not accept all the terms of the offer but purports to accept the offer subject to a variation in its terms, no contract is formed. Rather, a counter-offer has been made by the offeree, who thereby becomes the offeror.

Acceptance of an offer must be clearly communicated.

Business offers are usually made subject to express terms. For example, a business might offer to supply a specified machine at a quoted price. The offer might contain a proviso — that acceptance of the offer can be made during a limited time period. The offer might also state that acceptance must be communicated in accordance with the terms of the quotation.

IRREVOCABLE OFFERS

An offeree might want to assure himself that an offer will not be revoked by the offeror before the offeree can accept it. This normally occurs in the tendering process, for example. Upon instructions from the owner, bidders submit offers or tenders that have been made irrevocable for a specific period of time. At any point during that period, the offer may be accepted and a contract will be formed. For reasons which will be noted, "contract consideration" is necessary where such irrevocable offers are submitted or such bids must be submitted under seal, in order to be binding.

THE OPTION CONTRACT

The option contract is another means of keeping an offer open for a certain period of time. The right to accept the offer is preserved until the offeree chooses to exercise the option. The offeror is thus precluded from revoking the offer. Something of value — for example, a payment of nominal amount — must be made at the time of entering into the option agreement in order to make the option contract enforceable.

An option agreement may be advantageous in many business situations. For example, an individual might want to purchase a particular business, but may be unwilling to make a firm offer until having completed a review of its financial and other business records. To prevent the owner from selling the business until completion of the investigation, the prospective purchaser may be able to persuade the owner to enter into an option agreement. For an agreed price (which is usually substantially less than the total purchase price of the business), the owner of the business becomes obligated to sell only to the prospective purchaser, during a specified period. And he can sell only upon the terms set out in the option agreement. A specific time limit is stipulated in the option to purchase agreement. If not exercised by the specified time, the exclusive option to purchase will expire.

Option agreements are particularly common in mining contracts. The party purchasing the option might wish to carry out exploration work before deciding to expend a large sum in acquiring property rights, for example.

Purchasing options might also be desirable in land development. A prospective purchaser might want to find out if he can acquire various pieces of land from various owners in a particular area before he makes a large expenditure on an overall land purchase for development purposes.

MANNER OF COMMUNICATION

(a) Timing

Accepting an Offer   The law has developed certain general "rules" to specify when communications are effective. There are several different ways to communicate. For example, suppose the parties establish the mail as the means of communication between them. If one party decides to accept an offer, the acceptance is effected when posted. Another example: the parties might establish the telegram as the means of communication. The "rule": a communication is effected at the time the message is delivered to the telegraph operator.

Unless the two parties agree to communicate by post or telegram, the communication of the acceptance of an offer is effected only when it is actually received by the offeror.

Revoking an Offer   Similar rules, however, do not apply to the timing of the revocation of an offer. Notwithstanding what means of communication is used, the general rule is that revocation is not effective until the offeree actually receives notice of the revocation.

Complications can arise. For example, an offeror might decide to revoke his offer. He communicates the revocation through the mails, but his letter takes a few days to reach the offeree. In the meantime, the offeree has written, effecting the acceptance of the offer by mailing his acceptance. The acceptance is valid. Thus, any offeror who intends to revoke an offer should do so as expeditiously as possible, by telephone or telex, for example.

(b) Governing Law   There is also a "rule" that relates to the determination of the law applicable to a contract. The general rule is that the law of the place where the acceptance of the offer becomes effective is applicable (unless otherwise agreed upon). For example, suppose an equipment supplier located in the Province of Ontario has provided a quotation by mail to a prospective customer located in the State of New York. The equipment supplier should expressly state in the quotation that any contract resulting from the acceptance of the offer will be governed by the laws of the Province of Ontario. The supplier will thus avoid the argument that the law of the State of New York   63 will apply to the contract (if, for example, acceptance of the offer is communicated by mail from New York State).

In 1983, the Nova Scotia Supreme Court, Appeal Division, decided *The Queen et al* v. *Commercial Credit Corp. Ltd.*[1] The decision confirms the "rule" that says acceptance is effective on despatch when the acceptance is mailed, and confirms that the rule also applies where acceptance is made by courier. In the Commercial Credit case, an offer of conditional sales was prepared by Commercial Credit, who was acting as agent for the parties to the contract. The offer was sent by courier to the offeree, who was located outside Nova Scotia. The acceptance was sent back by courier. The court held that the contract was therefore not made within Nova Scotia. Therefore a particular Nova Scotia statute, the Instalment Payment Contracts Act, did not apply. In its decision, the court stated in part:

> I am inclined to agree with the conclusion of the trial judge that the mailbox doctrine does apply here, although for slightly different reasons. It seems to me that in relation to both of the conditional sale contracts in question the purchaser and the vendors had nominated Commercial Credit as their agent to arrange for the execution of the contract documents. Commercial Credit employees prepared the documents and made certain that they were properly executed and then advanced the funds. They were the ones that chose the method of communication and having done so on behalf of both parties the mailbox doctrine was brought into play. Its extension to a courier service was sound in principle and, in my opinion, the contracts were therefore made outside of Nova Scotia when their acceptances were sent back to Commercial Credit. The Instalment Payment Contracts Act does not apply.

THE BATTLE OF THE FORMS

An equipment supplier usually attaches to its quotations certain terms and conditions pursuant to which the manufacturer is prepared to sell its product. These terms and conditions may describe warranty rights, terms of payment,

[1] 4 D.L.R. (4th) 314

termination, governing law, indemnities, etc. Often the offeree purports to accept the offer; but his offer is actually a counter-offer, because he demands terms and conditions of sale that differ from those attached to the original offer or quotation. Engineers involved in such equipment supply contracts should be cautious to ensure that acceptance of an offer (or counter-offer) is not made without a clear understanding of the terms and conditions that apply to the sale. As a general rule, the terms and conditions stipulated in an accepted counter-offer will prevail unless the person examining the counter-offer takes exception to any unsatisfactory terms or conditions.

Terms and conditions of sale should be examined and negotiated. As a practical matter, however, the terms and conditions—the "fine print"—are too often overlooked. If a contract dispute later occurs, the resolution of the dispute could be complicated. Sufficient attention should be paid to terms and conditions at the time of acceptance of the offer to prevent unnecessary complications.

CHAPTER SEVEN

INTENT

MUTUAL INTENT

The engineer should make sure that any contract document specifies the agreement between the parties on all essential terms.

LETTERS OF INTENT

The use of "letters of intent" in business is a very common practice. Businesses use the letter to express interest in proceeding with a particular transaction, usually on the basis of further negotiation and subsequent agreement. Sometimes letters of intent are clearly agreements to agree, rather than well-defined agreements. The agreements to agree do not constitute enforceable contracts: the courts will not enforce an agreement to agree. It is, in fact, no agreement at all.

To illustrate: in 1976, the Ontario Court of Appeal heard the case of *Bahamaconsult Ltd.* v. *Kellogg Salada Canada Ltd.*[1] There were certain omissions in a letter of intent relating to the sale of the shares of a company. The court noted:

> The trial Judge found that the document of October 10, 1969, was a contract complete in itself, and that while it was the intention of the parties to draw a further agreement, the subsequent agreement was only to spell out the mechanics of the transfer of the shares, and of the closing of the sale. With respect, we think that the trial Judge erred in so finding. We are all of the opinion that the document of October 10th does not contain certain essential terms, and that it was the intention of the parties that these terms would be negotiated between them and embodied in a subse-

[1] 75 D.L.R. (3d) 522

quent agreement. Since the parties were unable to agree upon those terms, there was no enforceable contract. The applicable principle of law is stated in the oft-quoted words of Parker, J., in *Von Hatzfeldt-Wildenburg* v. *Alexander*, [1972] Ch. 284 at pp. 288-9:

> It appears to be well settled by the authorities that if the documents or letters relied on as constituting a contract contemplate the execution of a further contract between the parties, it is a question of construction whether the execution of the further contract is a condition or term of the bargain or whether it is a mere expression of the desire of the parties as to the manner in which the transaction already agreed to will in fact go through. In the former case there is no enforceable contract either because the condition is unfulfilled or because the law does not recognize a contract to enter into a contract. In the latter case there is a binding contract and the reference to the more formal document may be ignored.

The court noted that both parties had referred to the document in question as "a letter of intent". Essential terms of the contract were missing; those terms could only be agreed on by further negotiation between the parties.

A letter of intent that does not contain all essential terms is not an enforceable contract. It can, however, serve a useful purpose: it may establish terms for negotiation and it may create some moral obligation between the parties to continue to negotiate in good faith.

To the inexperienced, the letter of intent can present considerable difficulties. A letter of intent could constitute an agreement, if it were sufficiently detailed. The engineer should be cautious when presented with "letters of intent"; he should consult a lawyer if he is in doubt as to the true nature of the letter. The precise drafting of contracts is better left to lawyers. The engineer in business can greatly simplify the contract preparation process by listing negotiated business terms, but it is advisable to seek legal advice when negotiating significant terms and when drafting the contract document.

CHAPTER EIGHT

CONSIDERATION

Consideration is an essential part of an enforceable contract. As Black's Law Dictionary points out, it is the cause, motive, price, or impelling influence that induces a contracting party to enter into a contract. Consideration can be described as something of value that is exchanged by contracting parties. A promise made by an engineer to design a structure in return for the payment of a fee is an example of a situation where consideration exists. Each party to the contract promises something in return for the other party's undertakings. The payment of money is not essential: consideration may consist of an exchange of promises, each promise representing something of value.

The courts are not normally concerned with the adequacy of consideration. There are exceptional circumstances, however. For example, if it is established that the contract was entered into under conditions amounting to undue influence, duress or fraud, the courts will provide relief.

Where consideration is not present in the form of promises or other mutual exchange of something of value, no contract is formed unless the document is "sealed." There are two kinds of seals. A mechanical device is used to imprint corporate seals on documents executed by corporations; the personal seal of the individual is a small red adhesive wafer. The ancient practice remains with us today and is recognized by the courts as a substitute for consideration. Originally, the use of the seal was considered an act of great importance, a clear indication that the promisor intended to be bound by his promise. The party making the promise is required to affix the seal to the document expressing the promise or undertaking.

The use of the seal is important in tendering procedures.

Often tenders submitted by bidding contractors are required to be irrevocable for a specific period of time; for example, an offer might be binding for twenty days following the date of the opening of the tenders. An "irrevocable" offer without consideration or a seal is simply a gratuitous promise; it is not legally binding. The offeror may revoke the offer at any time before its acceptance. When the offeror promises to hold an offer open for a specified period, separate consideration is required for the promise of irrevocability to be binding. This separate consideration is usually achieved through the use of a seal.

EQUITABLE ESTOPPEL

But should a party that makes a gratuitous promise (that is, a promise without consideration) be entitled to escape its moral obligations? Such obligations are strictly moral, and are not legally binding, but can still raise questions of an equitable nature. An example is the 1963 case, *Conwest Exploration Co. Ltd. et al* v. *Letain*[2], a decision of the Supreme Court of Canada. An option agreement that related to certain mining claims owned by the optionor had a time limit. The optionee had to take certain steps by a specified date in order to be entitled to exercise the option to acquire the mining claims. Before the option's expiry, the optionor became aware that the optionee would not be able to fulfill his obligations by the expiry date. The optionor implied that the time for fulfillment was extended. However, the promise to extend was not accompanied by consideration; hence, it was not strictly binding. Subsequently, the optionor reverted to his strict contractual rights, and insisted that the original expiry date must apply. The Supreme Court of Canada held that it would be inequitable if the optionor were permitted to enforce the original contract in the circumstances and that the optionor should therefore be "estopped" from reverting to his strict contractual rights.

The Conwest case is very important. Remember that, pursuant to contract law, consideration (or a seal) must be present in order to make an amendment to a contract enforceable — otherwise the amending promise is gratui-

[2] 41 D.L.R. (2d) 198

tous. Conwest provides a basis on which to argue that where the terms of a contract are amended without the consideration that would make the amending promise enforceable, there may be relief for the party that relies upon the gratuitous promise. The concept whereby such relief may be provided is called promisory or equitable estoppel. A court will only exercise its discretion to apply the concept of promisory or equitable estoppel, however, to avoid an obviously inequitable result.

The concept of equitable estoppel has been examined in other cases. The 1968 decision by the Supreme Court of Canada in *John Burrows Ltd.* v. *Subsurface Surveys Ltd. et al*[3] is an example. The plaintiff sought to enforce the terms of a promisory note. The terms were as follows:

> FOR VALUE RECEIVED Subsurface Surveys Ltd. promises to pay to John Burrows Ltd. or order at the Royal Bank of Canada the sum of forty-two Thousand Dollars ($42,000.00) in nine (9) years and ten (10) months from April 1st, 1963, payable monthly on the first day of May, 1963, and on the first day of each and every month thereafter until payment, provided that the maker may pay on account of principal from time to time the whole or any portion thereof upon giving thirty (30) days' notice of intention prior to such payment.
>
> In default of payment of any interest payment or installment for a period of ten (10) days after the same became due the whole amount payable under this note is to become immediately due.
>
> SUBSURFACE SURVEYS LTD.
[Sgd.] G. Murdoch Whitcomb
President

Although payments were made late, the holder of the note did not insist on all the terms. Continuing indulgences were granted to Subsurface Surveys Ltd. Eleven payments were accepted more than ten days after they were due. The parties eventually had a falling out. When one of the interest payments was thirty-six days overdue, the holder of the note decided to insist on the default clause. Subsurface Surveys was notified that immediate payment of the principal amount must be made, in accordance with the terms of the note.

Subsurface Surveys protested on the basis that the noteholder should be equitably estopped from enforcing its strict contractual rights in all of the circumstances of case. Subsurface Surveys argued that the holder of the note was contradicting an implied agreement between the two parties. The default clause of the note had been disregarded several times by the noteholder; Subsurface Surveys inferred that they had an agreement with the noteholder with respect to the default clause. The Supreme Court of Canada concluded that this evidence did not warrant such an inference.

In the John Burrows decision, the Supreme Court of Canada referred to the following statements of earlier court decisions on the principles involved:

> . . . it is the first principle upon which all Courts of Equity proceed, that if parties who have entered into definite and distinct terms involving certain legal results — certain penalties or legal forfeiture — afterwards by their own act or with their own consent enter upon a course of negotiation which has the effect of leading one of the parties to suppose that the strict rights arising under the contract will not be enforced, or will be kept in suspense, or held in abeyance, the person who otherwise might have enforced those rights will not be allowed to enforce them where it would be inequitable having regard to the dealings which have thus taken place between the parties . . .

> The principle, as I understand it, is that where one party has, by his words or conduct, made to the other a promise or assurance which was intended to affect the legal relations between them and to be acted on accordingly, then, once the other party has taken him at his word and acted on it, the one who gave the promise or assurance cannot afterwards be allowed to revert to the previous legal relations as if no such promise or assurance had been made by him, but he must accept their legal relations subject to the qualification which he himself has so introduced, even

though it is not supported in point of law by any consideration, but only by his word.

Justice Ritchie of the Supreme Court then stated in the John Burrows case:

> It seems clear to me that this type of equitable defence can not be invoked unless there is some evidence that one of the parties entered into a course of negotiation which had the effect of leading the other to suppose that the strict rights under the contract would not be enforced, and I think that this implies that there must be some evidence from which it can be inferred that the first party intended that the legal relations created by the contract would be altered as a result of the negotiations.
>
> It is not enough to show that one party has taken advantage of indulgences granted to him by the other for if this were so in relation to commercial transactions such as promisory notes it would mean that the holders of such notes would be required to insist on the very letter being enforced in all cases for fear that any indulgences granted and acted upon could be translated into a waiver of their rights to enforce the contract according to its terms.

On the facts, the John Burrows case was distinguished from the Conwest case.

In 1979, the Ontario Court of Appeal decided *Owen Sound Public Library Board* v. *Mial Developments Ltd. et al*[4], in which the issue of equitable estoppel was raised in an action for breach of contract. The contract in question was a construction contract, which provided that payments were to be made by the owner within five days of an architect's certificate. If the owner should fail to pay any sum certified as due by the architect within seven days, the contractor would be entitled to terminate the construction contract with the owner. The architect had certified such a sum as due. Soon after that, the parties agreed upon certain action; as a result, the owner assumed that the due date for payment to the contractor was being extended. Instead of making a payment, the owner had requested the contractor to have the corporate seal of one of its subcontractors

[4] 26 O.R. (2d) 459

affixed to a document supporting the architect's certificate. The contractor undertook to obtain the corporate seal. The payment date passed, but the contractor did not obtain the corporate seal. The contractor later purported to terminate the contract because of the owner's failure to pay within the time limit. The Court of Appeal concluded that the contractor's conduct had led the owner to believe that the time limit for payment would be extended until the subcontractor's sealed document had been provided. The court concluded that the owner's assumption was reasonable and held that the contractor should be estopped from invoking his strict contractual termination rights. Enforcement of contractual rights would be clearly inequitable. The contractor was attempting to take advantage of the owner's contractual default, but that default had been induced by the contractor's conduct.

The issue of equitable estoppel can be of particular significance to the engineer who is acting as a contract administrator. If an engineer waives any particular contractual rights, he may be faced with the argument that he (or the party on whose behalf he is acting) ought subsequently to be equitably estopped from reverting to his strict contractual rights. The success of the argument will depend upon the particular circumstances of each case.

CHAPTER NINE

CAPACITY

MINORS

In order for a contract to be binding and enforceable, all parties must have the necessary capacity to enter into a contract. Under the common law, not everyone has the "necessary capacity." For example, a contract with a minor is enforceable by the minor but unenforceable by the other party, unless it can be established that the contract concerned something that was necessary to the minor (for example, food, clothing, shelter, and so on) or unless the contract is ratified by the minor upon reaching the age of majority. The age of majority is now eighteen in Ontario, Manitoba, Saskatchewan, Alberta and Prince Edward Island; it is nineteen in Nova Scotia, New Brunswick and Newfoundland.

The age of majority is also nineteen in British Columbia. However, the Infants Act[1] of that province prevents the ratification of a contract made by a minor. That is, a contract made by a minor will generally remain unenforceable even if the minor attempts to ratify the contract after he or she has reached the age of majority.

DRUNKS AND LUNATICS

Contracts for non-necessaries entered into by lunatics or intoxicated persons are enforceable by the lunatic or drunkard but unenforceable by the other party — on two conditions. The other party to the contract had to be aware of the state of insobriety or lunacy. And the incapacitated party must repudiate the contract within a reasonable period of time. Anyone who claims to have signed a contract while inebriated will obviously have some very significant evidentiary difficulties: he must substantiate that he was drunk

[1] R.S.B.C. 1979, c. 196

when he entered into the contract, and he must show that the other party appreciated that he was drunk.

CORPORATIONS

Caution should be exercised in dealing with corporations. The engineer must make sure that it is within the powers of the contracting corporation to carry out the obligations described in the contract. If it is clearly beyond the power of the corporation to enter into the contract, the contract will not be enforceable. It is particularly important, when dealing with corporations that have been created by special statute of the federal or provincial legislature (such as a railway company, for example), to determine the nature of the corporation. Its incorporating statute must provide that the purpose of the proposed contract is within the powers of the corporation. During negotiations, it is advisable to require that the corporation expressly represent, in the contract, that it has the necessary capacity to enter into the contract, and that the contract will be enforceable against it.

In day-to-day business dealings with a corporation, reliance upon representatives of the corporation is appropriate as established in the case of *Royal British Bank* v. *Turquand*, an English case reported in 1856. A corporation is bound by the acts of its officials, provided such acts are within the actual, usual, or apparent scope of each such official's authority, and the party dealing with the corporation has no knowledge to the contrary, and provided there are no suspicious circumstances or prohibitions in the corporation's public documents. If there is any doubt about the authority of an official to act on behalf of a corporation, appropriate enquiries should be made, including a review of the corporation's public file. The file will include the corporation's charter documents and a listing of its directors and officers. A file is kept by the appropriate government department for each corporation.

CHAPTER TEN

LEGALITY

CONTRARY TO STATUTE LAW

A contract will not be enforced if the purpose of the contract is unlawful, that is, if it is illegal or void because it is contrary to any statute.

There are many examples of contracts contrary to statutory law. They include:

1. a contract contrary to the provisions of the Bankruptcy Act (Canada).[1] For example, the Act provides that where property is transferred between related parties and the transferor becomes bankrupt within one year of the transfer, the transfer is void as far as the Trustee in Bankruptcy is concerned. The Act also provides that if, within three months before bankruptcy, an insolvent party transfers property to a creditor with the intent of giving that creditor a preference over other creditors, the transfer is fraudulent and void;

2. a contract that is contrary to provincial workmen's compensation legislation. For example, section 17 of the Worker's Compensation Act of Ontario[2] provides that a contract between an employer and workman is invalid if it fixes an amount of compensation in lieu of compensation pursuant to the Act;

4. a contract that is contrary to the provisions of the Combines Investigation Act (Canada).[3] For example, a contract might repre-

[1] R.S.C. 1970, c. B-3
[2] R.S.O. 1980, c. 539
[3] R.S.C. 1970, c. 314

sent an attempt to prevent or unduly lessen competition, or to engage in "bid-rigging";

5. a contract that defeats a workman's lien rights contrary to section 15 of the Mechanics' Lien Act of Ontario;

6. a contract for services where the party to perform is required to be licensed pursuant to a statute or by-law. Failure to license may expressly preclude the right to contract for such services. However, as will be noted, case decisions to date have varied.

An illustration of Example Six is the 1958 decision of *Kocotis* v. *D'Angelo*[4]. The Ontario Court of Appeal heard the case. An electrician began an action for payment for work done and material supplied. The electrician was not properly licensed as an electrical contractor pursuant to a local by-law. In its decision, the court stated:

> It is plain to me that the object of the by-law was to protect the public against mistakes and loss that might arise from work done by unqualified electricians. It was not to secure the revenue from certificates or from licenses, because only certain qualified persons could obtain such certificates or licenses. It was plainly intended by the by-law to prohibit a maintenance electrician from undertaking the work of a master electrician or electrical contractor, and no maintenance electrician could lawfully contract for any electrical work. . . . Such a contract would be illegal and could not be enforced in the Courts.

The Kocotis decision was followed in the 1974 case of *Calax Construction Inc.* v. *Lepofsky*[5]. The case involved an unlicensed building contractor. The Ontario High Court of Justice concluded that the contract was illegal and unenforceable. The court referred to an excerpt from Cheshire and Fifoot, Law of Contract, at p. 334, 8th ed (1972):

> The general principle, founded on public policy, is that any transaction that is tainted by illegality in which both parties are equally involved is beyond the pale of

[4] [1958] O.R. 104
[5] [1974], 5 O.R. (2d) 259

the law. No person can claim any right or remedy whatsoever under an illegal transaction in which he has participated.

But the 1979 decision in *Monticchio* v. *Torcema Construction Ltd. et al*[6] represented a departure from the precedents. The Ontario High Court of Justice reviewed the earlier decisions on the question of licensing. The court pointed out that because the plaintiff was not a licensed drain contractor, the contract itself might be illegal. But the court felt that that was not a complete defence against the contractor's claim for payment. The by-law required only that the contractor be licensed; there was no prohibition against the sale of material, thus the court held that the contractor ought to at least be paid for material supplied. The judgment also indicated that a claim for payment for services on a time basis might succeed even though the contract was held to be void. The Monticchio case suggests a change in the attitude of the court with respect to compensation for unlicensed contractors. Whether such change will be endorsed generally by the courts remains to be seen.

CONTRARY TO COMMON LAW

A contract that contravenes statutory law may be illegal and/or void; a contract that is against public policy may be illegal and/or void according to common law.

Contracts may contain provisions that are against public policy. An example is a contract that contains restrictive covenants in restraint of trade. The court presumes initially that any agreement in restraint of trade is against public policy, and therefore void. However, a party seeking to enforce a restrictive covenant can overcome the court's initial presumption. The party must prove that, between the parties to the contract, the restrictive covenant is a reasonable one, and that it does not adversely affect the public interest.

An example is a contract for the purchase and sale of a business. The purchaser may require the vendor to covenant not to compete with the purchaser in a similar business in a specified area and over a specified period of time. Such a provision is generally referred to as a "non-competition agreement." Such an agreement might read:

> The vendor shall not for a period of five years from the date of closing, anywhere within the Province of Ontario, either alone or in conjunction with any individual, firm, corporation, association or other entity, whether as principal, agent, shareholder, employee or in any other capacity whatsoever carry on, or be engaged in, concerned with or interested in, directly or indirectly, any undertaking similar to any of the business carried on by the company being purchased within the respective territories in which such business is then carried on.

A purchaser seeking to enforce a non-competition agreement must persuade the court that the terms are reasonable between the parties, and that the nature of the vendor's services are such that the public interest would not be adversely affected if the covenant were enforced. There is no way of predicting what the court will determine to be "reasonable" in terms of time and geographic area. Each case will turn on its own facts. If the court is not persuaded that the terms are reasonable, the restrictive clause will not be enforced. If the court determines that the provisions are unreasonable, it will not intervene to enforce more reasonable terms.

Engineers often encounter similar restrictive covenants in employment contracts. Such contracts may attempt to restrict the employee after he leaves such employment. The courts will apply principles of reasonableness and public policy to determine the enforceability of non-competition clauses in employment contracts. The courts are reluctant to enforce restrictive covenants that would severely limit the former employee's ability to earn a livelihood; each decision will depend upon the particular circumstances.

CHAPTER ELEVEN

THE STATUTE OF FRAUDS

A contract may be verbal or written. Written contracts may be formed through correspondence. A contract can also be formed in part by correspondence and in part by discussions between the parties.

An agreement between parties is best set out in the form of a single written contract that clearly details the agreement. Such a contract may, in fact, be essential in order to ensure that it is enforceable; the statute of frauds (of the various common-law provinces) stipulates that certain types of contracts must be in writing to be enforceable.

For example, section 4 of *The Statute of Frauds of Ontario*[1] states:

> 4. No action shall be brought whereby to charge any executor or administrator upon any special promise to answer damages out of his own estate, or whereby to charge any person upon any special promise to answer for the debt, default or miscarriage of any other person, or to charge any person upon any agreement made upon consideration of marriage, or upon any contract or sale of lands, tenements or hereditaments, or any interest in or concerning them, or upon any agreement that is not to be performed within the space of one year from the making thereof, *unless the agreement upon which the action is brought, or some memorandum or note thereof is in writing and signed by the party to be charged* therewith or some person thereunto by him lawfully authorized.

Various types of contracts are referred to in the Statute

[1] R.S.O. 1980, c. 481

of Frauds. Those most likely to be relevant to the engineer are:

1. contracts relating to interests in land (that is, "any contract or sale of lands, tenements or hereditaments, or any interest in or concerning them");
2. those agreements that are not to be performed within the space of one year from the making thereof; and
3. guarantees of indebtedness.

Agreements relating to ownership interests and leasehold interests in land must be in writing to be enforceable. Contracts for the construction of buildings, on the other hand, need only be in writing if the contract cannot be performed within a year, although a written contract is certainly preferable to an oral one. The engineer should ensure that legal advice is obtained regarding interests in real property — land — affected by agreements. Real-property law is a matter that is most appropriately handled by lawyers.

A contract between an engineer and client is not usually a contract that must be in writing pursuant to the Statute of Frauds. Complications may arise, however, if performance by either party cannot be completed within one year.

A contract of guarantee must also be in writing in order to be enforceable. A distinction between a guarantee and an indemnification was discussed earlier in the text[2]. There is a further distinction between the two: an indemnification need not be in writing to be enforceable. In some circumstances, however, it may be difficult to distinguish between a contract of guarantee and one of indemnification. It is advisable to put both kinds of agreement in writing.

DERIVATION OF STATUTE

A statute of frauds is in force in each of the various common-law provinces of Canada. The statute is derived from the English Statute of Frauds. One purpose of the original statute was to answer concern about property interests. The statute was developed to prevent property

[2] *Supra*, at page 9.

interests being lost through fraudulent testimony about verbal agreements to convey property interests.

UNENFORCEABLE CONTRACTS NOT VOID

Although a verbal contract may be unenforceable because of the Statute of Frauds, it will not be treated as void: the courts will recognize its existence for certain purposes. For example, suppose that someone does not honour a verbal agreement to convey real property. The courts will not permit the defaulting party to retain a deposit cheque. The verbal agreement will be recognized so that the non-defaulting party may recover his deposit.

DESIRABILITY OF WRITTEN FORM

There is an obvious problem with any verbal agreement: it may be extremely difficult to substantiate the terms of the contract. This difficulty is best avoided by ensuring that all contracts are in written form.

CHAPTER TWELVE

MISREPRESENTATION, DURESS, AND UNDUE INFLUENCE

MISREPRESENTATION

A misrepresentation is a false statement or assertion of fact. If a misrepresentation is made to induce a party to enter into a contract, the misled party may apply to the court to have the contract rescinded. The court will treat the contract as voidable at the option of the party misled. When a contract is rescinded, it is cancelled or set aside.

An innocent misrepresentation is a false assertion made by a party who does not appreciate that the statement is false.

A fraudulent misrepresentation has been described, by the English Court of Appeal in *Derry* v. *Peek*[1], as a statement made "(1) knowingly, or (2) without belief in its truth, or (3) recklessly, careless whether it be true or false." The court noted that a party who makes a careless statement can have no real belief in the truth of what he states.

If a person deceived by a misrepresentation has entered into a contract, there are remedies available. The choice of remedy depends upon the kind of misrepresentation: innocent or fraudulent.

An innocent misrepresentation is remedied by rescission of the contract. The deceived party must repudiate the contract within a reasonable length of time. The deceived party is also generally entitled to claim compensation for damages in respect of any costs he may have sustained as a result of entering into the contract.

Where the misrepresentation is fraudulent, a deceived party is generally entitled to rescind the contract and to claim compensation for reasonable costs incurred as a

[1] [1889] 14 App. CAS. 337

result of entering into the contract. He can also sue for damages for deceit.

In addition, the Hedley Byrne decision has established potential liability for a negligent misrepresentation or negligent misstatement.

MISREPRESENTATIONS IN ENGINEERING SPECIFICATIONS

Contractors rely on engineering plans and specifications. If those plans contain misrepresentations, a contractor may be entitled to rescind the construction contract. An example is *Township of McKillop* v. *Pidgeon and Foley*[2]. The defendant contractor had submitted its tender based on a price estimated by an engineer. Later, the contractor discovered that considerably more excavation had to be done than estimated. (The job required approximately 16% more work than had been estimated.) Because of the error in the specifications, the contractor terminated its contract; the contractor then sued for breach of contract. The court heard evidence from a number of witnesses, including civil engineers and experienced surveyors. The court concluded that the error of 16% was excessive and would practically deprive the contractor of any profit; 16% might result in a loss to the contractor, in circumstances where he should not be asked to incur such loss. As the trial judge noted, contracts frequently stipulate that architects' or engineers' estimates are not binding upon the property owner. The judge noted that errors in estimates should not entitle the contractor to any further money and that, when contractors had sued in such cases, they had occasionally failed. However, the judge stated that there was no doubt the contractor had entered into the contract upon the faith of the estimate. It would be unreasonable, the judge stated, to expect the contractor to do the work of the engineer. The judge concluded that no deceit was involved; instead, a mistake had arisen from an innocent misrepresentation in the tendering documents. The defendant contractor was thus entitled to repudiate the contract.

[2] [1908] 11 O.W.R. 401

DURESS

If a contract is induced by means of intimidation, it is voidable. Such intimidation is termed "duress." Duress can be defined as threatened or actual violence or imprisonment used as a means of persuading a party to enter into a contract. The actual or threatened violence or imprisonment must be directed at the contracting party or a close relative. For example, lawful imprisonment — as the result of criminal prosecution — might be threatened. The court may nevertheless provide equitable relief. The case of *Mutual Finance Co. Ltd.* v. *John Wetton & Sons Ltd.*[3] is an example. A family member had forged a previous guarantee. Disclosure was threatened in an attempt to execute a second guarantee. At the time of the coërcion, the party threatening disclosure knew that the alleged forger's father was in ill-health, and that the shock of the disclosure might kill him. The guarantee was held to be unenforceable.

UNDUE INFLUENCE

Undue influence is similar to duress, but arises in less drastic circumstances. Undue influence occurs where one party to a contract dominates the free will of the other party to such an extent as to be able to coërce the dominated party into an unfair agreement. In such circumstances the dominated party is entitled to be relieved of his contractual obligations. Undue influence is an equitable concept. It is not frequent in business situations, where parties are at arms' length. It allows family members (for example, husband and wife or parent and minor child) to repudiate a contract where bargaining positions are unequal and undue influence occurs.

[3] [1937] 2 K.B. 389

CHAPTER THIRTEEN

MISTAKE

The subject of mistake in contract is of interest to engineers. It is often raised in connection with the submission of bids during the construction tendering process.

The common law has long recognized that it may be equitable to provide some relief if a mistake is made by one or both of the parties to a contract. But the courts will intervene to provide relief to a contracting party that has made a mistake only in rare circumstances.

RECTIFICATION

If contracting parties have clearly reached agreement but have recorded the provisions of the agreement inaccurately in a written contract, a "common mistake" has occurred. One of the parties to the agreement can apply to the court for an order of rectification. The order is used to correct an obvious common mistake. The party applying for the order must persuade the court that the written contract is inconsistent with the terms agreed upon by the parties; the mistake must be of a secretarial or recording nature.

UNILATERAL MISTAKE

A unilateral mistake is a mistake made by only one party to a contract. Unilateral mistakes by contractors in tendering have resulted in several interesting case decisions.

For example, in 1960 the British Columbia Court of Appeal heard the case of *Imperial Glass Ltd.* v. *Consolidated Supplies Ltd.*[1]. The contractor (or offeror) had used the wrong figure in calculating the price at which it would supply certain items. The offeree was aware that the offeror

---

[1] 22 D.L.R. (2d) 759

had made the mistake; however the offeror had not been induced to make the mistake by any representation of the offeree. The court was satisfied that the offeree's conduct was not fraudulent. The offeree's conduct might be open to question on moral or ethical grounds, but the court would not relieve the contractor from the consequences of his mistake.

But more recent decisions of Ontario courts hold that a contractor may be relieved of the consequence of unilateral mistake in certain circumstances.

An example is the 1977 decision of the High Court of Justice of Ontario in *Belle River Community Arena Inc.* v. *W.J.C. Kaufmann Co. et al*[2]. In submitting a bid, the defendant contractor had incorrectly transferred a figure from a summary sheet. The contractor's bid was therefore approximately $70,000 lower than intended. The total bid price was $641,603. The bid was submitted under seal, and was irrevocable for sixty days. When the contractor discovered his mistake, he attempted to withdraw his tender. There was no disagreement that the error had been made. The plaintiff refused to allow the contractor to withdraw the tender. More than a month after being informed of the mistake, the plaintiff attempted to accept the contractor's tender. The Ontario court was critical of the plaintiff's motive for accepting the tender. In finding in the contractor's favour, the court pointed out that the plaintiff had not submitted to the contractor a formal contract executed by the plaintiff. Hence the plaintiff had not technically obtained an unequivocal refusal from the contractor to enter into the contract. The plaintiff entered into a contract with another tenderer, then sued the defendant contractor for the difference between the amounts of the two tenders. Before deciding the case, the court considered the British Columbia Court of Appeal decision in *Imperial Glass Ltd.* v. *Consolidated Supplies Ltd.*[3]. The court noted a distinction in the nature of the mistake made in the two cases. In the Imperial Glass case, the court pointed out, the mistake consisted of using the wrong price in the calculation; in the Belle River case, the mistake consisted of omitting to transfer a figure from a summary

[2] (1977) 15 O.R. (2d) 738
[3] *Supra*, at page 89

sheet to an adding-machine tape. In his judgment, Justice Southey stated in part:

> There are American cases on the point which appear to go both ways. These American cases are referred to in Corbin on Contracts (St. Paul; 1960), vol. 3, p. 679, where the author, after recognizing the logic of the principle followed in the Imperial Glass case, expressed the view that the result of its application is frequently unjust, depending on the circumstances of the case. I am impressed with his statement, at p. 682, that a "just and reasonable man will not insist upon profiting by the other's mistake" and that "If he does insist, it seems reasonably certain that he will get either a law suit or a poor job performed with a continuing sense of grievance." The conclusion of the learned author as to the course that should be followed by the Courts is stated at p. 688:
>
> Courts refusing to decree recission for unilateral mistake often say that to do otherwise would tend greatly to destroy stability and certainty in the making of contracts. In some degree, this may be true; but certainty in the law is largely an illusion at best, and altogether too high a price may be paid in the effort to attain it. Inflexible and mechanical rules lead to their own avoidance by fiction and camouflage. A sufficient degree of stability and certainty will be maintained if the court carefully weighs the combination of factors in each case, is convinced that the substantial mistake asserted was in fact made, and gives due weight to material changes of position. Proof of the mistake should be required to be strong and convincing; but in many cases it is evident that such proof existed.

The Ontario High Court decided the Belle River case in favour of the contractor. The plaintiff appealed the decision to the Court of Appeal. In 1978, the Court of Appeal[4] upheld the trial judgment decision in favour of the contractor; the authorities had established a principle: an offeree cannot accept an offer that he knows has been made by mistake, and that affects a fundamental term of a contract. As the Court of Appeal pointed out, in substance the purported offer, because of the mistake, was not the offer the offeror

[4] (1978) 20 O.R. (2d) 447

intended to make, and the offeree knew that. The situation would be quite different, the Court of Appeal noted, if the offeree had not known the offer contained a mistake, and had accepted it at face value. The court also noted that in the United States, the weight of authority is very strongly on the side of the contractor who submits a tender by mistake, or one whose tender contains a mistake when the mistake is known to the person to whom the tender is made.

The Belle River case was applied in a 1979 decision of the Ontario Court of Appeal. The case was *Ron Engineering et al.* v. *The Queen in right of Ontario et al*[5]. A bid deposit cheque of $150,000 was paid with a tender submitted to the defendant, The Water Resources Commission. The tender concerned work to be done for the Commission in the City of North Bay. The tender contained a mistake similar to the one in the Belle River case: an amount had been omitted from the final price. In *Ron Engineering et al.* v. *The Queen*, the omitted amount was $750,058; the tender price was $2,748,000. The contractor was unable to contact the Commission before the tenders were open. Within an hour subsequent to the opening of the tenders, the contractor spoke to the Commission. He also sent a telegram notifying the Commission of the error; the telegram arrived the following morning. There was no doubt as to the genuineness of the error. The next highest bidder had tendered a price of $3,380,464. The trial judge found in favour of the Water Resources Commission.

The contractor appealed the decision, and the Court of Appeal found in favour of the contractor. The court stated, in part:

> The trial Judge, as I have said, dismissed the action. In fairness to him, it should be pointed out that his judgment was given some four months before the judgment of this Court in *Belle River Community Arena Inc.* v. *W.J.C. Kaufmann Co. et al.* (1978), 20 O.R. (2d) 447, 87 D.L.R. (3d) 761, holding that an offeree cannot accept an offer which he knows has been made by mistake which affects a fundamental term of the contract. In our view, the principles enunciated in that case ought to be applied to this case. The error in question

[5] (1979) 24 O.R. (2d) 332

has been found to be, as it obviously was, material and important. It was drawn to the attention of the Commission almost at once after the opening of tenders. Notwithstanding that, the Commission proceeded as if the error had not been made and on the footing that it was entitled to treat the tender for what it said on its face.

However, the Ontario Court of Appeal's decision in Ron Engineering was set aside in 1981 by a decision of the Supreme Court of Canada.[6] The decision has sparked considerable controversy in the construction industry. The Supreme Court, focussing on the issue of whether the contractor's tender deposit was to be forfeited, pointed out that there was a contract relating to the tender arrangements which was separate from the construction contract itself; and that the mistake in question was not communicated to the Commission at the time of tender submission and did not affect the contract relating to the tender arrangements. The following provision was contained in the Information for Tenderers:

"Except as otherwise herein provided the tenderer guarantees that if his tender is withdrawn before the Commission shall have considered the tenders or before or after he has been notified that his tender has been recommended to the Commission for acceptance or that if the Commission does not for any reason receive within the period of seven days as stipulated and as required herein, the Agreement executed by the tenderer, the Performance Bond and the Payment Bond executed by the tenderer and the surety company and the other documents required herein, the Commission may retain the tender deposit for the use of the Commission and may accept any tender, advertise for new tenders, negotiate a contract or not accept any tender as the Commission may deem advisable."

The Supreme Court held that because of the provision the contractor was contractually required to forfeit its tender deposit.

[6] 119 D.L.R. (3d) 267

Note that the Supreme Court of Canada, in deciding Ron Engineering, focused on the separate contract relating to the tendering arrangements and the contractual obligation to forfeit the tender deposit. It was not prepared to accept, as the Ontario Court of Appeal had, that the mistake was relevant to the contractual obligation to forfeit the tender deposit. But note that the Supreme Court did not expressly overrule the Belle River decision and future decisions may distinguish Ron Engineering and Belle River on their respective facts. However, the decision of the Supreme Court of Canada in Ron Engineering has undoubtedly complicated this area of the law. Predictability of case decisions in this area may well continue to be a difficult matter.

The court was prepared to distinguish between Belle River and Ron Engineering to the contractor's benefit in *Calgary* v. *Northern Construction Company Division of Morrison — Knudsen Company Inc. et al*[7], a 1982 case that involved a clerical error of $181,000 on a tender price of $9,342,000. When the contractor refused to execute the contract, the owner sued for the difference between the contractor's tender price and the second-lowest bidder's price, which was $9,737,000. The Alberta Queen's Bench applied Belle River and distinguished the Ron Engineering case. The Bench pointed out, in part:

> The similarities between the case at bar and Ron Enrg. are numerous and include:
> 1. The contractor's error in completing the formal tender was clerical in nature;
> 2. The error was not apparent on the face of the tender;
> 3. The error was promptly reported to the owner by the contractor;
> 4. The error was an honest one, committed unwillingly, and the conduct of the contractor was free from improper or dishonest motive;
> 5. The formal tender was irrevocable within the stated time period;
> 6. The contractor did not purport to withdraw its tender at any time.
> However, there are two crucial dissimilarities that dis-

[7] (1982) 23 Alta. L.R. (2d) 388

tinguish Ron Enrg. and render it inapplicable to the case at bar:

1. The city of Calgary accepted the contractor's tender. . . .

2. . . . The parallel clause in the information to tenderers herein is cl. 8 quoted in para. 9 of the facts herein. It contains no provision similar to para. 13 in Ron Enrg. . . .

Consequently, the case at bar remains to be decided by determining the applicability of the law of mistake to the formation or enforcement of the contract arising from the acceptance by the city of the contractor's tender. The authoritative case on that issue is the Ontario Court of Appeal decision in Belle River Community Arena Inc. v. W.J.C. Kaufman Co. Ltd . . . considered by the Supreme Court in Ron Enrg. but neither overruled nor disapproved by that court. . . .

CHAPTER FOURTEEN

CONTRACT INTERPRETATION

Parties to a contract sometimes dispute the meaning of part of the contract. Such disputes can be referred to the court. The court examines the specific wording of the part of the contract in question; and interprets the contract to determine its most reasonable meaning. The court may refer to dictionary definitions and to the intent of the parties who have entered into the contract. The parties to the contract will be bound by the court's determination of the most reasonable interpretation.

In interpreting the contract, the court may listen to witnesses. The witnesses may testify as to the intention of the persons who signed the contract; they may also discuss the contract's subject matter. The court may be required to judge the relative credibility of the witnesses. It is obviously preferable to avoid the problems involved in determining contract meaning by ensuring that contracts are prepared with sufficient clarity in order that the likelihood of the need for court interpretation will be minimized.

PAROL EVIDENCE RULE

A contract should embody all terms agreed upon by both parties. Problems can occur when terms that are agreed upon verbally are not included in the written contract that embodies the agreement. If a condition is agreed upon verbally but is not included in the contract, the condition is not part of the contract. The contract law rule that precludes evidence of the omitted condition is called the "parol evidence rule." It is most important that contracts be carefully drafted and that no agreed-upon conditions are omitted from the final contract form.

There are, however, exceptional circumstances in which courts will not always apply the parol evidence rule. For example, where it can be substantiated that a contract was to be effective only if an agreed-upon condition were to occur. The court considered such a situation in *Pym* v. *Campbell*[1]. A contract concerning shared ownership of the invention of a machine was entered into. It was established at trial that, during the financial negotiations, the parties had agreed that the purchase of the invention rights would be conditional: the invention would have to be approved by two engineers. There was no mention of this condition in the written contract. Two engineers were approached, but only one expressed a favourable opinion of the invention. The second engineer refused to do so. The defendants contended that the condition precedent had not been met, and that therefore no contract was formed. The court accepted the defendants' argument, and admitted evidence of the condition precedent. In part, the court stated:

> No addition to or variation from the terms of a written contract can be made by parol: but in this case the defence was that there never was any agreement entered into. Evidence to that effect was admissible; and the evidence given in this case was overwhelming. It was proved in the most satisfactory manner that before the paper was signed it was explained to the plaintiff that the defendants did not intend the paper to be an agreement till Abernethie had been consulted . . .

The "parol" evidence rule relates to evidence extrinsic to or "outside" the written contract prior to the execution of the contract. Only in exceptional circumstances is a contract affected by extrinsic evidence. But parties to a contract are free at any time to alter the terms of the contract after it has been signed, provided both parties agree and provided the essential contract elements are present in the amended contract.

IMPLIED TERMS

Occasionally, the parties to a contract overlook the inclusion of an obvious term. Where it is clearly reasonable to do

[1] [1856] 119 E.R. 903

so, the courts may give business efficacy to an agreement through "implication of terms." A leading case example is known as "*the Moorcock*."[2] The plaintiff was the owner of a steamship called the *Moorcock*. He paid for space at the defendants' wharf and jetty on the Thames. While the *Moorcock* was docked, the tide went out; the *Moorcock* settled on a ridge of hard ground and was damaged. The court held that the parties must have intended that the vessel would have been safe at low tide and hence implied a term accordingly in finding the defendants liable.

A more recent example is the case of *Markland Associates Ltd.* v. *Lohnes*[3], a 1973 decision of the Nova Scotia Supreme Court, Trial Division. The court held, in the absence of express terms, that the building contract in question implied several things: that the materials and workmanship should be of a proper standard or quality; that the work was to be carried out in a proper and workmanlike manner; that the work and materials, when completed and installed, would be fit for the purposes intended; and that the work would be completed in a reasonable time and without undue delay.

In 1961, the Ontario Court of Appeal heard *Pigott Construction Co. Ltd.* v. *W.J. Crowe Ltd.*[4] The court had to decide the advisability of implying a term into a contract. The court referred to earlier decisions involving implied terms in summarizing the principle:

> I have for a long time understood that rule to be that the Court has no right to imply in a written contract any such stipulation, unless, on considering the terms of the contract in a reasonable and business manner, an implication necessarily arises that the parties must have intended that the suggested stipulation should exist.

In 1983, the Ontario Court of Appeal heard *G. Ford Homes Ltd.* v. *Draft Masonry (York) Co. Ltd.*,[5] a case involving the supply and installation of two circular staircases. The court decided the contract implied that the staircases would comply with the requirements of the Ontario Building

[2] [1889] 14 P.D. 64
[3] [1973] 33 D.L.R. (3d) 493
[4] 27 D.L.R. (2d) 258
[5] 43 O.R. (2d) 401

Code. The subcontractor, G. Ford Homes Ltd., a fabricator and installer of residential staircases, was engaged to provide the staircases. Its representative attended at the homes in question, but declined an opportunity to review the architectural plans, which indicated the requisite clearance to comply with the Code. Instead, he took some measurements and offered a selection of staircases to the contractor. The installed stairways did not comply with the Ontario Building Code because the head room was one and a half inches short of the specified minimum. The building inspector said the staircases had to be replaced; and the subcontractor commenced a lawsuit to recover the cost of supplying and installing the stairs. The Ontario Court of Appeal pointed out that the subcontractor was an "expert" in the manufacture and installation of stairs, and was fully aware of the requirements of the building code. The court also said it was natural and reasonable, in the circumstances of the case, to rely upon the subcontractor to supply and install the staircases in compliance with the Ontario Building Code, and that it would be unrealistic to come to any other conclusion. The court pointed out that there could be no business efficacy to the contract without implying such a term, and that to sanction the installation of such a staircase in contravention of the Code would be tantamount to sanctioning an illegal contract. The principle enunciated in 1889 in the Moorcock case was applied.

CHAPTER FIFTEEN

DISCHARGE OF CONTRACTS

There are several ways to accomplish the discharge of a contract.

PERFORMANCE AS A MEANS OF DISCHARGE

When all parties to a contract have completed their respective obligations, the contract is at an end. So long as any obligations described in the contract remain unfulfilled, the contract remains in effect.

Some contracts provide that obligations will continue beyond initial performance and payment for services and materials. An example is an equipment supply contract that contains warranty provisions; the manufacturer undertakes to remedy defects within a specified time period. In building contracts, the contractor normally undertakes similar warranty obligations.

AGREEMENT TO DISCHARGE

The parties to a contract are always free to amend the contract; thus they can subsequently agree to cancel or terminate the contract upon mutually agreeable terms and conditions.

DISCHARGE PURSUANT TO EXPRESS TERMS

It is advisable to include, in a contract, provisions whereby any or all parties may terminate the contract upon the occurrence of certain events. For example, a contract might terminate upon the bankruptcy of one of the parties. Construction contracts often provide for termination if an engineer determines that the contractor has failed to complete the work properly, or has otherwise failed to substantially comply with the requirements of the contract.

DISCHARGE BY FRUSTRATION

At times, without default by either party to a contract, changing circumstances may radically change the obligations of the parties. If this happens, the contract will have been "frustrated," and is discharged by such frustration. However, the doctrine of frustration may not be used to justify discharge of a contract simply because circumstances have made performance more onerous than contemplated. Such an application of the doctrine would be contrary to the general principles that support the binding effect of contracts. The doctrine of frustration will be applied by a court only where exceptional circumstances, which were not contemplated by the parties, have arisen, and only where discharge by frustration is the only practical and reasonable solution.

For example, in 1917 the English House of Lords heard the case of *Metropolitan Water Board* v. *Dick, Kerr and Company, Limited*[1]. A contract had been entered into in July of 1914 for the construction of a reservoir over a six-year period. But because of special wartime legislation, the contractor was ordered to cease work in 1916 by the Ministry of Munitions. The character and duration of the wartime interruption changed the contract; when the contract was resumed, it was a different contract than that which had been entered into. The House of Lords held that the contract had been discharged by frustration, in the circumstances.

Equipment supply agreements and construction contracts often contain a "*force majeure*" provision. The *force majeure* clause usually provides that time for completion will be extended in the event of war, riot, insurrection, flood, labour dispute, or other events that arise beyond the control of either party. The contract being discussed in *Metropolitan Water Board* v. *Dick, Kerr and Company, Limited* did contain a *force majeure* provision. The Water Board

[1] [1918] A.C. 119

argued that the cease-work order should have been dealt with by an extension of time, according to the provision. The House of Lords did not apply the *force majeure* provision, but rather emphasized the very exceptional wartime circumstances affecting the contract. The case illustrates the very important principle that the doctrine of frustration will be applied to discharge a contract only in most exceptional circumstances.

In 1956, the House of Lords heard *Davis Contractors Ltd. v. Fareham Urban District Council*[2]. Completion of a building contract had been delayed due to the scarcity of labour. Neither party was in default. The contract required the contractor to build seventy-eight houses within an eight-month period. Because of the labour shortage, twenty-two months were needed to complete construction. The House of Lords did not accept the argument that the contract had been frustrated, concluding that there had been an unexpected turn of events, which simply rendered the performance more onerous than contemplated. The House of Lords pointed out:

> But, even so, it is not hardship or inconvenience or material loss itself which calls the principle of frustration into play. There must be as well such a change in the significance of the obligation that the thing undertaken would, if performed, be a different thing from that contracted for.

> Two things seem to me to prevent the application of the principle of frustration to this case. One is that the cause of delay was not any new state of things which the parties could not reasonably be thought to have foreseen. On the contrary, the possibility of enough labour and materials not being available was before their eyes and could have been the subject of special contractual stipulation. It was not made so. The other thing is that, though timely completion was no doubt important to both sides, it is not right to treat the possibility of delay as having the same significance for each. The owner draws up his conditions in detail, specifies the time within which he requires completion, protects himself both by a penalty clause for time

exceeded and by calling for the deposit of a guarantee bond and offers a certain measure of security to a contractor by his escalator clause with regard to wages and prices. In the light of these conditions the contractor makes his tender, and the tender must necessarily take into account the margin of profit that he hopes to obtain upon his adventure and in that any appropriate allowance for the obvious risks of delay. To my mind, it is useless to pretend that the contractor is not at risk if delay does occur, even serious delay. And I think it a misuse of legal terms to call in frustration to get him out of his unfortunate predicament.

A similar decision was reached in 1963, when the Manitoba Court of Appeal heard *Swanson Construction Company Ltd.* v. *Government of Manitoba; Dominion Structural Steel Ltd., Third Party*[3]. A contractor was forced to work in winter conditions rather than summer conditions, as planned, because the work site was not available soon enough. The contractor argued frustration of contract. But the court refused to invoke the doctrine of frustration. The court pointed out that in many building contracts, some delay in performance may occur; the contractor should have adjusted his tender price accordingly.

[3] 40 D.L.R. (2d) 162

CHAPTER SIXTEEN

BREACH OF CONTRACT

If a party to a contract fails to perform obligations specified in the contract, then the defaulting party has breached the contract. The innocent party is entitled to certain remedies; the particular remedy will depend upon the nature of the breach and the terms of the contract. For example, a breach of contract may entitle the non-defaulting party to sue for damages sustained as a result of the breach. The non-defaulting party may also be entitled to regard the contract as discharged because of the breach.

An obligation essential or vital to the contract is called a "condition"; an obligation that is not essential to the contract is called a "warranty." Breach of a condition or of a warranty may entitle the non-defaulting party to damages. But only breach of a condition that is of fundamental importance to the contract will entitle the non-defaulting party to consider the contract discharged by the breach.

Note, however, that the term "warranty" has several meanings. It can be used to describe a minor term of a contract; at other times, it can be used to mean "guarantee." For example, a manufacturer could guarantee the performance of his equipment, by issuing a warranty. The warranty he issues may be an essential term of the equipment supply contract. Establishing whether a provision of a contract is a condition or a warranty may be a key issue in a law suit. In the case of *Piggot Construction Co. Ltd.* v. *W.J. Crowe Ltd.*[1], the Ontario Court of Appeal quoted from the Law of Contract, Cheshire & Fifoot, 5th ed., page 488:

> Breach, no matter what form it may take, always entitles the innocent party to maintain an action for

[1] *Supra*, at page 99

damages, but it does not always discharge the contract. . . . when can a breach be regarded as a cause of discharge? The manner in which from time to time the answer to this question has been judicially expressed has not been altogether uniform, and it has been clouded by a distinction between dependent and independent promises that appeared of greater importance in the past than it does in the modern law. But at the present day it is possible to state with some confidence what the position is.

A breach of contract is a cause of discharge only if its effect is to render it purposeless for the innocent party to proceed further with performance. Further performance is rendered purposeless if one party either shows an intention no longer to be bound by the contract or breaks a stipulation of major importance to the contract. . . .

It may, indeed, be said in general that any breach which prevents substantial performance is a cause of discharge. Whether performance is substantially prevented or only partially affected is, of course, a question that depends upon the circumstances of each case.

In the Pigott Construction case, the contractor was under an obligation to proceed as expeditiously as possible; he was also obligated to provide temporary heat in the buildings during winter construction. The Court of Appeal held that neither obligation could be regarded as fundamental; neither obligation affected the substance and foundation of the transaction between the parties. Hence a breach of either provision could not be regarded as sufficient cause to discharge the contract.

It is often difficult to establish whether a breach might entitle the non-defaulting party to treat the contract as terminated. To avoid the difficulty, construction contracts very often contain a special provision: if the engineer determines that the contractor's performance has been inadequate, then the contract may be terminated by the engineer's client, the owner.

REPUDIATION

When one party to a contract expressly tells the other party that he has no intention of performing his obligations, the declaring party has repudiated the contract. He need not express his intentions verbally; he might indicate by his conduct that he will not perform his contractual obligations. The non-defaulting party can either ignore the breach — in which case the contract continues — or he can assume that the contract has been discharged by the repudiation. If the non-defaulting party treats the contract as discharged, he may claim damages against the defaulting party. The right to elect to discharge the contract makes it impossible for a defaulting party to avoid contractual obligations by announcing that he has no intention of fulfilling the contract. If the non-defaulting party elects to discharge the contract, he is required to communicate his intention to the defaulting party "with reasonable dispatch."

REMEDIES

A non-defaulting party is entitled to damages for losses incurred as a result of breach of contract. The injured party may also be entitled to a *quantum meruit* remedy; he may also be eligible for equitable remedies called "specific performance" and "injunction."

The court must determine the amount of damages to be awarded as a result of a breach of contract, by applying long-established principles. As stated in the landmark 1854 English case decision in *Hadley* v. *Baxendale*[2]:

> Where two parties have made a contract which one of them has broken, the damages which the other party ought to receive in respect of such breach of contract should be such as may fairly and reasonably be considered either arising naturally, i.e., according to the usual course of things, from such breach of contract itself, or such as may reasonably be supposed to have been in the contemplation of both parties, at the time they made the contract, as the probable result of the breach of it.

[2] (1854) 9 Exch. 341

Hence, damages should flow naturally from the breach or be reasonably forseeable by both parties at the time of entering into the contract. If the contract were entered into under special circumstances, and if those special circumstances were communicated between the parties at the time when the contract was formed, then those special circumstances would be taken into account in determining the damages resulting from the breach. The Hadley v. Baxendale judgment is of further assistance:

> Now, if the special circumstances under which the contract was actually made were communicated by the plaintiffs to the defendants, and thus known to both parties, the damages resulting from the breach of such a contract, which they would reasonably contemplate, would be the amount of injury which would ordinarily follow from a breach of contract under those special circumstances so known and communicated. But, on the other hand, if these special circumstances were wholly unknown to the party breaking the contract, he, at the most, could only be supposed to have had in his contemplation the amount of injury which would arise generally, and in the great multitude of cases not affected by any special circumstances, from such a breach of contract. . . .

The plaintiffs in the Hadley v. Baxendale case operated a mill. The plaintiffs asked the defendants, who were carriers, to deliver a broken crank shaft to its manufacturer for repairs. Through the defendants' neglect, delivery of the shaft was delayed. The crank shaft was essential to the mill's operation, but the plaintiffs did not communicate its importance to the defendants. The plaintiffs brought an action for damages for lost profit during the delay period. As the court noted, however, the defendants were not told that lost profits would result from a delay in the delivery of the shaft.

Today, contracting parties often seek to limit the extent of damages for which they might be responsible. Liability may be limited in the terms of the contract itself. For example, an equipment supply contract might state that:

In no event whatsoever will the manufacturer be

responsible for any indirect or consequential damages howsoever caused.

DUTY TO MITIGATE

A party that suffers a loss through a breach of contract must take reasonable steps to mitigate or reduce the amount of damages suffered. The plaintiff is expected to behave in a reasonable manner in mitigating damages. If he does not, his conduct will be taken into account when the court is fixing the damage award.

PENALTY CLAUSES

Contracts often contain provisions whereby a party is required to pay prescribed damages if a certain event occurs — for example, if the contract is not completed by a specified date. However, the parties must make a genuine attempt at the time of entering into the contract to pre-estimate the amount of damages likely to occur as a result of such breach; otherwise, the court will not uphold such provisions. As previously noted, the amount of damages awarded by a court will be based upon the actual damages that result from the breach and in contemplation of (or foreseeable to) the parties at the time of the formation of the contract. Hence a court will not enforce a penalty clause that does not represent a genuine pre-estimate of damages.

QUANTUM MERUIT

Suppose that certain services have been requested and performed, but that no express agreement was reached between the parties as to what payment would be provided in return for the services. In such a situation, the court will award payment by implying that the party performing the services ought to be paid a reasonable amount, that is, an amount determined on the basis of *quantum meruit*—"as much as is reasonably deserved" for the time spent and materials supplied.

Quantum meruit may apply in other situations. For example, a contract might expressly provide for payment, but if the party obligated to pay repudiates the contract and the 109 innocent party elects to treat it as discharged, *quantum meruit* may apply. For example in 1968, the Supreme Court of Canada decided *Alkok* v. *Grymek*[3]. The defendant owner had repudiated a construction contract with the plaintiff. The contract provided that the owner would pay the contractor a fixed amount, in accordance with an agreed-upon schedule, for completion of various parts of the work ''upon the Architect's certificate (when the Architect is satisfied that payments due to Sub-Contractors have been made).'' The contractor failed to satisfy the architect that sub-contractors had been paid. As well, the owner and the architect complained that there were defects in the construction, which had been delayed. The owner terminated the contract and engaged other contractors to complete the building. The court determined that the contractor's failure to satisfy the architect that sub-contractors had been paid did not amount to breach of an essential term of the contract. The breach did not justify the owner's termination of the contract. Nor did the evidence of defective workmanship or delay go to the root of the contract. The courts decided that the owner's repudiation of the contract was not appropriate. The contractor succeeded in his claim to recover for work done on a *quantum meruit* basis.

SUBSTANTIAL COMPLIANCE

A contractor might substantially comply with the terms of a contract, yet fail to comply with some minor aspect of the contract's provisions. The contractor will be entitled to be paid the contract price less the cost of damages caused by any such failure. This principle is called the doctrine of substantial compliance. For the doctrine to apply, however, the facts must substantiate that the contract deficiencies are of a minor nature. An example is the 1951 decision of the Ontario Court of Appeal in *Fairbanks Soap Co. Ltd.* v. *Sheppard*[4]. The court had to decide whether the contractor was entitled to payment for equipment supplied and installed. The contractor had substantially complied with the terms of the contract; there were minor defects, which were

---

[3] [1968] S.C.R. 452

[4] [1952] 1 D.L.R. 417

remediable without excessive cost. The Court of Appeal referred to the applicable principles as follows:

> On the question of substantial compliance, the case of *H. Dakin & Co.* v. *Lee*, [1916] 1 K.B. 566, is a leading case. The law was there laid down by Ridley J. in the Divisional Court — and the judgment of the Divisional Court was sustained on appeal — in the following language [p. 569]: "It seems to me, however, from the authorities that where a building or repairing contract has been substantially completed, although not absolutely, the person who gets the benefit of the work which has been done under the contract must pay for that benefit. . . ."

> The principle stated in *Dakin* v. *Lee*, supra, is simply this, that the person who has done the work and/or supplied the materials should be paid what he deserves for what he has done. Here the trial Judge has arrived at an amount of which he concluded the defendant was deserving, by deducting the sum of $600 as the cost of making the necessary adjustments and adding the necessary parts to put the machine in proper running order.

SPECIFIC PERFORMANCE AND INJUNCTION

The remedies of specific performance and injunction are equitable remedies; they supplement the remedy of damages. The courts will not grant the remedies of specific performance or injunction where damages provide sufficient relief.

SPECIFIC PERFORMANCE

To remedy a contract dispute, the courts may, where appropriate, require a party to a contract to perform a contractual obligation. This remedy is called "specific performance." It is most often granted in cases concerning contracts for the sale of land. The courts presume that, when one has contracted to purchase particular land and

111

the contract is breached by the vendor, a damage award of money will not be satisfactory. Therefore the vendor will be required to convey the land, in accordance with the agreement of purchase and sale. A breach of contract for the sale of a unique item of personal property — for example, an antique automobile — may also result in a court award of specific performance. The vendor will be required to fulfill his obligation to sell the item to the purchaser only where the property in question is sufficiently unique that damages for breach of contract will clearly not provide an adequate remedy to the purchaser.

Where it would have to supervise the performance of an obligation, the court will not grant the remedy of specific performance. Hence, breach of a contract for engineering services, construction, manufacturing, or installation of machinery will not result in an award of specific performance.

INJUNCTION

An injunction is a court order that prohibits or restrains a party from the performance of some act, such as a breach of contract. A court will not grant the remedy of injunction unless the contract contains a "negative covenant"; a negative covenant is a promise not to do something. In a non-competition agreement, for example, the promise not to compete for a specific period of time within a defined geographical area is a negative covenant. A court might order an injunction to restrain a party from breaching the covenant. Before an injunction will be granted, however, the court will apply tests of reasonableness as to time and geographic limitations, and will consider public policy with respect to such "restraint of trade" contracts.

CHAPTER SEVENTEEN

FUNDAMENTAL BREACH

The doctrine of fundamental breach has received considerable attention by our courts, particularly in the past ten
years. As the case illustrations will indicate, the doctrine
may be very significant to engineers.

The doctrine of fundamental breach may be applied to a
contract that contains an exemption clause; essentially, it
renders the exemption clause ineffective in the event of a
fundamental breach of contract. An "exemption clause" is a
provision whereby contracting parties may limit the extent,
in whole or in part, of liability that arises as a result of
breach of contract.

An example is the case *Harbutt's Plasticine Ltd.* v. *Wayne
Tank and Pump Co. Ltd.*[1] A contract was entered into for the
design and installation of storage tanks for stearine, a
greasy wax that is one of the main ingredients of plasticine.
As part of the contract, the contractors designed a plastic
pipe-line wrapped with electrical heating tape; the pipe-line
was to be used to liquefy the stearine, in order to convey it
from one point to another. The plastic pipe became dis-
torted under the heat. It sagged, cracked and the stearine
escaped and became ignited. The plaintiff's factory was
completely gutted by the fire. The trial judge concluded that
the contractor was in fundamental breach of contract. The
court stated:

> In breach of their contract the defendants designed,
> supplied and erected a system which was thoroughly —
> I need not abstain from saying *wholly* — unsuitable for
> its purpose, incapable of carrying it out unless drasti-
> cally altered, and certain to result not only in its own
> destruction but in considerable further destruction and
> damage . . . the supply of the useless and dangerous

[1] [1970] 1 All E.R. 225

durapipe, coupled with the useless thermostat was a breach of the basic purpose which might be described as total, going to the root of the contract.

The contract contained a provision that limited the contractor's liability for accidents and damage to £2,300. The Court of Appeal held that, because of the fundamental breach, the contractors were not entitled to rely on the liability-limiting provision. The contractors were held liable for the cost of reinstating the factory, an amount determined at trial to be in excess of £170,000.

The Harbutt's Plasticine case provided an important principle: in the event of a fundamental breach, that is a breach of such a nature as to go to the very root of the contract, an exemption clause in a contract would not afford protection to the party that committed the fundamental breach.

The Harbutt's Plasticine precedent has been applied by Canadian courts. However, the precedent was recently dramatically overruled in a 1980 decision by the English House of Lords, in a case called *Photo Production Ltd.* v. *Securicor Transport Ltd.*[2] The House of Lords stated that the whole foundation of the Harbutt's Plasticine case was unsound.

In Photo Production, a security contract was entered into between a manufacturer and a security company. During a night patrol at the factory, one of the employees of the security company started a fire. The fire spread out of control and destroyed the factory and its contents, together valued at £615,000. The contract contained an exemption clause that limited the contractor's liability:

> Under no circumstances shall the Company [Securicor] be responsible for any injurious act or default by any employee of the Company unless such act or default could have been foreseen and avoided by the exercise of due diligence on the part of the Company as his employer; nor, in any event, shall the Company be held responsible for; (a) Any loss suffered by the customer through burglary, theft, fire or any other cause, except insofar as such loss is solely attributable

[2][1980] 1 All E.R. 556

to the negligence of the Company's employees acting within the course of the employment. . . .

No negligence was alleged in the Photo Production case. (The House of Lords noted that the trial judge had found the motives of the employee who started the fire to be "mysteries which it was impossible to solve.") The trial judge held that the defendants were entitled to rely on the exemption clause. The Court of Appeal reversed the trial judge's decision, and applied the doctrine of fundamental breach, as in Harbutt's Placticine. The House of Lords expressly reversed the decision of the Court of Appeal. The House of Lords overruled the application of the fundamental breach doctrine and enforced the provisions of the exclusion clause. In an interesting discussion relating to express and implied contractual terms, the House of Lords stated:

> A basic principle of the common law of contract, to which there are no exceptions that are relevant in the instant case, is that parties to a contract are free to determine for themselves what primary obligations they will accept. They may state these in express words in the contract itself and, where they do, the statement is determinative; but in practice a commercial contract never states all the primary obligations of the parties in full; many are left to be incorporated by implication of law from the legal nature of the contract into which the parties are entering. But if the parties wish to reject or modify primary obligations which would otherwise be so incorporated, they are fully at liberty to do so by express words. . . .

> Applying these principles to the instant case, in the absence of the exclusion clause which Lord Wilberforce has cited, a primary obligation of Securicor under the contract, which would be implied by law, would be an absolute obligation to procure that the visits by the night patrol to the factory were conducted by natural persons who would exercise reasonable skill and care for the safety of the factory. That primary obligation is modified by the exclusion clause. Securicor's obligation to do this is not to be absolute,

but is limited to exercising due diligence in their capacity as employers of the natural persons by whom the visits are conducted, to procure that those persons shall exercise reasonable skill and care for the safety of the factory.

The doctrine of fundamental breach has been applied in Canada. For example, in 1979, the Ontario High Court of Justice decided *Murray* v. *Sperry Rand Corporation et al*[3]. The vendor of a farm harvestor was prevented from relying upon a disclaimer clause in his contract with the purchaser. The "disastrous failure of the machine" to achieve the promised level of performance precluded reliance on the disclaimer. The Ontario High Court stated that the disclaimer clause in the contract would not protect the vendor against breach of a fundamental term of the contract. The court referred to a number of cases in Canadian courts where the fundamental breach doctrine has been applied, in rendering exemption clauses ineffective. The court referred specifically to an excerpt from the judgment of Lord Denning, of the Court of Appeal in England. Lord Denning also gave judgment in *Harbutt's Plasticine*.

> . . . it is now settled that exempting clauses of this kind, no matter how widely they are expressed, only avail the party when he is carrying out his contract in its essential respects. He is not allowed to use them as a cover for misconduct or indifference or to enable him to turn a blind eye to his obligations. They do not avail him when he is guilty of a breach which goes to the root of the contract.

The Supreme Court of Canada referred to the overruling decision in the *Photo Production* decision in its 1980 decision in *Beaufort Realties (1964) Inc. and Belcourt Construction (Ottawa) Limited and Chomedey Aluminum Co. Ltd.*[4] The case involved the effect of a waiver of lien clause signed by the subcontractor, Chomedey Aluminum. The Court of Appeal of Ontario had found that the clause was, in effect, an

[3] 23 O.R. (2d) 457
[4] [1980] 2 S.C.R. 718

exclusionary or exemption clause. The contractor had failed to pay the subcontractor and was therefore in fundamental breach of the subcontract. The issue was whether or not the exclusionary waiver clause applied in the circumstances of the fundamental breach. The clause provided:

"ARTICLE 6. The Subcontractor hereby waives, releases and renounces all privileges or rights or privilege, and all lien or rights of lien now existing or that may hereinafter exist for work done or materials furnished under this Contract, upon the premises and upon the land on which the same is situated, and upon any money or monies due or to become due from any person or persons to Contractor, and agrees to furnish a good and sufficient waiver of the privilege and lien on said building, lands and monies from every person or corporation furnishing labour or material under the subcontractor."

The Supreme Court of Canada, in referring to the *Photo Production* decision, indicated that the question of whether such a clause was applicable where there was a fundamental breach was to be determined according to the true construction or meaning of the contract (not on the *Harbutt's Plasticine* rationale that, as a rule of law, fundamental breach precluded reliance on an exemption clause). In its determination of what that true meaning was, the Supreme Court decided that the clause should not apply in the circumstances of the contractor's fundamental breach. The Ontario Court of Appeal had pointed out, in effect, that it would not be fair and reasonable for the subcontractor to continue to be bound by its waiver of lien rights as the contractor had deliberately refused to perform its basic payment obligations under the subcontract. The Supreme Court of Canada did not expressly refer to the "fair and reasonable" rationale of the Ontario Court of Appeal. Nevertheless, in the end result, the equitable outcome as determined by the Ontario Court of Appeal was preserved in the *Beaufort Realties* decision by the Supreme Court of Canada.

As a practical matter, the engineer in business should pursue the negotiation of exemption clauses limiting liability where appropriate, in terms as advantageous as possible.

CHAPTER EIGHTEEN

THE AGREEMENT BETWEEN CLIENT AND ENGINEER

A contract between a client and a professional engineer must include all the essential contract elements.

A contract between a client and an engineer will not usually specify the measure of the standard of care in performance that is expected of the engineer. The contract will simply state that the engineer is to provide engineering services in connection with a particular project. The document may detail the scope of such services, but it will not necessarily specify the degree of care that is required of the engineer in carrying out those services. That degree of care will be an implied term in the contract. As pointed out earlier, an engineer is liable for incompetence, carelessness or negligence that results in damages to his client; he is responsible as a professional if he does not perform with an ordinary and reasonable degree of care and skill. The standard of performance expected of the engineer in contract is essentially the same as the standard expected in tort law, unless otherwise provided by a particular contract.

Most engineers are likely aware of the frequency of court actions against professionals. The potential magnitude of damage claims flowing from breach of contract for negligently performed engineering services can be enormous! Professional engineers should carry appropriate and adequate professional liability insurance coverage.

THE AGENCY RELATIONSHIP

By entering into a client-engineer agreement, the engineer usually enters into an agency relationship in which the client is the principal and the engineer is the agent. As an agent, the engineer must be careful to act only within the scope of his authority as agreed upon with his principal. If an engineer exceeds the scope of his authority, he may be liable to his principal for damages resulting from his actions. For example, suppose an engineer acts as agent on behalf of a client to negotiate the terms of a construction contract. He should seek the client's approval of all terms before confirming acceptance of the contract, unless the client has otherwise clearly authorized the engineer.

THE ENGINEER'S REMUNERATION

The client-engineer agreement should be in written form. The contract should clearly outline the nature of the project, the nature of the services that are required, the basis of payment, and all general terms and conditions mutually acceptable to both client and engineer. If an engineer is retained by a client to perform services, and if he undertakes to do so without agreeing with his client on the amount of remuneration to be received, the law implies that the engineer shall be paid a reasonable amount for his services on a *quantum meruit* basis. A suggested schedule of fees, published by a provincial engineering association, should provide a reasonable basis on which to determine remuneration.

ESTIMATED FEE

When an engineer enters into a contract with a client, he should estimate, if required and appropriate, the amount of his total fee cautiously. He should also emphasize to the client that his quoted total fee is only an estimate. The issue of discrepancies between estimates and final costs has come before the courts. An example is the 1979 decision of the Ontario High Court of Justice in *Kidd* v. *Mississauga Hydro-Electric Commission et al*[1]. In proposing to undertake a study, a consulting engineer estimated that the cost of his support staff would be $5,000.00. The actual cost of the support staff was $14,447.00. The consulting engineer brought an action to recover the full cost of the support staff. The court held that, in the circumstances, the engineer's client was entitled to rely upon the engineer's exper-

[1] 97 D.L.R. (3d) 535

tise in making the estimate. The following excerpt from the court's judgment is of interest:

> . . . I consider that the reference to $5,000.00 has a major effect upon the liability of the defendant. Admittedly the plaintiff could not give a precise estimate of the cost of support staff, but he was an experienced consultant — and even if he were not, it surely is incumbent upon a professional man to estimate the cost of services at something closer to the eventual figure than was done here . . . . I do not, of course, mean to say that all estimates are necessarily binding. Clearly they are not, and the plaintiff here might well have been allowed, because of the vagueness of his estimate, a substantial margin of error. But where the eventual figure is almost three times the original estimate, it is my view that the estimator should be held to that original figure.
>
> I can find no authority directly supporting the conclusion just reached. Normally if the contract fails to set a price (and certainly no firm price was set here) the Courts will set a reasonable price upon a *quantum meruit* and it is here conceded that, the merit of the study aside, the support staff work was done and the charges therefore were appropriate. But the essential distinction here is that a figure was mentioned, that it was wildly inadequate, and the defendant committed itself to payment because that figure was mentioned. This may be no more than another example of the negligent misrepresentation principle enunciated in *Hedley Byrne & Co. Ltd.* v. *Heller & Partners Ltd.*, [1964] A.C. 465. The duty upon the representor was there expressed by Lord Reid at p. 486, as follows:

> A reasonable man, knowing that he was being trusted or that his skill and judgment were being relied on, would, I think, have three courses open to him. He could keep silent or decline to give the information or advice sought; or he could give an answer with a clear qualification that he accepted no responsibility for it or that it was given without that reflection or inquiry which a careful answer would require; or he could simply answer without any such qualification. If he chooses to adopt the last course he must, I think, be held to have accepted some responsibility with the inquirer

121

which requires him to exercise such care as the circumstances require.

In the case at bar it seems to me the plaintiff adopted the third course, In the light of (a) the plaintiff's familiarity with reports of this nature and the work involved, and (b) the eventual cost of the support staff work, I cannot conceive that the answer was given carefully. This is an action in contract for payment not one in tort for negligence, but the obligations of the plaintiff and the consequences for breach must be at least as great.

It may be also that the contract can be viewed as one for the payment of support staff at a cost of approximately $5,000, and because the charge was not close to that figure the Court will give judgment for the only figure mentioned. . . .

STANDARD-FORM ENGINEERING AGREEMENTS

Recommended forms of agreement for professional engineering services between client and engineer and between engineers and other consultants are available from provincial associations, such as the Association of Professional Engineers of Ontario, and from other sources, such as the Association of Consulting Engineers of Canada. The standard-form engineering agreements currently available have been carefully developed. The forms set out very good basic contract formats. Some require more detail of completion than others with respect to project definition, the description of engineering services to be provided and the engineer's fee for services rendered. The general terms and conditions set out in the forms cover important aspects of the contractual relationship between the parties. But additional terms, conditions or modifications to the standard form may be necessary. A standard-form contract may constitute a satisfactory form of agreement between parties, but the standard-form contract may not always suffice. Each contract should be "tailored" so that it accurately records the particular agreement between the parties, a drafting process that is usually best left to lawyers. The importance of ensuring that contracts are competently drafted cannot be overemphasized.

LIMITING LIABILITY BY CONTRACT

The doctrine of fundamental breach has been discussed, and we have considered its applicability in Canadian cases. Any contract must take the doctrine into account. There is no reason a contract between an engineer and client cannot contain a provision whereby the engineer limits, to some extent, his or her liability for damages resulting from performance of engineering services. Such a provision may well be totally unacceptable to the client, however. Insistence upon an unreasonable provision may well result in the loss of a prospective client. An example of an unreasonable clause might be one that limits liability to an amount less than the engineer's fee for the project.

A more reasonable approach is to limit the engineer's potential liability to the extent of his professional liability insurance coverage. If such an approach is taken, the details of the liability coverage should be communicated to the client, so that he can assess the appropriateness of the coverage.

ENGINEER'S COMPLIANCE WITH THE LAW

An engineer who provides engineering services is expected to comply with common-law principles relating to tort and contract. In addition, he or she must comply with all statutes and regulations applicable to the particular nature of engineering services performed. The engineer is expected to have a reasonable knowledge of applicable statutes and regulations. He or she should ensure an awareness of requirements by investigating applicable federal and provincial laws relevant to the industry within which particular engineering services are being provided.

There are many federal and Ontario statutes of a technical nature. The engineer should keep his knowledge of relevant statutes and regulations up to date. Government sources and provincial engineering associations should be of assistance. He should also obtain legal advice on particular matters as may be required. The following list of technical statutes is illustrative rather than exhaustive:

1. The Hazardous Products Act (Canada), R.S.C. 1970, c. H-3
2. Consumer Packaging and Labelling Act (Canada) S.C. 1970-71-72, c. 41
3. The Boilers and Pressure Vessels Act, R.S.O. 1970, c. 45
4. The Building Code Act, R.S.O. 1980, c. 51
5. The Construction Lien Act, 1983, S.O. 1983, c. 6.
6. The Drainage Act, R.S.O. 1980, c. 126
7. Elevating Devices Act, R.S.O. 1980, c. 135
8. The Environmental Assessment Act, R.S.O. 1980, c. 140
9. The Environmental Protection Act, R.S.O. 1980, c. 141
10. Public Transportation and Highway Improvement Act, R.S.O. 1980, c. 421
11. The Mining Act, R.S.O. 1980, c. 268
12. The Municipal Act, R.S.O. 1980, c. 302
13. The Occupational Health and Safety Act, R.S.O. 1980, c. 321
14. The Occupiers' Liability Act, R.S.O. 1980, c. 322
15. The Ontario New Home Warranties Plan Act, R.S.O. 1980, c. 350
16. The Operating Engineers Act, R.S.O. 1980, c. 363
17. The Pits and Quarries Control Act, R.S.O. 1980, c. 378
18. The Planning Act, 1983, c. 1.

An examination of the list will indicate the diversity of statutes with which an engineer may be required to be familiar. The statutes to be complied with will vary according to the nature of the contract. For example, in a contract dealing with real property (land), requisite approvals may be required to subdivide land; and relevant statutes may include the Planning Act and the Municipal Act. (Legal advice should be obtained where interests in real property are involved.)

In addition to statutes, there are many codes and building regulations with which the engineer must comply. For example, electrical codes, provincial building codes and municipal by-laws that relate to structural, fire, health and other safety requirements. Compliance with municipal zoning or licencing by-laws may also be required.

In fulfilling a contract, the engineer must be careful to comply with all applicable laws; otherwise, serious problems may arise. Failure to comply with building permit requirements, for example, may expose the engineer's client to substantial additional cost or other loss, for which the engineer may find himself responsible.

As already indicated, an engineer should be especially cautious when involved in a contract dealing with real property. The body of law concerned with land is singularly complex. Much of it is derived from concepts developed in feudal England. As a result, the laws tend to be filled with archaic terms and somewhat unusual concepts. It is extremely important to obtain legal advice where interests in real property are involved.

Although a comprehensive review of the law of real property is outside the scope of this text, there are some aspects of it that should be of particular interest to engineers. For example, many governments have actively attempted to plan the growth of communities they oversee. In Ontario, this desire for planned growth has led to a system of "subdivision control." The Planning Act of Ontario provides that, with certain exceptions, land shall not be divided (that is, sold in separate parts to different parties) unless a "consent" under the Planning Act has been obtained or the sale is in accordance with a "registered plan of subdivision." When the owner wants to divide land into parcels, he or she seeks a consent to the "severance" from the appropriate government body. This duty is often performed by the "committee of adjustments" for the municipality where the land is located.

When a person (for example, a land developer) buys one large parcel of land and wants to sell it in many small parts, the owner usually registers a plan of subdivision. The owner submits a detailed plan to the municipality. Generally, this is a lengthy process and involves negotiations between the developer and the municipality; also a variety of government agencies usually consider the plan.

The Planning Act is not limited to commercial land

125

developers; rather, it applies whenever someone seeks to sell a piece of land that "abuts" (touches) other land owned by the same person.

The penalties for violating the Planning Act are severe. Section 49(21) of the Planning Act provides that any sale or agreement that contravenes the Act fails to "create or convey any interest in land." The effect of this section is dramatic. Suppose A "buys" land from B, who owns a piece of abutting land. If A and B have not obtained a consent, and if the sale is not in accordance with a plan of subdivision, A and B have violated the Planning Act. Section 49(21) of the Act effectively "voids" the sale, so A does not own the land, even if he paid for it. Recovering the purchase price from B may prove difficult or impossible. To avoid this problem, A's lawyer should find out who owns adjoining land when he or she performs the "search."

The control of land subdivision is one of the methods used by government to control development. However, the Planning Act allows municipalities to review development even if no division of land is involved. A municipality may designate an area as one where "site-plan control" is in effect. In a site-plan-control area, detailed plans for any development must be approved by the municipality. Often municipalities demand that plans for particular projects be modified.

Following is a list of provincial statutes relating to the control of developments:

> Alberta: Planning Act, R.S.A. 1980, c. P-9.
> British Columbia: Municipal Act, R.S.B.C. 1979, c. 290.
> Manitoba: Planning Act, S.M. 1975, c. 29.
> New Brunswick: Community Planning Act, R.S.N.B. 1973, c. C-12.
> Newfoundland: Urban and Rural Planning Act, R.S.Nfld. 1970, c. 387.
> Nova Scotia: Planning Act, S.N.S. 1983, c. 9.
> Prince Edward Island: Planning Act, R.S.P.E.I. 1974, c. P-6.
> Quebec: Land Use Planning and Development Act, S.Q. 1979, c. 51.
> Saskatchewan: Planning and Development Act, R.S.S. 1978, c. P-13.

CHAPTER NINETEEN

THE QUESTION OF CONCURRENT LIABILITY IN TORT AND CONTRACT

Unless otherwise stated in a contract, the standard of care expected of an engineer in performing services pursuant to a contract is the same standard of care by which an engineer's performance is measured in tort. This "overlap" raises the question of whether an engineer can be concurrently liable for both breach of contract and tort. The consequences of simultaneous liability raise some rather startling possibilities. For example, the measure of damages for breach of contract may not always be the same as the measure of damages arising in tort. And limitation periods may differ in contract and in tort.

An illustration is provided by the 1967 decision in *Schewebel* v. *Telekes*[1]. The action against a notary public alleged negligence in acting for the plaintiff in the purchase of a home. The Ontario Court of Appeal concluded that the plaintiff's action was not in tort but in contract; the court noted that the duty of care arose by virtue of a contractual relationship, and had no existence apart from that relationship. The court concluded that, where breach of contractual duty is involved, the limitation period of six years runs from the breach of duty, rather than from the time that breach was or ought to have been discovered. In tort, however, as the Ontario Court of Appeal noted in 1976 in *Dominion Chain Co. Ltd.* v. *Eastern Construction Co. Ltd. et al.*[2], and as the Supreme Court of Canada confirmed in 1984 in *City of Kamloops* v. *Nielsen et al.*[2a] the limitation period starts to

---

[1] [1974] 3 O.R. (2d) 481
[2] *Supra*, at page 50.
[2a] [1984] 29 C.C.L.T. 97

run not when the services are performed, but when the damage is first detected or ought to have been detected.

Questions may also arise with respect to the respective liabilities of concurrent tortfeasors. Suppose, for example, that one of the tortfeasors has precluded liability by virtue of a contract with the plaintiff. The point is illustrated in the Dominion Chain Case. Dominion Chain Co. Ltd. entered into separate contracts with a contractor and with an engineer in connection with the construction of a factory. The factory roof developed very serious leaks five years after construction. Dominion Chain initiated an action against the contractor and the engineer, but the trial judge dismissed the action against the contractor because a clause in the contract limited the contractor's liability. As owner, Dominion Chain had, in the contract, waived its right to make claims against the contractor after the guarantee period had expired. Although the contractor was not contractually liable to the owner because the guarantee period had expired, the trial judge concluded that the damage to the roof was, however, the result of negligence by both the contractor and the engineer, apportioned 75% and 25% respectively. The trial judge then applied Section 2 of The Negligence Act of Ontario[3]. The Act provides that where two persons are found at fault or negligent, they are jointly and severally liable to the person suffering the damage. Between themselves, however, in the absence of any contract, each is liable to make contribution and indemnify the other in the degree in which they are respectively found to be at fault or negligent. The trial judge concluded, therefore, that as only the engineer was required to satisfy the owner's damages, the contractor should contribute to the engineer 75% of such damages. The trial judge's decision was appealed. The Ontario Court of Appeal[4] did not agree with the trial judge. Noting that a contractor and an engineer may be liable in tort as well as in contract for negligent performance of contractual duties, the Court of Appeal held that the contractor was not required to contribute 75% of the damages to the engineer. The court pointed out that Section 2 of The Negligence Act did not apply unless both the contractor and the engineer, as joint tortfeasors, were liable

[3] R.S.O. 1980, c. 315

[4] 68 D.L.R. (3d) 385

to the plaintiff, Dominion Chain Co. Ltd. The contractor had escaped such liability because of its contract with the plaintiff; thus it was not liable to contribute 75% of the damages to the engineer.

The decision of the Court of Appeal in Dominion Chain was appealed by the engineer. The Supreme Court of Canada[5] concluded that, because of the contract between the owner and the contractor, the contractor was not liable to make contribution to the engineer. However, the court focussed on contractual provisions to decide the appeal; there was no direct consideration of the question of concurrent liability in tort and contract.

Hence, in Dominion Chain, the Ontario Court of Appeal concluded that an engineer or a contractor may be concurrently liable in tort as well as in contract. But the Supreme Court of Canada has not since made a decision on the principle of concurrent liability; the question has yet to receive its direct consideration.

The issue of concurrent liability in tort and contract has recently attracted considerable attention, but that is not to imply that it is an issue that has not yet come before the Supreme Court of Canada. On the contrary: in 1973, in *Halvorson Inc.* v. *Robert McLellan & Co. et al.*[6], an engineer was sued for negligent modification of a winch system. The Supreme Court of Canada stated, at page 74:

> . . . Halvorson's only possible claim is against McLellan & Co. for negligent performance of its contract for erection services, not in tort as was contended.

In addition, in 1973, the British Columbia Court of Appeal decided *Sealand of the Pacific Ltd.* v. *R.C. McHaffie Ltd. et al*[7]. Damages were awarded for breach of contract as a result of an architect's failure to enquire as to the fitness of certain experimental material. The British Columbia Court of Appeal considered whether tort liability should arise where the relationship was governed by contract. The court concluded that the facts in the case did not meet the test suggested by the Supreme Court of Canada in *J. Nunes*

[5] [1978] 2 S.C.R. 1346
[6] [1973] S.C.R. 65
[7] [1974] 6 W.W.R. 724

Diamonds Ltd. v. *Dominion Electric Protection Co.*[8], as follows:

> Furthermore, the basis of tort liability considered in *Hedley Byrne* is inapplicable to any case where the relationship between the parties is governed by a contract, unless the negligence relied on can properly be considered as "an independent tort" unconnected with the performance of that contract . . . . This is specially important in the present case on account of the provisions of the contract with respect to the nature of the obligations assumed and the practical exclusion of responsibility for failure to perform them . . .

To summarize, the concept of concurrent liability in tort and contract has been endorsed by the Ontario Court of Appeal. But earlier decisions of the British Columbia Court of Appeal and of the Supreme Court of Canada indicate a reluctance to endorse the concept. Hence, the law on the point is presently in a somewhat uncertain state in Canada; English and American case decisions, however, have endorsed the concept[9].

---

[8] [1972] S.C.R. 769
[9] The Canadian Bar Review, June, 1980, "The Negligent Contract-Breaker", B. Morgan, p. 299.

CHAPTER TWENTY

THE DUTY OF HONESTY

When an engineer enters into a contract, he assumes a duty of care in performing his services. Implicit in that duty of care is the duty of the engineer to act with absolute honesty.

The penalties for dishonesty can be severe. Where fraud is involved, a contract may be repudiated and damages may be awarded for the tort of deceit. In addition, fraud is a criminal offence; it is punishable, on conviction, by imprisonment for up to ten years. Section 338 of the Criminal Code[1] (Canada) provides, in part:

> (1) Every one who by deceit, falsehood or other fraudulent means, whether or not it is a false pretence within the meaning of this Act, defrauds the public or any person, whether ascertained or not, of any property, money or valuable security, (a) is guilty of an indictable offence and is liable to imprisonment for ten years. . . .

The engineer is usually retained as the agent of his client. A relationship of trust exists between an agent and his principal; the duty of good faith that arises from that trust is a very important one. Section 383 of the Criminal Code deals with violation of the principal-agent relationship. The section deals with secret commissions — bribes and kickbacks. It provides:

> (1). Every one commits an offence who
>   (a) Corruptly
>   (i) gives, offers or agrees to give or offers to an agent, or
>   (ii) being an agent, demands, accepts or offers or agrees to accept from any person, a reward, advantage or benefit of any kind as consider-

[1] R.S.C. 1970, c. C-34

ation for doing or forbearing to do, or for having done or forborne to do, any act relating to the affairs or business of his principal or for showing or forbearing to show favour or disfavour to any person with relation to the affairs or business of his principal; or

(b) with intent to deceive a principal gives to an agent of that principal, or, being an agent, uses with intent to deceive his principal, a receipt, account, or other writing
(i) in which the principal has an interest,
(ii) that contains any statement that is false or erroneous or defective in any material particular, and
(iii) that is intended to mislead the principal.

A conviction for taking secret commissions can result in imprisonment.

Various sections of the Criminal Code and sections of other statutes — such as the Income Tax Act (Canada) and the Combines Investigation Act (Canada) — provide substantial sanctions to deal with dishonesty. The sanctions include fines and imprisonment, and emphasize the importance of honesty and integrity in Canadian business dealings.

The engineer should also be aware that, under section 110 of the Criminal Code, it is an offence for a government employee to accept any gift from a person who has dealings with that government, unless the head of the employee's government branch consents in writing. It is also an offence to give any such gift or confer a benefit on a government employee if the person giving the gift or conferring the benefit has dealings of any kind with the government. The offence is punishable by imprisonment for up to five years.

CHAPTER TWENTY-ONE

CONSTRUCTION CONTRACTS

The engineer is not normally a party to a construction contract; the engineer usually has a separate contract with the owner (client). Under the separate contract, the engineer may undertake to prepare plans and specifications, to assist in the tendering process, and to administer the construction contract between the owner and the contractor.

As administrator, the engineer may make decisions of major significance to the rights and obligations of the owner and the contractor. For example, many construction contracts provide that the engineer shall, in the first instance, interpret the provisions of the contract; and be the judge of the performance of the respective obligations of the parties to the construction contract. The words "in the first instance" are included for the purpose of reaching timely decisions during construction yet leaving to a more appropriate forum — for example, a court or arbitrator — the ultimate decision as to how the contract ought to be interpreted. Some examples of aspects of administration of construction contracts with respect to which the engineer is often authorized by both the owner and the contractor to make decisions are as follows:

(1) in the preparation of payment certificates;
(2) in the preparation of certificates to evidence substantial and final completion of the work;
(3) in the event of delays during construction, the engineer may determine the appropriateness of extending time for completion;
(4) in the determination of whether the contractor has failed to fulfill his obligations to an extent that would justify termination of the construction contract;

(5) in the valuation of changes or "extras" to the contract, the engineer may decide appropriate changes in contract price and in time for completion;

(6) in determining whether actual subsurface conditions differ materially from those conditions described in the plans or specifications for the work;

(7) in the event of emergencies, the engineer is usually authorized to direct the contractor's work methods to ensure safety to property and workmen;

(8) to inspect the progress of the construction and to reject work that does not comply with the contract documents.

The manner in which an engineer ought to discharge decision-making powers has been the subject of court decisions. In 1953, the Ontario Court of Appeal decided *Brennan Paving Co. Ltd.* v. *Oshawa*[1]. The court considered the conduct of an engineer who acts as agent for the owner, and who also acts as certifier of payment certificates. The court concluded that as certifier, the engineer is required to act judicially and in an independent and unbiased manner; he should not act as agent on behalf of his principal. The court stated, in part:

> Where, as here, the engineer's certificate is a condition precedent to payment, the engineer occupies two positions: first, one as agent of the owner under the contract; second, a quasi-judicial position as certifier between the parties: Hudson on Building Contracts, 7th ed., p. 286. The two positions are distinct and separate. Different duties attach to them and different consequences flow from the performance or breach of those duties. Under the law of principal and agent he may, within the scope of his duties, bind his principal. As certifier deciding between the parties he must act judicially. . . . To act judicially as certifier requires him, where the question arises, to consider and give effect to any conduct on his part as agent vis-a-vis the contractor which has bound the owner as his principal

[1] [1953] 3 D.L.R. 16

to the advantage of the contractor. In this connection he must act qua certifier as independently as if some other person rather than himself had been the agent of the owner under the contract. All that seems crystal clear to me.

In 1960, the Supreme Court of Canada decided *Kamlee Construction Ltd.* v. *Town of Oakville*[2]. The construction contract provided that the "decision of the engineer shall be final and binding upon both the contracting parties as to the interpretation of the specifications and as to the material and workmanship." The contractor disagreed with the decisions of the engineer. A "battle of wills" developed between the engineer's representatives and the contractor's representatives; the factions disagreed on many basic questions concerning method and detail. The Supreme Court of Canada held that the contractor was not entitled to repudiate the contract on the basis of the engineer's conduct. Under such a contract, the court held, an engineer is required to act "judicially"; he must make decisions dictated by his own best judgment. He must decide the most efficient and effective way to carry out the contract; his judgment must not be affected by the fact that he is being paid by the owner.

The question of the manner in which the engineer carries out his duties was also considered in another case: the 1959 decision in *Croft Construction Co.* v. *Terminal Construction Company*[3]. Contracting parties had agreed that payment to the contractor would be based on calculations by the engineer. The court upheld that the engineer's figures would govern the payments, even if the engineer had made an honest mistake. The Ontario Court of Appeal stated in part:

> It is well considered that a computation of the character in question is conclusive and binding upon the parties in the absence of fraud or bad faith or, unless the person entrusted with the duty of making it, has knowingly and wilfully disregarded his duty. It is not suggested here that there was any fraud or bad faith on the part of the engineer. . . .

The immunity of a certifier from any loss caused by his

[2] [1961] 26 D.L.R. (2d) 166
[3] 20 D.L.R. (2d) 247

lack of skill has come into question. In 1974, the House of Lords decided *Sutcliffe* v. *Thackrah et al*[4]. An architect who acted as the owner's agent in preparing payment certificates was, the House of Lords held, under a duty to the owner to exercise care; the architect was, in fact, liable to the owner for negligent over-certification unless he could show that he was acting as an arbitrator in preparing the certificates. The architect was unable to substantiate that he was acting as an arbitrator; thus he was liable for any loss caused by his lack of skill or negligence. The House of Lords concluded that immunity would be extended only to an arbitrator. In his capacity as certifier on behalf of the owner, immunity was not available to the architect.

To summarize, where an engineer is empowered to make decisions that are final and binding upon the parties to a construction contract, the engineer must act judicially notwithstanding that he was originally retained by the owner. In acting judicially, he must act independently of the owner (his principal) and in good faith. Provided he does so, his decisions will be binding upon the parties. In addition, an engineer may be liable for loss caused by negligent certification, if future Canadian court decisions apply Sutcliffe v. Thackrah.

CERTIFICATES FRAUDULENTLY PREPARED

Canadian courts have heard cases that involve fraudulently prepared engineers' certificates. In *Grant, Smith & Co.* v. *The King*[5], certificates prepared by an engineer in collusion with a drilling contractor represented a fraudulent attempt to overstate rock quantities. The certificates were set aside by the court.

INSPECTION SERVICES

In administering a construction contract, an engineer normally acts as an inspector. In doing so the engineer must discharge his duties competently; he must demonstrate a reasonable degree of care and skill.

[4] [1974] All E.R. 859
[5] [1920] 19 Ex. C.R. 404

Unless his contract provides otherwise, the engineer will be expected to inspect all significant aspects of construction. The inspection may be done by the engineer himself, or he may select competent representatives. The courts expect a high standard from professionals; the standard is illustrated in a 1976 decision of the Ontario Court of Appeal in *Dabous* v. *Zuliani et al.*[6]. An architect entered into a contract for the design and supervision of the construction of a house. During the construction, a metal chimney was installed too close to wooden joists; the oversight eventually resulted in fire damage to the house. The court considered the architect's inspection of the chimney installation, and stated:

> Prior to the installation of this prefabricated chimney which caused the fire, the builder had installed another prefabricated chimney in this house which serviced the furnace in the basement. This chimney was installed in direct contact with the wooden joist at the first-floor level and was observed by the architect who cautioned the builder against this practice and directed correction. The prefabricated fire-place was late in arriving and because of some urgency in completing the building, the fire-place together with its chimney was installed on a week-end and the area where the prefabricated chimney passed through the second floor level was boxed in and covered with gyprock. As a result, the offending installation was not observed by the architect. It should perhaps be added that the architect took no steps to have some of the gyprock removed, so that he might examine the chimney installation, although that would have involved trifling cost. . . .
>
> The proper installation of this type of chimney was critical to the safety of the dwelling. The fact of a previous similar improper installation and its correction should have magnified the concern of the architect rather than diminished it as was argued on their behalf. The failure of the defendant architects to ensure that the chimney leading from the fire-place was properly

[6] 68 D.L.R. (3d) 414

installed, even if this required the removal of some of the concealing gyprock, was a failure to meet the reasonable standard of care which they owed to the plaintiff and the appeal of the architects against their liability was therefore dismissed. . . .

The decision may seem harsh to some. However, it illustrates the very high degree of care expected by the courts.

THE ENGINEER'S ADVICE TO THE CONTRACTOR

In a construction contract, the engineer is normally expected to inspect rather than actually supervise the work methods of the contractor. Most construction contracts provide that the contractor shall have complete control of construction methods and procedures. However, consistent with tort law principles, the engineer may be expected to advise a contractor in circumstances where the contractor is reasonably relying on the engineer's expertise. This may well require the engineer to make a difficult judgment call; and he must be extremely careful in doing so as unwarranted interference with a contractor's work methods may give rise to a damage claim.

Some contracts provide that the engineer is to approve the contractor's work methods, in which case the engineer's obligations are more clear. To illustrate, in 1977, the Supreme Court of Canada decided *Demers et al.* v. *Dufresne Engineering et al.*[7] During the construction of bridge piers, the contractor failed to use sufficient vertical reinforcing steel in constructing a caisson. The caisson exploded under pressure, and had to be rebuilt at a cost of $1,400,000. The Supreme Court of Canada held the engineer 50% liable for the damage. In part, the court stated:

> The explosion of the caisson was due to a glaring error in the method of performing the work that was selected by the contractor; having failed to take the low

resistance of concrete in tension into account, the latter did not provide for the use of vertical reinforcing steel. The engineer was aware of this incorrect method of doing the work; if he had not been aware of it, I would have had no hesitation in saying that he ought to have been since this was such an enormous error. By remaining silent, the engineer implicitly approved the work method chosen by the contractor. Moreover, he also implicitly approved the minor alteration which consisted in adding a small quantity of vertical reinforcing steel and which, even having regard to the preliminary calculations made by his representative. . . was obviously inadequate. By committing these two errors the engineer effectively allowed the work to be performed incorrectly, and this caused the accident. The contractor's error indicates how much he was in need of the engineer's guidance in order to perform the work properly; this need for guidance gave rise to the engineer's obligation to give it to the contractor, to see, in short, that the error be corrected. By failing to carry out this contractual obligation, the engineer became liable toward the contractor.

CONTRACT ADMINISTRATION

The engineer should ensure that the construction contract is administered in accordance with its terms. All too often, a contract is administered in a manner that is to some extent contrary to its terms. For example, payment dates may be overlooked; contract extras may proceed without written authorization required by the contract; parties may ignore notice requirements that were stipulated in the contract. The conduct of the parties during construction may bear little resemblance to the conduct that was contemplated when the contract was signed. Conceivably, the issue of equitable estoppel might arise; for example, if contract "extras" proceed without written authorizations, as contractually required, a party may be equitably estopped from denying that it had waived its contractual rights. It is better to avoid complicating the matter; this can best be achieved by closely administering the contract in accordance with its terms.

139

The engineer-administrator on a construction project should keep very detailed records. Thus he will have evidence of the manner in which the contract was administered and the circumstances of the actual construction. The records should include a daily diary; carefully drafted minutes of meetings with contractors' representatives, owner and engineer; and detailed notes of all developments, which might give rise to claims, during the construction. The engineer might be asked later to recollect events during construction; for example, in connection with subsequent delay and interference claims.

DRAWINGS AND SPECIFICATIONS

One of the most important services provided by the engineer on a construction project is the preparation of conceptual and detailed drawings and specifications to describe the work. The engineer's description of the work will form the basis of contractors' prices; and the engineer's client will rely upon the plans and specifications as well.

During construction, disputes often arise as a result of incomplete or ambiguous specifications. For example, where mechanical hardware — door locks, fasteners, and so on — is mentioned in the specifications; although quantity is specified, there may be no reference to a particular product or manufacturer. If the contractor installs hardware of poorer quality than that anticipated by the project owner, and if the construction contract has a stipulated-price or lump-sum basis, then a dispute may well arise. It is surprising how often an owner and a contractor will begin construction without detailed drawings and specifications; in an attempt to expedite construction, usually to avoid escalating costs or to take advantage of more favourable weather conditions. Such action might reflect the best intentions. But it can obviously lead to disputes about the true meaning and intent of the contract documents.

Detailed project drawings and specifications should include all required dimensions, units of measurement, quality of materials, and also product designations of parts and equipment. Product standards should include references to recognized testing authorities, such as the Canadian Stand- Association ("CSA") or the American Society for Testing Materials ("ASTM"), wherever possible.

The importance of detailed specifications was illustrated in the 1979 decision in *Trident Construction Ltd.* v. *W.L. Wardrop and Assoc. et al*[8]. Justice Wilson, of the Manitoba Queen's Bench, displayed a sympathetic attitude to the contractor where the engineer had failed to specify a proper design. The Judge considered whether the likelihood of disaster might have been detected if the contractor had investigated or re-worked the engineer's design:

> In the building trade in Manitoba not only does the owner rely upon a consulting engineer to prepare competent and reliable structural drawings for the erection of a building in accordance with those drawings, but also the contractors who were called upon to tender for those buildings on the basis of such drawings and specifications, must also rely upon the accuracy and competency of these drawings. The normal practice is for the engineers to take months to research and prepare the plans and specifications involved in a project for which they are paid substantial sums and to give the contractors only a few weeks to prepare and to submit competitive bids for the construction of the building based on such plans and specifications. In this time frame it is impractical for any building contractor in Winnipeg to check out independently the structural design of buildings involved in the plans and specifications prior to bidding. During the few weeks open to him he is fully involved in doing take-offs and getting and collating prices. During that time he has to go through volumes of specifications and many sheets of plans to establish what materials, machinery and equipment he has to order, and to compute the labor involved in obtaining and procuring, fabricating, constructing and equipping such a plant. The task is made much more difficult by the series of late, extensive and complex addenda that are usually issued up to the very day on which tenders are called. The general contractor must also obtain bids from the various sub-contractors, and the sub-contractors must in turn obtain quotations from their various suppliers and sub-sub-contractors, and the whole must be gathered together

[8] *Supra*, at page 32.

to make up the total bid of the general contractor within the bidding time allowed. There in fact is no time for anything else except the foregoing under the standard bidding procedures for a large project . . . and the bidding represented no exception to the general rule.

THE TENDERING PROCESS

Where contractors submit competing bids, in the project tendering process, the acceptance of any one of these bids constitutes a contract — or the basis for the formation of a contract — between the successful contractor and the owner. The selection depends on the particular terms the owner has outlined in its tendering documentation. As the owner's agent, the engineer is usually involved in the preparation of tendering documentation.

The "Information to Tenderers" package should be tailored to the particular project. It will normally include a general description of the nature of the project; plans and specifications; information with respect to where more detailed data may be obtained (for example, a reference to soils reports); bid deposits or bid bonds that will be required at the time of submitting the tender; and the date, time, and place for submission of tenders. The package also normally includes the statement that the lowest or any tender will not necessarily be accepted by the owner.

A tender is a contractor's offer to complete construction as described in the bid submission. Some tendering procedures are set up so that the owner's acceptance of the contractor's offer will constitute a contract between the owner and the contractor. It is important to include a form of the construction contract that the owner is prepared to sign as part of the documents delivered to the contractor prior to its bid submission. The engineer should advise the client of the need for preparing a contract form that is appropriately "tailored" to the project — a drafting process that is best left to a lawyer who can prepare the contract on the basis of the engineer's and the client's instructions.

Contractors who submit bids on construction projects and on equipment-supply contracts will often qualify the basis upon which their bids are submitted. They might, for example, take exception to terms and conditions included in the owner's form of contract. Such qualifications change the basis of the proposed contract. Until the owner is prepared to accept the contractor's revised terms and conditions, the formation of the contract will be delayed. Usually there is a straightforward business negotiation between the owner's and the contractor's representatives; the parties try to work out an agreeable basis for the contract so the work may proceed. The engineer might be engaged by the owner to assist in the negotiation process. The engineer should monitor closely the details of the negotiation; he should document the final agreement between the parties. A well-drafted contract can then be finalized and signed. Where work proceeds before detailed terms and conditions are finalized, the potential for contract disputes increases. Whenever construction proceeds before contract documents have been finalized, the door is open to unnecessary headaches in contract administration.

The contract should be finalized and executed at the earliest possible opportunity. The contract provides the engineer-administrator with a defined basis upon which to proceed.

TYPES AND FORMS OF CONSTRUCTION CONTRACTS

Under common law, parties have the right to choose their contract terms and conditions; thus there is no prescribed format for construction contracts. There are, however, certain types of contractual arrangements and contract formats that are being used in the industry. Some of these formats have been reduced to "standard forms" that are widely accepted. However, the engineer should adopt a critical approach to the use of standard-form construction contracts (as he should to the use of any standard-form contract). The parties should closely examine a proposed standard form to determine if it reasonably reflects the agreement they wish to express. Any modifications to the contract should be clearly and appropriately drafted (preferably by a lawyer) and incorporated into the wording of the contract prior to its execution.

Some examples of different types of contracts currently in use in the construction industry are listed below.

1. Stipulated-Price or Lump-Sum Contract   This type of contract gives the owner the benefit of knowing the total price he will have to pay to the contractor for the completion of the construction (subject to additions or deductions to or from the work as the course of construction proceeds) in accordance with the terms of the contract documents. When the stipulated-price contract form is used, it is essential that detailed plans and specifications form the basis of the contractor's price. The engineer should carefully define and fully detail the work involved at the outset. If these details are provided after the price has been tendered, the contractor may claim that the work is beyond the scope of the contract as the contractor understood it at the time of bidding; he may claim that additional compensation is warranted.

The stipulated-price contract may involve a considerable degree of risk for the contractor. For example, he might incur extra costs if subsurface, dewatering, or weather problems arise. The contractor should set his initial price accordingly.

The stipulated-price contract does provide the owner with the advantage of a reasonable approximation of the total cost of the construction. But a word of warning: if the contractor has submitted an unrealistically low price for the work, he may conceivably try to cut costs and look for opportunities to claim extra compensation. Insufficiently detailed specifications may well assist a contractor in such attempts.

2. Unit-Price Contract   This type of contract is often used for projects where it is difficult to predetermine quantities. For example, in an excavation project, the extent of varying subsurface conditions might not be determinable in advance. Bids are submitted on the basis of price per unit of item. In preparing specifications, the engineer should ensure that the quantity units on which prices will be based are clearly spelled out; he should also list alternatives. In excavation projects, for example, he should request prices for removal of either rock or earth.

3. Cost-Plus Contracts

(1) **Cost plus Percentage**   This type of contract provides compensation to the contractor for his costs incurred; as

well, it provides a reasonable percentage to cover the contractor's overhead and profit. The cost-plus approach is often used on large-scale projects where there is not enough time to finalize detailed plans and specifications; to take the time may not be practicable in light of the urgency to proceed with construction. In large-scale projects, there is also the likelihood of changes in the work that the owner may wish to effect from time to time. Note that the cost-plus contract provides no incentive to the contractor to reduce costs: the contractor is being paid a percentage of the total construction costs. The engineer–administrator should closely monitor the progress of the work and the contractor's accounts in order to ensure that the work is performed at a reasonable cost. It is advisable for the owner to be expressly entitled to access to all of the contractor's project records. This will facilitate the extensive, detailed administration that is usually necessary.

(ii) **Cost plus Lump-Sum Fee**   This contract approach is much like the cost-plus-percentage arrangement. But the contractor does not receive a percentage of the project costs: instead, he is paid a fixed amount. This may be to the owner's advantage. However, although the contractor receives no incentive to increase the total cost of the contract, there is also no incentive to reduce costs. As with the cost-plus-percentage arrangement, the engineer–administrator should closely monitor the work to ensure that the contractor is not being careless in co-ordinating and scrutinizing work that is performed by the various trades.

(iii) **Cost plus Lump-Sum Fee plus Bonus**   In this type of arrangement, the contractor is provided with an incentive to reduce costs: for every dollar saved on an agreed estimated total cost, the contractor may receive an additional compensation in the form of an agreed-upon percentage of the saving. This approach makes good sense for the owner, as long as the agreed estimate is a reasonable one. Usually, the owner will expect his engineer to ensure him of the reasonableness of the contractor's estimate. An inflated estimate would obviously increase the contractor's likelihood of benefiting from the bonus arrangement.

4. Guaranteed Maximum Price plus Bonus   Like the cost-plus-bonus contract, the guaranteed-maximum-price contract incorporates an incentive to the contractor to effect savings on a cost-plus project. The contractor receives a fixed fee as well as an agreed-upon percentage of savings. The guaranteed-maximum-price contract offers the owner a further advantage over a basic cost-plus contract: the guaranteed-maximum-price feature. The amount of the guaranteed maximum price should be determined on the basis of detailed plans and specifications rather than on the basis of a reasonable estimate. Again, the owner usually expects his engineer to assure the reasonableness of the contractor's maximum price.

5. Design-Build Contracts   With this type of contract it is normally the contractor — rather than the owner — who arranges to obtain the necessary engineering design services, to finalize the design detail. The detailed design is often finalized as the construction work proceeds. Thus construction may proceed promptly; detailed plans and specifications for subsequent phases are finalized at a later date. The work often proceeds on a cost-plus-bonus basis; this appeals to owners who wish to avoid retaining professionals. In design-build contracts, the engineer is usually the agent of the contractor. But the contract normally entitles the owner to retain, at his option, his own engineering representative. The owner's engineer will double-check the sufficiency of the design services provided; he will also ensure that construction proceeds in compliance with the agreed-upon plans and specifications.

PROJECT MANAGEMENT

The design-build contract is often used in connection with projects that are organized on a "project-management" basis. The owner usually enters into a contract with a project manager; the project manager acts as the owner's agent. He acts on the owner's behalf to arrange for professional design services and to hire contractors to complete the construction. The project manager usually purports to have the experience and contacts necessary to facilitate and expedite the design, tendering and construction stages. In return for acting on the owner's behalf, the project manager receives a fee; this fee is in addition to the professional design fee and the contracting cost, which the owner would incur in any event. The project manager simplifies the construction process for the owner; theoretically, the project manager's fee is the premium the owner is prepared to pay in order to receive the advantages of the project manager's experience, contacts and administrative expertise. Hiring a project manager may, in fact, lead to overall cost savings on the project.

PRIME CONTRACT AND SUBCONTRACTS

Where the owner enters into a construction contract with a general contractor who in turn enters into subcontracts with various trade contractors, a contractual relationship, called "privity of contract," exists between the owner and the general contractor; privity of contract exists between the general contractor and each of its trade subcontractors. But no privity of contract exists between the owner and any of the subcontractors. The administration of the contract between the owner and the general contractor should be consistent with the administration of the contract between the general contractor and each of its subcontractors. To ensure consistency, the general terms and conditions of the head contract — between the owner and the general contractor — should be included in each of the subcontracts wherever applicable. If this consistency of terms and conditions is not achieved, there is no assurance that the general contractor will be capable of passing on to the subtrades the engineer-administrator's decisions. Inconsistency increases the likelihood of contract administration difficulties. For example, suppose mechanical extras are authorized and valued by the engineer pursuant to the terms of the head contract. And suppose the general contractor does not provide, in the mechanical subcontract, that extras are to be valued by the engineer. If the mechanical subcontractor disputes the value of the extras, unnecessary difficulties may well arise. The subcontractor may be entitled to claim an amount for the extras in excess of the engineer's valuation. The general contractor will then have a problem, which may conceivably adversely affect an otherwise smooth contract administration.

The engineer-administrator can promote smooth contract administration by ensuring that the general contractor is aware of the need for consistency in the general conditions of the head contract and the general conditions of each subcontract.

EMERGING TRENDS IN CONTRACTING

A further caution about the use of "standard-form contracts" arises because of the developing trend, particularly on larger projects, to depart from the "traditional" contract arrangements. For example, the popular "fast-track" or phased-construction approach, where construction proceeds on the designed portions of a project while other portions are still being designed, often involves the services of a construction manager who co-ordinates the project and also might do some construction work. In such a situation, it isn't possible to achieve a traditionally structured single-stipulated-price contract. Such special projects require specially drafted contracts.

The use of multiple-prime contractors ("multi-primes") on projects is another developing trend. Again, the traditional standard-form contracts are not appropriate. Multi-primes may, for example, be used by developers who see themselves as general contractors and who parcel out the work of the various trades on individual prime-contract arrangements. As construction managers or project managers, engineers may be required to co-ordinate and schedule multi-primes. The project contracts must be appropriately negotiated and should realistically describe the responsibilities and protect the interests of the various participants in the construction project.

As professionals in the construction industry find new approaches to respond to project requirements, the need for "hybrid" contracts follows. Engineers play a key role in that developing process and should seek the advice of an experienced lawyer before finalizing such contracts. Contracts that are prepared by contract administrators and that do not receive attention from legal counsel may create unnecessary complications when difficulties and claims later arise.

DELAY AND INTERFERENCE CLAIMS

Claims by contractors against owners for damages resulting from delays and interference caused by the owner's representative are not at all uncommon in the construction industry today. Claims on account of delay may result when enquiries from the contractor are not properly answered; the contractor may be required to delay construction until he receives a reply to his query. Claims of interference result when the works of subcontractors overlap or when a project is not well co-ordinated. The engineer-administrator should ensure that responses to contractors' enquiries are provided promptly and that the overall project is co-ordinated to minimize delay and interference claims.

BONDS

Bonds are commonly used on construction projects and in many equipment-supply contracts. A basic understanding of bonding is important to the engineer. The most common forms of bonds are the bid bond, the performance bond and the labour and material-payment bond.

Bonds are contracts, the bonding company agreeing (the "surety") to guarantee the performance of a specified contractual obligation. In common bonding terminology, the "principal" is the party whose performance of the contractual obligation is guaranteed by the bonding company, or surety. The principal is normally a contractor or subcontractor. The term "obligee" is used to describe the party for whose benefit the bond is provided. The obligee is often the owner.

It is extremely important to appreciate that a bond is not insurance. If the bonding company is required to incur expense in performing its obligations, it will seek to recover its expenses from the principal.

Often the principal (contractor) is a corporation. Bonding companies often require shareholders or principal officers of a corporation that is named as principal in a bond to indemnify the surety against any expense incurred by the Surety. The bonding company may then look to both the corporation, as principal, and to the individuals who provide the indemnities to recover any payments the bonding

149

company may be required to make as it fulfills its obligations to the obligee.

Bonds are essentially contracts among three parties, the surety, the principal and the obligee. In effect, the surety indemnifies the obligee against loss arising from the principal's failure to perform contractual obligations.

BID BOND

The bid bond is used in tendering. If the principal's tender or bid is accepted, the principal is required to enter into a formal contract with the obligee. If the principal fails to enter into the formal contract, he or she must pay to the obligee the difference in money between the amount of the bid and the amount the obligee must pay another party for the work, up to the face amount of the bid bond. Should the principal fail to pay, the surety has to pay it. However, the surety will then charge the total costs involved back to the principal.

PERFORMANCE BOND

A performance bond indemnifies the obligee if the principal doesn't perform his or her contractual obligations. The indemnity, however, is limited to the amount specified in the performance bond. The performance bond is normally provided when the formal contract is executed. The performance bond identifies the contract that the principal must fulfil. Sometimes performance bonds are for all of the contract price; or they can be for a limited amount.

At the time of tendering, it is common practice to require bidders to provide agreements to bond, or consent letters that say the surety will provide performance or other bonds pursuant to the tender instructions.

LABOUR AND MATERIAL-PAYMENT BOND

The purpose of a labour and material-payment bond is to guarantee that all claimants will be paid for labour and materials provided to the principal for the project described in the bond. In the traditional contractual arrangement between an owner and a general contractor, the potential

150

claimants are usually subcontractors and material suppliers who have contracts directly with the principal (contractor). Because there is usually no contract between the bonding company and such claimants, the owner should be described, in the labour and material-payment bond, as the obligee who acts as trustee for the benefit of such claimants.

The form of bond chosen is most important. Bonds should be reviewed by legal counsel where necessary.

LETTERS OF CREDIT

The use of letters of credit on construction contracts and on equipment-supply contracts is becoming more common, particularly when a job is to be performed outside Canada. For example, someone might ask for a letter of credit instead of a performance bond. Letters of credit are normally provided by chartered banks or trust companies. The letters provide an assurance that funds are available if, for example, a contractor defaults in performance. Depending upon their terms, letters of credit can amount to "blank cheques" for the person in whose favour the letter is written and legal advice should be obtained where unusual terms are encountered. Often the terms of the letter of credit will provide that the bank or trust company must pay the holder of the letter if he or she provides a certificate or affidavit saying a contractual default has occurred. Being required to provide a letter of credit can significantly complicate matters for a contractor as it normally impacts directly on the contractor's line of credit with the bank or trust company.

CHAPTER TWENTY-TWO

ARBITRATION

A lawsuit is not always the best way to resolve a dispute between contracting parties. The dispute may sometimes be resolved by a somewhat less formal procedure called arbitration. The engineer is often involved in arbitrations; he may be party to the dispute, an expert witness, or the arbitrator. An engineer who acts as an arbitrator is expected to act entirely impartially and independently of the parties to the dispute.

An arbitration provision is usually included in engineering and construction contracts. The wording of the arbitration provision may indicate that arbitration is mandatory — that is, the parties must submit disputes to arbitration; they may not proceed to resolve the dispute by way of a lawsuit. An example of a mandatory arbitration provision is as follows:

> All matters in difference between the parties hereto in relation to this agreement shall be referred to arbitration.

But not all arbitration provisions indicate mandatory arbitration; the clause might provide that disputes will be submitted to arbitration if both parties agree to so arbitrate upon the request of one of the parties. Such a clause is simply notice that arbitration is available as a means of resolving a dispute.

Is a mandatory arbitration provision desirable? The question invokes considerable discussion amongst engineers and contractors. Proponents of arbitration emphasize that it is generally a more expeditious method of resolving a dispute than is a lawsuit; as well, arbitration provides a forum whereby disputes over matters of a technical nature can be brought before an arbitrator who is already familiar with that general subject matter. It is difficult to argue with the soundness of such reasoning, as long as the dispute is of a technical nature.

But sometimes a dispute relates to the legal interpretation of a contractual provision; sometimes a dispute involves a very substantial amount of money. In such disputes, the mandatory arbitration provision may not be desirable. In addition, the parties might agree that the award of the arbitrator shall be final and binding, but either party may still appeal an arbitrator's decision to the courts. An appeal would be appropriate, for example, if the arbitrator has made an error in law or has exceeded his jurisdiction, perhaps by deciding a matter that is not within the scope of the dispute as presented to him. If an appeal is made against the award of an arbitrator, then the initial arbitration becomes merely an extra step in the court process; the parties may well have been better off to proceed by way of a lawsuit from the outset. It is impossible to predict the nature of contractual disputes; thus the non-mandatory, or notice-of-arbitration, provision offers an advantage: neither party is limited in its method of resolving disputes. If the parties want a technical matter settled by arbitration, then arbitration is available. Or one of the parties can proceed by way of court action.

APPOINTMENT OF ARBITRATOR

Some contracts describe the manner in which an arbitrator is to be appointed and detail the general procedure that will govern the arbitration. For example, an arbitration clause may provide that each party to the dispute shall appoint a representative arbitrator, and that the two representative arbitrators shall then appoint a chairman, thereby creating a three-man arbitration board. The contract may also provide that, if the two representative arbitrators cannot agree upon the selection of the chairman, the chairman will be appointed by a court.

THE ARBITRATIONS ACT

Engineering and construction contracts usually provide that arbitration will be governed by a provincial arbitration statute. The Arbitrations Act of Ontario[1] is one example. The Act deals with the appointment of an arbitrator or arbitrators, and empowers the arbitrator to administer oaths to the parties and witnesses; it enables him to make an award within prescribed time periods. The Act provides that the court may remove an arbitrator where the arbitrator has misconducted himself; it prescribes the procedure for appealing an arbitration award; it provides for agreement as to arbitrator's fees. The Act also provides that where parties to an arbitration do not otherwise expressly provide, the arbitration shall take place before a single arbitrator. The Act requires that the parties to the arbitration produce, on oath, all books and records relating to the matter in dispute.

Procedure during an arbitration is less formal than a law suit. But court procedures relating to the admission of evidence and the examination and cross-examination of witnesses by legal counsel are generally followed.

APPEALS

An agreement that precludes the appeal of an arbitrator's decision to the court will not be enforced by the courts. The question was considered by the Nova Scotia Supreme Court in *Re Thomas Hackett*[2]. The court listened to a submission relating to a contractual provision. It was argued that the arbitration described in the contract was to be a private arrangement between the parties, and that the provisions of the Arbitration Act of Nova Scotia did not apply. The court stated:

> But there is one thing that the parties cannot do and that is agree that no application can be made to the Courts. Whatever effect, then, is to be given to this last clause of the submission, it cannot prevent the application to the Court to set aside the award. Even if the Arbitration Act did not apply, there would still be a right of application. Such right existed at common law. . . .

[1] R.S.O. 1980, c. 25
[2] [1939] 2 D.L.R. 332

CHAPTER TWENTY-THREE

LIEN LEGISLATION

Every engineer in construction should be aware of provincial legislation that creates certain lien rights and that requires amounts to be held back from contractors until a specified time. In Ontario, the act is called The Construction Lien Act, 1983 of Ontario, and came into force on April 2, 1983. The new Act significantly amended the old Mechanics' Lien Act of Ontario. The other common-law provinces also have lien legislation. In Alberta, British Columbia and Manitoba, for example, the statute is called the Builders' Lien Act. In other common-law provinces the statute is called the Mechanics' Lien Act. In the Yukon and Northwest Territories it is called the Mechanics' Lien Ordinance. Engineers are often administrators of construction contracts; it is important that the engineer be aware of the necessity to comply with lien legislation.

DIFFERENCES IN PROVINCIAL LIEN ACTS

The general purpose of the various mechanics', construction and builders' lien acts of the provinces is the same. But differences arise from province to province. Some of these differences concern matters of key significance to the engineer/contract-administrator. For example, calculation of the percentage holdback and the time of releasing holdback funds varies from province to province. The engineer-administrator should be familiar with applicable statutory requirements in the province in which the construction is taking place. The following table indicates, very generally, the respective percentage holdbacks and time periods in the various provinces after completion or abandonment of the contract, or otherwise as provided by the lien statute, before the holdback can be released. (It is extremely important to

	Percentage Holdback	Time before holdback can be released
Alberta	− 15%	− 35 days
British Columbia	− 10%	− 40 days
Manitoba	− 7.5%	− 40 days
Ontario	− 10%	− 45 days (Note: Ontario has two holdbacks, "basic" and "finishing")
New Brunswick	− 20%, if contract price doesn't exceed $15,000	− 60 days
	15%, if contract price exceeds $15,000 (a minimum of $3,000 must be held back)	− 60 days
Newfoundland	− 10%	− 30 days
Northwest Territories	− 10%	− 30 days
Nova Scotia	− 10%	− 45 days
Prince Edward Island	− 20%, if contract price doesn't exceed $15,000	− 60 days
	− 15%, if contract price exceeds $15,000 (a minimum of $3,000 must be held back)	− 60 days
Saskatchewan	− 20%, if contract price doesn't exceed $25,000	− 37 days (or 60 days, if contract involves oil or gas wells or pipelines)
	− 15% for a contract worth more than $25,000 (a minimum of $5,000 must be held back)	− 37 days
Yukon	− 10%	− 30 days

refer to the specific provincial statutes for more complete
details, particularly in connection with the time period dur-

ing which lien claims can be made and the timing of holdback release.)

Essentially, until any lien is filed or until the owner is
given notice in writing that a lien is claimed, an owner is
protected if he retains the required percentage holdback of
the value of the work done or materials furnished as construction proceeds. If an owner releases the holdback too
soon, he may find that he has to pay additional funds to satisfy lien claimants. Hence, knowledge of and compliance
with the applicable lien Act is very important.

PERSONS ENTITLED TO LIEN RIGHTS

The Construction Lien Act of Ontario provides, in effect,
that anyone who supplies services or materials to an
"improvement" for an owner, contractor or subcontractor
is entitled to a lien. The term "improvement," as defined
in the Construction Lien Act, means:

> i. any alteration, addition or repair to, or
> ii. any construction, erection or installation on,
> any land, and includes the demolition or removal of
> any building, structure or works or part thereof, and
> "improved" has a corresponding meaning.

In Alberta, the Builders' Lien Act provides the following
definition:

> "improvement" means anything constructed, erected,
> built, placed, dug or drilled, or intended to be con-
> structed, erected, built, placed, dug or drilled, on or
> in land except a thing that is neither affixed to the
> land nor intended to be or become part of the land.

RIGHTS AGAINST OWNER WHERE NO CONTRACT EXISTS

Construction lien rights exist in addition to any other rights
that may exist at law. Privity of contract normally exists
between an owner and a general contractor, but not
between an owner and a subcontractor. Thus the lien rights
provide the subcontractor with a cause of action directly
against the owner. The subcontractor (or supplier or

worker) would otherwise be limited in an action for breach of contract against the contractor. The lien Acts were designed to provide some degree of protection for parties who do not have privity of contract with the owner by providing a right to sue the owner directly under the Act. They also provide a specialized forum for resolution of payment disputes that arise during the course of construction projects.

EFFECT OF LIEN

The practical impact of a lien claim on a construction project can be most significant. In Ontario, when an owner receives written notice of a lien claim, the owner is obligated to retain both the holdback amount and the amount of the lien claim. Lien legislation in the other common-law provinces has the same effect: to generally ensure the retention of both the holdback amount and the amount of the lien claim. If an owner does not comply with the statutory requirements to hold back, and if a lien is filed, the owner may be liable to pay additional funds to satisfy the lien claim. Ultimately, the court might order the owner to sell his interest in the land to satisfy the lien claim if the owner is unable to or refuses to otherwise pay the amount of the claim. (Crown lands, however, may not be sold to satisfy lien claims.)

Lien legislation is admittedly complex. The engineer, as contract administrator, should obtain legal advice if he receives notice of any lien claim. The owner might receive no written notice of lien claims during the course of the construction project. The engineer should still obtain legal advice, to ensure that he can document compliance with the lien Act, to confirm the date at which holdback monies may be released and to arrange to conduct a search at the appropriate registry office or land-titles office, to ensure that no lien claims have been registered before the engineer releases any portion of the holdback fund.

An engineer may be required to file a lien claim. For example, he may be authorized to do so by a contractor in connection with a particular project. The engineer should obtain legal advice to ensure that the claim is made within the statutory-limitation period, and that it is otherwise in compliance with the applicable provincial lien Act.

THE NEW ONTARIO CONSTRUCTION LIEN ACT, 1983

At the time of writing this second edition, the Construction Lien Act, 1983 of Ontario (the "new Act") is still relatively new. The new Act contains significant changes from the old Mechanics' Lien Act ("the old Act"). People involved in the construction industry in Ontario have had to adjust their thinking. Some of the major differences between the old Act and the new Act that may be of particular interest to engineers are:

(a) **The holdback amount** − Pursuant to the new Act, the amount of the holdback is reduced from fifteen per cent to ten per cent of the price of services or materials as they are supplied. Unlike the old Act, which provided for one holdback, the new Act creates two holdbacks. The first, or basic, holdback, is for work or services performed before it is certified that the contract is substantially performed. The second, or holdback for finishing work, is designed to give the finishing trades a claim against ten per cent of the value of the remainder of the contract for the services and materials supplied from the date of substantial performance to the date the contract is completed. Because there are two separate holdbacks, lien claimants who want to make a claim for work done before the contract is substantially performed and for work done after it is done must file separate liens for such work.

(b) **Release of holdback** − The rules for determining when the holdbacks may be paid out have been changed. Under the new Act, holdback may be released when all liens that may be claimed against that holdback have expired or have been satisfied, discharged or provided for by payment into court, under the provisions of the new Act.

The new rules for determining the period of time for retaining holdback are intended to provide a more certain date for holdback release. Note that the new Act states times at which the payer *may* make payment of the remaining ninety per cent of the contract and the holdback without jeopardy, and does not state that the payer *must* pay at such times. Therefore, there is no obligation to release holdback at a certain time under the new Act; however, the obligation to release holdback funds is usually covered in the construction contract or subcontract.

The new Act provides for certification of the *completion* of a subcontract to allow for the release of holdbacks related to a certified complete subcontract. Note that, pursuant to the new Act, the determination of whether a subcontract has been completed may be made, upon the contractor's request, by the payment certifier (for example, the engineer) or by the owner and contractor jointly.

(c) **Certification of Substantial Performance** – There are new statutory provisions dealing with certification or declaration of substantial performance of the contract, and for certification of completion (rather than substantial performance) of a subcontract. These concepts are important. They are two of the trigger points that determine when holdbacks can safely be paid out and when lien rights will expire. The definition of "substantial performance" in the new Act is the same as it was in the old Act, except for the quantitative limits, which have been increased. Section 2(1) of the new Act provides:

2. – (1) For the purposes of this Act, a contract is substantially performed,

(a) when the improvement to be made under that contract or a substantial part thereof is ready for use or is being used for the purposes intended; and

(b) when the improvement to be made under that contract is capable of completion or, where there is a known defect, correction, at a cost of not more than,

(i) 3 per cent of the first $500,000 of the contract price,

(ii) 2 per cent of the next $500,000 of the contract price, and

(iii) 1 per cent of the balance of the contract price.

The new Act also defines when a contract is deemed to be completed. Section 2(3) of the new Act provides:

2. – (3) For the purposes of this Act, a contract shall

be deemed to be completed and services or materials shall be deemed to be last supplied to the improvement when the price of completion, correction of a known defect or last supply is not more than the lesser of,
(a) 1 per cent of the contract price; and
(b) $1,000.

The rules relating to certification or declaration that a contract is substantially performed are mandatory; once they are invoked by the contractor, the parties must comply with the rules. On the application for certification made by the contractor, the payment certifier (usually an architect or engineer) or, if there is no payment certifier on the project, the owner and contractor together, must determine whether the contract has been substantially performed, and a certificate in the prescribed form must be signed. Once the contract is certified, the payment certifier, if any, must, within seven days of the date of executing the certificate, give or send a copy to the owner and the contractor. The contractor must publish a copy of the certificate in a "construction trade newspaper" as defined in the new Act (for example, the *Daily Commercial News*). If he does not do so, anyone may publish a copy of the certificate.

If the contract is not certified as substantially performed, any person may apply to the court and the court may declare the contract to be substantially performed. The person who brings the application must publish a copy of the court declaration in a "construction trade newspaper."

(d) **Damages for Non-Certification** — If an engineer doesn't certify substantial performance, he may be liable for damages. The new Act provides that anyone who is required to certify substantial performance (often, an engineer designated by the contract) and fails to do so within a reasonable time — even though there is no reasonable doubt that the contract has been substantially performed — will be liable to anyone who suffers damages as a result. In addition, a certifier who fails to deliver the certificate to the owner and contractor within seven days of certification will also be liable to anyone who suffers damage as a result.

163

Everyone should closely monitor the progress of a project, and check the construction-trade newspapers regularly. Under the new Act, the contractor must disclose, upon request in writing and within a reasonable time, the date of publication of certificates.

(e) **Who May Lien** − As noted earlier in this chapter, any person who supplies services or materials to an improvement will have a lien upon the property interest of the owner in the premises. The new Act makes it clear that an "improvement" for which a person can claim a lien may include demolition or removal. In addition, the new definition of "premises" and the new definition of "materials" indicate that the lien applies not only to the improvement and the land upon which the improvement is made, but also to materials supplied to the improvement but not yet incorporated into the improvement.

The new Act also provides that, where the construction of the improvement has not commenced, anyone (for example, an engineer) who supplies designs, plans, drawings or specifications that enhance the value of the land is entitled to a lien. However, architects do not have lien rights. Liens by architects have been specifically excluded from the new Act because of lobbying by architects. Careful consideration may have to be given to the appropriateness of retaining holdbacks from amounts paid to architects, for example, where engineers or others are retained as subconsultants. Even though architects can't file lien claims, and therefore will argue that the owner shouldn't retain a holdback on account of architectural services, architects' subconsultants may well have lien rights against the owner.

(f) **Prohibition Against Waiver of Lien Rights** − Unlike the old Act, which permitted lien rights to be waived, the New Act provides that an agreement to waive lien rights is void.

(g) **Limits on Amount of Lien Claim** − Under the new Act, a lien may be claimed only for the price of services and materials supplied prior to the time of the claim; not, as under the old Act, for work that is to be done in the future. The purpose of this provision is to reduce exaggerated lien claims. In addition, the new Act provides that anyone making a frivolous or fictitious claim for lien will be liable to any person who suffers damage as a result.

(h) **Preservation of Lien Claims** — The term "preservation" is used in the new Act. It is a new term to describe the method of claiming a lien. The method is similar to the method in the old Act, although time limits have changed. Under the old Act, thirty-seven days were allowed for claiming a lien following the supply of services or materials; the new Act allows forty-five days. When the forty-five-day period commences depends on the circumstances. Bear in mind that there are two holdbacks (the basic holdback and the finishing holdback) and that different liens may apply to each. (If an engineer is planning to preserve a lien, it is advisable to have a lawyer do so.)

The following is a general summation of the time limits, under the new Act, that apply to determine when the lien must be preserved:

(I) The lien of a contractor (as opposed to a subcontractor) for services or materials supplied before the date certified or declared to be the date of substantial performance must be preserved before the end of the forty-five-day period following the date of publication of substantial performance or the date the contract is either completed or abandoned — whichever is earlier.

(II) Where there is no certification or declaration of substantial performance, or for services or materials supplied after the certified date of substantial performance, the lien of a contractor must be preserved before the end of the forty-five-day period following the date the contract is completed or abandoned, whichever occurs first.

(III) The lien of any other person (subcontractors, suppliers and so on) for services or materials supplied on and before the certified date of substantial performance of the contract must be preserved before the end of the forty-five-day period next following the earliest of:

(i) the date of publishing the certificate or declara-

165

tion of substantial performance of the contract;
(ii) the date on which he last supplies services or materials to the improvement; and
(iii) the date a subcontract is certified to be complete (where the services or materials were supplied under that subcontract).

(IV) Where there is no certification or declaration of substantial performance of the contract, or for services or materials supplied after the certified date of substantial performance of the contract, the lien of any person other than the contractor must be preserved before the end of the forty-five-day period following the date on which he last supplies services or materials to the improvement and the date a subcontract is certified to be complete (where the services or materials were supplied under that subcontract) − whichever is earlier.

As with any lawsuit, the engineer should understand that a lawyer ought to be retained to advise and act on behalf of the engineer or the engineer's client in any lien action.

(i) **Priority of Mortgages** − Many readers may be aware of certain difficulties that lending institutions − such as banks and trust companies − have raised with the new Act, particularly because a lien claimant is given priority over the lender in certain circumstances (to the extent of any deficiency in the holdbacks required by the new Act).

The new Act distinguishes between three classes of mortgages: the building mortgage (that is, a mortgage taken to finance the construction project); the prior mortgage (that is, any mortgage registered prior to the time a lien first arises); and the subsequent mortgage (that is, any mortgage registered after the time a lien first arises). The new Act gives lien claimants priority over building mortgages taken out at the outset of the project, long before any lien might arise, insofar as holdback deficiencies are concerned.

However, the new Act permits a financial-guarantee bond to be registered on title. If such a bond is registered, the liability for deficiencies in holdbacks will expire if the lender (the mortgagee) sells the property.

This provision is designed to allow a mortgagee to sell the premises in the event of a default under the mortgage free of the liability for such deficiencies in holdbacks. Lien claimants can then claim against the surety (the bonding company) on the bond for such deficiencies.

THE TRUST FUND

In Ontario, the trust obligations provided under the old Act have been included and added to in the new Act. Suppose a contract states that the owner must pay the contractor a certain sum when an authorized person — an engineer — certifies. That sum constitutes a trust fund in the hands of the owner for the benefit of the contractor, and no part of the trust fund can be appropriated or converted for use by the owner except in accordance with the trust-fund provisions of the Construction Lien Act. Similar trust-fund provisions also extend to amounts received by contractors and subcontractors; such amounts are subject to a trust for the benefit of those who have supplied services or materials. The funds cannot be used otherwise until the specified beneficiaries have been paid in full.

Similar trust-fund provisions are included in mechanics' lien legislation in British Columbia, Saskatchewan, Manitoba and New Brunswick.

In Ontario, new trust obligations under the new Act include and extend to all amounts received by an owner after substantial performance, and to amounts received by an owner as a result of a sale of the premises (less reasonable expenses of the sale and amounts to discharge mortgages).

In the event of non-payment of trust monies, and where lien rights have expired, an action under the trust-fund provisions to recover misappropriated trust funds may provide a remedy.

ENGINEERS' RIGHTS TO LIEN CLAIMS

As already noted, pursuant to the new Act in Ontario, engineers' entitlement to lien claims is now confirmed by stat-

167

ute, provided the engineers' services enhance the value of the land.

In the other common-law provinces, where the engineer's right to lien is not yet statutory, what constitutes "necessary services of engineers and architects" to qualify for lien claims remains a question to be decided by the courts of those provinces. There have already been a number of such court decisions.

In 1971, the British Columbia Supreme Court decided the *Application of Erickson/Massey*.[1] An architect prepared plans for, and supervised the construction of, a building. The court held that he was entitled to a lien under the Mechanics' Lien Act of British Columbia. An earlier decision held that an architect was not entitled to a claim for lien. But the earlier decision was distinguished: the architect had only prepared plans. He had not supervised the construction of the building.

But providing supervisory services is not necessarily a prerequisite for an engineer's entitlement to a lien in all provinces. For example, in 1965, the Supreme Court of Alberta decided *Englewood Plumbing & Gas Fitting Ltd.* v. *Northgate Development Ltd. et al.*[2] The court held that an architect was entitled to file a lien claiming payment for his services in the preparation of plans although the architect had performed no supervisory services in connection with the construction.

In 1975, the Supreme Court of Ontario decided *Armbro Materials and Construction Ltd.* v. *230056 Investments Limited et al.*[3] An engineer had prepared plans for sewers, water mains and roads in a subdivision; the plans had to be approved by municipal authorities. The engineer was also retained to supervise construction of the services. Approval of the municipality was obtained, but construction did not proceed for financial reasons. The engineer made a claim for lien. The court distinguished the particular plans of the engineer from architectural plans, and noted that the engineering plans had improved the value of the land. The engineer was entitled to his claim for lien. The court stated:

[1] [1971] 2 W.W.R. 767
[2] [1966] 54 W.W.R. 225
[3] 9 O.R. (2d) 226

. . . those engineering services are so inextricably linked with the land. They are different from the plans of an architect. The plans of an architect are, may I say, "up in the air", and they can fit everywhere, and if they do not fit that specific parcel, then they become a stock plan and they can be sold to someone else who has another lot, and therefore those plans do not need as much protection because they have a merchantable value. They can be sold to someone else if the original man who ordered the plans cannot pay for them, or does not need them any more, but those engineering plans are very specific. They are not "in the air" — they run with the land. The owners could sell those 17 acres now at a much higher price than he could before those plans were made and approved. It is the approval that gives a good deal of value to the lands because it is a long process and a difficult one but once it is obtained, it is attached to the lands and the purchaser can benefit with those plans immediately. He does not have to begin all over again. He carries on from there.

Therefore, I find that those plans, approved as they are, advance the value of the land considerably and they are specifically for that parcel of land and therefore, I think it would be unjust and unfair not to grant a lien to the people who have increased the value of the land.

LIEN STATUTES:

Alberta: The Builders' Lien Act, R.S.A. 1980, c. B-12

British Columbia: The Builders' Lien Act, R.S.B.C. 1979, c. 40

Manitoba: The Builders' Lien Act, S.M. 1980-81, c. 7

New Brunswick: The Mechanics' Lien Act, R.S.N.B. 1973, c. M-6

Newfoundland: The Mechanics' Lien Act, R.S.Nfld. 1970, c. 229

Nova Scotia: The Mechanics' Lien Act, R.S.N.S. 1967, c. 178

Ontario: The Construction Lien Act, S.O. 1983, c. 6

Prince Edward Island: The Mechanics' Lien Act, R.S. P.E.I. 1974, c. M-7

Saskatchewan: The Mechanics' Lien Act, R.S.S. 1978, c. M-7

Yukon: Mechanics' Lien Ordinance, R.O.Y.T. 1971, c. M-5

North West Territories: Mechanics' Lien Ordinance R.O.N.W.T. 1974, c. M-8

CHAPTER TWENTY-FOUR

THE COMBINES INVESTIGATION ACT

The Combines Investigation Act[1] is a federal statute designed to protect and advance business competition. The Act prescribes certain offences and very significant penalties. The scope of offences under the Act is broad: it deals, for example, with formation of monopolies, misleading advertising, bid rigging, price fixing, and conspiracy to unduly limit competition.

An increasing number of convictions, particularly in the area of misleading advertising, attests to the Act's significance. "White collar crime" is undoubtedly a "high-profile" matter today; the engineer in business should be aware of the Act. Its broad scope is perhaps best illustrated through examining selected sections of the statute.

MISLEADING ADVERTISING

Section 36(1), which deals with misleading advertising, provides:

> No person shall, for the purpose of promoting, directly or indirectly, the supply or use of a product or for the purpose of promoting, directly or indirectly, any business interest, by any means whatever,
>
> > (a) make a representation to the public that is false or misleading in a material respect;
> >
> > (b) make a representation to the public in the form of a statement, warranty or guarantee of the performance, efficacy or length of life of a product that is not based on adequate and proper test

[1] R.S.C. 1970, c. C-23

thereof, the proof of which lies upon the person making the representation;

(c) make a representation to the public in a form that purports to be

(i) a warranty or guarantee of a product, or

(ii) a promise to replace, maintain or repair an article or any part thereof or to repeat or continue a service until it has achieved a specified result

if such form of purported warranty or guarantee or promise is materially misleading or if there is no reasonable prospect that it will be carried out; or

(d) make a materially misleading representation to the public concerning the price at which a product or like products have been, are or will be ordinarily sold, and for the purposes of this paragraph a representation as to price is deemed to refer to the price at which the product has been sold by sellers generally in the relevant market unless it is clearly specified to be the price at which the product has been sold by the person by whom or on whose behalf the representation is made.

Conviction can result in a fine "in the discretion of the Court" — that is, there is no maximum limit — or to imprisonment for five years, or to both.

BID-RIGGING

The offence known as "bid-rigging" (that is, collusion leading to the submission of fraudulent contract tenders or bids) is defined in section 32.2(1) of the Act as follows:

in this section "bid-rigging" means

(a) an agreement or arrangement between or among two or more persons whereby one or more of such persons agrees or undertakes not to submit a bid in response to a call or request for bids or tenders, and

(b) the submission in response to a call or request for bids or tenders, of bids or tenders that are

> arrived at by agreement or arrangement between or among two or more bidders or tenderers,

where the agreement or arrangement is not made known to the person calling for or requesting the bids or tenders at or before the time when any bid or tender is made by any person who is a party to the agreement or arrangement. Section 32.2(2) provides:

> Every one who is a party to bid-rigging is guilty of an indictable offence and is liable on conviction to a fine in the discretion of the court or to imprisonment for five years or to both.

CONSPIRACY

The section of the Act that deals with conspiracy (and focusses on preventing interference with competition) is very broadly worded. Section 32(1) provides:

> Every one who conspires, combines, agrees or arranges with another person
> (a) to limit unduly the facilities for transporting, producing, manufacturing, supplying, storing or dealing in any product,
> (b) to prevent, limit or lessen, unduly, the manufacture or production of a product, or to enhance unreasonably the price thereof,
> (c) to prevent, or lessen, unduly, competition in the production, manufacture, purchase, barter, sale, storage, rental, transportation or supply of a product, or in the price of insurance upon persons or property, or
> (d) to otherwise restrain or injure competition unduly, is guilty of an indictable offence and is liable to imprisonment for five years or a fine of one million dollars or to both.

The court must determine in each case, whether the "lessening of competition," for example, is undue; interpreting the meaning of "undue" in any particular circumstances may provide considerable latitude for argument.

173

TRADE ASSOCIATIONS

Certain activities of trade associations — associations of manufacturers and contractors within particular industries — are permitted under the Act. Pursuant to section 32(2) of the Act, the permitted activities or agreements must relate to the following subjects:

(a) the exchange of statistics
(b) the defining of product standards
(c) the exchange of credit information
(d) the definition of terminology used in a trade, industry or profession
(e) co-operation in research and development
(f) the restriction of advertising or promotion, other than a discriminatory restriction directed against a member of the mass media
(g) the sizes or shapes of the containers in which an article is packaged
(h) the adoption of the metric system of weights and measures
(i) measures to protect the environment

The activities listed are legitimate subjects of exchange between trade-association members only insofar as no agreement or arrangement is entered into that will lessen competition unduly in respect of prices, quantity or quality of production, markets or customers, or channels or methods of distribution; or which would restrict any person from entering into or expanding a business in the trade or industry. An exchange of statistics, for example, might appear to be an inherently innocent activity, but it could cross the fine line of illegality. Suppose, for example, that a statistical table of costs were used by members of a trade association as a basis for standard mark-ups; that use could lead to price-fixing. (*Competitors should strictly avoid any discussion of prices.*) As well, technical discussions within an association that discourage independent research by competing companies, or that establish industry standards which smaller, newer, or potential competitors may not be able to meet, may constitute an offence under the Act.

Association members must avoid discussion or other activity that would allocate market shares among firms, allocate markets in any geographical sense or allocate customers in any manner. An understanding that would limit transportation facilities or restrict channels or methods of distribution should be avoided.

Associations must be most cautious not to reach any understanding or pursue any activity (such as an agreement to refuse to deal) that would lessen competition unduly by restricting any person from entering into a particular business or industry.

CHAPTER TWENTY-FIVE

STATUTES GOVERNING THE ENGINEERING PROFESSION

Canada's common-law provinces and the territories have enacted legislation to govern the practice of professional engineering. The professional engineer should acquaint himself or herself with applicable legislation in the province in which he or she practices. The Professional Engineers Act, 1984 of Ontario[1] and the Engineering, Geological and Geophysical Professions Act of Alberta[2] are included as examples, and for convenience of reference, in the Appendix to this text.

PURPOSE OF LEGISLATION

The general purpose of the governing legislation is to regulate the practice of professional engineering, to protect the public interest. For example, sections 2(3) and 2(4) of the Professional Engineers Act, 1984 of Ontario provide:

> (3) The principal object of the Association is to regulate the practice of professional engineering and to govern its members, holders of certificates of authorization, holders of temporary licenses and holders of limited licences in accordance with this Act, the regulations and the by-laws in order that the public interest may be served and protected.
>
> (4) For the purpose of carrying out its principal object, the Association has the following additional objects:
>
> 1. To establish, maintain and develop standards of knowledge and skill among its members.
> 2. To establish, maintain and develop standards of

[1] S.O. 1984, c. 13
[2] R.S.A. 1981, c. E-11.1

               qualification and standards of practice for the practice of professional engineering.

3. To establish, maintain and develop standards of professional ethics among its members.
4. To promote public awareness of the role of the Association.
5. To perform such other duties and exercise such other powers as are imposed or conferred on the Association by or under any Act.

The regulations under the Professional Engineers Act, 1984 of Ontario respond to the objects of the Association by addressing a wide range of matters.[3] For example, the regulations detail the structure of the Association's Council and provide for such matters as procedures for election to Council, mediating disputed engineering fees, issuing licences and certificates of authorization, prescribing requisite examinations, designating specialists and consulting engineers, defining "professional misconduct" and setting out minimum requirements for professional liability insurance, as well as specifying the Code of Ethics of the Association.

DEFINITION OF PROFESSIONAL ENGINEERING

"Professional engineering" is defined in the various provincial statutes; the definitions are broad in scope. The "practice of professional engineering" is defined in section 1(m) of the Professional Engineers Act, 1984 of Ontario:

> practice of professional engineering means any act of designing, composing, evaluating, advising reporting, directing or supervising wherein the safeguarding of life, health, property or the public welfare is concerned and that requires the application of engineering principles, but does not include practising as a natural scientist.

"Practice of engineering" is defined in Section 1(m) of the Engineering, Geological and Geophysical Professions Act of Alberta:

[3] O. Reg. 538/84

"practice of engineering" means

(i) reporting on, advising on, evaluating, designing, preparing plans and specifications for or directing the construction, technical inspection, maintenance or operation of any structure, work or process

   (A) that is aimed at the discovery, development or utilization of matter, materials or energy or in any other way designed for the use and convenience of man, and

   (B) that requires in the reporting, advising, evaluating, designing, preparation or direction the professional application of the principles of mathematics, chemistry, physics or any related applied subject, or

(ii) teaching engineering at a university.

PROFESSIONAL ENGINEER'S SEAL

In all of the common-law jurisdictions in Canada, a professional engineer is required to stamp drawings and specifications with his or her seal. The seal is issued by the Provincial Association, and it indicates that the engineer is a registered Professional Engineer. It is extremely important that each engineer closely controls the use of his or her seal and ensures that it is only used where appropriate. Improper use of the engineer's seal in Ontario can result in disciplinary proceedings and fines of up to fifteen thousand dollars for individuals and up to thirty thousand dollars for corporations and partnerships. In Ontario, the Council of the Association of Professional Engineers of Ontario is empowered to make regulations "requiring and governing the signing and sealing of documents and designs by members of the Association, holders of temporary licences and holders of limited licences, specifying the forms of seals and respecting the issuance and ownership of seals." And Section 54 of the regulations under the Professional Engineers Act, 1984 provides:

> Every holder of a licence, temporary licence or limited licence who provides to the public a service that is within the practice of professional engineering shall sign, date and affix his seal to every final drawing,

179

specification, plan, report or other document prepared or checked by him as part of the service before it is issued.

Section 86(2)(e) of the Ontario regulations includes, as part of the definition of ''professional misconduct'':

> (e) signing or sealing a final drawing, specification, plan, report or other document not actually prepared or checked by the practitioner.

In Alberta, a professional engineer is required to use his or her seal pursuant to section 76 of the Engineering, Geological and Geophysical Professions Act of Alberta and Part 11 of the Regulations thereunder. Section 76 provides that:

> 76(1) A professional member, license or restricted practitioner shall sign and stamp or seal all documents or records in accordance with the regulations.
> (2) No person other than a professional member, licensee, permit holder or certificate holder shall use a stamp or seal issued by the Registrar under this Act.

PARTNERSHIPS AND CORPORATIONS

The regulatory provincial common-law statutes provide, in effect, that a partnership or corporation may be granted a certificate of authorization or be permitted to practise professional engineering, providing such professional engineering is practised under the responsibility and supervision of a member or of a licensed professional engineer and otherwise complies with the applicable provincial statute and regulations thereunder.

DISCIPLINARY HEARINGS

The regulatory statutes also authorize what disciplinary action may be taken against members or licensees for professional misconduct. Disciplinary action usually arises, in Ontario, for example, following the submission of a complaint to the Complaints Committee. The Committee examines the complaint and can then refer the matter to the Discipline Committee. The Discipline Committee is authorized (pursuant to section 29 of the Professional Engineers Act,

1984), when so directed by the Council, the Executive Committee or the Complaints Committee, to hear and determine allegations of professional misconduct or incompetence. Disciplinary action may result in reprimands, suspensions, fines and cancellation of membership and licenses. Decisions of disciplinary hearings may be appealed to the courts in accordance with the provisions of the applicable regulatory statute.

Section 86 of the Ontario regulations sets out important specific definitions of negligence and professional misconduct. Section 86 provides:

86. − (1) In this section, "negligence" means an act or an omission in the carrying out of the work of a practitioner that constitutes a failure to maintain the standards that a reasonable and prudent practitioner would maintain in the circumstances.

(2) For the purposes of the Act and this Regulation, "professional misconduct" means,

(a) negligence;

(b) failure to make reasonable provision for the safeguarding of life, health or property of a person who may be affected by the work for which the practitioner is responsible;

(c) failure to act to correct or report a situation that the practitioner believes may endanger the safety or the welfare of the public;

(d) failure to make responsible provision for complying with applicable statutes, regulations, standards, codes, by-laws and rules in connection with work being undertaken by or under the responsibility of the practitioner;

(e) signing or sealing a final drawing, specification, plan, report or other document not actually prepared or checked by the practitioner;

(f) failure of a practitioner to present clearly to his employer the consequences to be expected from a deviation proposed in work, if the professional engineering judgment of the practitioner is overruled by non-technical authority in cases where the practitioner is responsible for the technical adequacy of professional engineering work;

181

(g) breach of the Act or regulations, other than an action that is solely a breach of the code of ethics;

(h) undertaking work the practitioner is not competent to perform by virtue of his training and experience;

(i) failure to make prompt, voluntary and complete disclosure of an interest, direct or indirect, that might in any way be, or be construed as, prejudicial to the professional judgment of the practitioner in rendering service to the public, to an employer or to a client, and in particular without limiting the generality of the foregoing, carrying out any of the following acts without making such a prior disclosure:

1. Accepting compensation in any form for a particular service from more than one party.

2. Submitting a tender or acting as a contractor in respect of work upon which the practitioner may be performing as a professional engineer.

3. Participating in the supply of material or equipment to be used by the employer or client of the practitioner.

4. Contracting in the practitioner's own right to perform professional engineering services for other than the practitioner's employer.

5. Expressing opinions or making statements concerning matters within the practice of professional engineering of public interest where the opinions or statements are inspired or paid for by other interests;

(j) conduct or an act relevant to the practice of professional engineering that, having regard to all the circumstances, would reasonably be regarded by the engineering profession as disgraceful, dishonourable or unprofessional;

(k) failure by a practitioner to abide by the terms, conditions or limitations of the practitioner's licence, limited licence, temporary licence or certificate;

(l) failure to supply documents or information requested by an investigator acting under section 34 of the Act;

(m) permitting, counselling or assisting a person who is not a practitioner to engage in the practice of professional engineering except as provided for in the Act or the regulations.

PENALTIES

The offence provisions of the statutes that regulate engineering impose varying penalties for contravening statutes and ordinances. The penalty in Ontario, for example, for practising professional engineering without a licence or for holding oneself out as engaging in the practice of engineering without being properly licensed includes a fine of not more than fifteen thousand dollars for the first offence, and for each subsequent offence a fine of not more than thirty thousand dollars.

CERTIFICATES OF AUTHORIZATION

In Ontario, professional-engineering membership alone does not qualify engineers to offer to the public, or engage in the business of providing to the public, services that are within the practice of professional engineering. A certificate of authorization is also required. Applicants for certificates of authorization, including individual members, partnerships and corporations, must meet prescribed requirements and qualifications pursuant to Section 15 of the Professional Engineers Act, 1984. The registrar is authorized to refuse to issue, to suspend or to revoke a certificate of authorization where the registrar "is of the opinion, upon reasonable and probable grounds" that the certificate should be refused, suspended or revoked, upon the basis of past conduct or failure to meet requirements or qualifications.

All holders of certificates of authorization must have professional-liability insurance, in accordance with Section 88 of the regulations. Minimum coverage for each single occurrence must be not less than $250,000, with an aggregate policy limit for all occurrences of not less than $500,000 per year or, alternatively, an automatic-policy-limit-reinstatement feature. Any engineer who obtains such insurance should ensure that it complies with all the requirements of the regulations.

OVERLAPPING IN THE SCOPE OF ENGINEERING AND ARCHITECTURAL PRACTICES

As noted, the term "professional engineering" is broadly defined by the regulatory statutes and ordinances. Occasionally, the broad definitions lead to confusion; one problem is the distinction between the functions of an engineer and an architect. The problem has been considered by the courts.

For example, in 1939 the court heard *Rex* v. *Bentall*.[4] A professional engineer in British Columbia had planned and supervised the construction of a theatre; he was convicted for unlawfully practising as an architect.

In 1955, the Ontario County Court heard *Regina* v. *Margison and Associates, Limited*.[5] An engineering firm was charged with holding itself out as an architect. The court examined both the Professional Engineers Act and the Architects Act to decide whether a particular job was essentially one for an engineer or for an architect. But neither Act provided the court with definitions specific enough to distinguish between the two professions. The action against the engineer failed. The court stated, in part:

> I cannot but think that it was the intention of the legislation to give reciprocal privileges, at least to the extent necessary to cover the facts disclosed, and that it is up to a client to weigh the qualifications of firms of architects and engineers and decide which he wishes to employ, or indeed if he wishes to employ both, which is a common practice. Mr. Fleming contends that it is possible to decide whether a job is essentially one for an architect or one for an engineer. I can find nothing in the words of the legislation which enables the Court to draw such a line between the two professions, and I do not think that the Court should endeavour to do so until the Legislature passes appropriate provisions.

BACKGROUND TO CHANGES IN ONTARIO LEGISLATION

[4] [1939] 3 W.W.R. 39
[5] [1955] O.W.N. 705

In Ontario, however, the Professional Engineers Act, 1984 includes provisions intended to simplify the ''scope-of-practice'' dispute between professional engineers and architects. The provisions describe the nature of construction projects that can be designed by engineers alone, or by architects alone, or by both. (See, in particular, subsection 12[6] of the statute in the Appendix to this text.)

By way of background to the Professional Engineers Act, 1984, in the April, 1980 Report of the Professional Organizations Committee (appointed by the Attorney General for Ontario, in 1977), the following observations were made in respect to the scope-of-practice dispute:

> Between 1969 and 1976, legal action was taken by the Ontario Association of Architects (OAA) against five engineering firms for offering architectural services. The laying of charges was motivated by a desire on the part of the Association to obtain from the courts clarification of the scope of licensed practice laid down by The Architects Act and The Professional Engineers Act.[6] The essential thrust of the resulting judicial opinions was to the effect that the existing legislation sanctioned an overlapping in the functions of architects and engineers in the field of building design.
>
> While the legislation did not permit an engineer to hold himself out as an architect, it left the client free to determine whether he should hire an architect or an engineer or both. These opinions, of course, were conclusive only with respect to the facts before the courts in each case. Strictly speaking, they extended only to the design of steel, concrete, and reinforced concrete structures. In other words, it apparently remained illegal for an engineer to design any building made out of wood, masonry, or a host of other building materials. But nothing stood in the way of further court tests which, whatever their outcome, promised to contribute little to the constructive evolution of interprofessional relations in building design.

Representatives of the Association of Professional Engineers in Ontario (APEO) and the OAA reviewed the prob-

[6] Ontario Association of Architects, Brief to the Professional Organizations Committee, July, 1977.

lem and held meetings. Premised on two particular declarations of principle, agreement was reached. The first premise: engineers should confine their professional activity to the practice of engineering and architects to the practice of architecture. The second premise: a client should be free to select the prime consultant of his choice. The APEO-OAA agreement and the decision of the Professional Organizations Committee contemplated in part: that a Joint Practice Board, composed of three engineers and three architects appointed by the APEO and the OAA respectively, be instituted. The Board would be authorized to make recommendations to the APEO and the OAA and to handle complaints of an interprofessional nature. It would also be empowered to work on other matters, such as the co-ordination and publication of guidelines, standards, criteria and performance standards in the field of building design and construction.

The recommendations of the Professional Organizations Committee were implemented and resulted in revisions to regulatory statutes governing both engineers and architects. Section 48 of the Professional Engineers Act, 1984 of Ontario now provides for a Joint Practice Board composed of a chairman, three architects and three professional engineers, who are authorized to recommend the issuance of licences. Firms are now entitled to practise both professional engineering and architecture.

The Joint Practice Board is also authorized to assist in the resolution of "scope-of-practice" disputes. Sections 48(4) and 48(5) of the Professional Engineers Act, 1984 provide:

> 48(4) Where a dispute arises between an architect and a professional engineer or a holder of a certificate of authorization as to jurisdiction in respect of professional services, the Registrar may refer the matter to the Joint Practice Board and the Joint Practice Board shall consider the matter and assist the architect and the professional engineer or the holder of the certificate of authorization to resolve the dispute in accordance with the rules in section 12.
>
> (5) Proceedings shall not be commenced under this Act in respect of a matter mentioned in subsection (4) except upon the certificate of the chairman of the Joint

Practice Board that the Board has considered the matter and has been unable to resolve the dispute.

CODE OF ETHICS

Section 91 of the regulations pursuant to the Professional Engineers Act, 1984 of Ontario sets out the APEO's Code of Ethics. The code contains standards of conduct designed for the protection of the public. Members and licensees must subscribe to and follow those standards in the practice of professional engineering.

Every engineer should therefore be familiar with his or her provincial code of ethics. The Ontario Code of Ethics, as now included in the regulations, is as follows:

91. The following is the Code of Ethics of the Association:

1. It is the duty of a practitioner to the public, to his employer, to his clients, to other members of his profession, and to himself to act at all times with,
   i. fairness and loyalty to his associates, employers, clients, subordinates and employees,
   ii. fidelity to public needs, and
   iii. devotion to high ideals of personal honour and professional integrity.

2. A practitioner shall,
   i. regard his duty to public welfare as paramount,
   ii. endeavour at all times to enhance the public regard for his profession by extending the public knowledge thereof and discouraging untrue, unfair or exaggerated statements with respect to professional engineering,
   iii. not express publicly, or while he is serving as a witness before a court, commission or other tribunal, opinions on professional engineering matters that are not founded on adequate knowledge and honest conviction,
   iv. endeavour to keep his licence, temporary licence, limited licence or certificate of authorization, as the case may be, permanently displayed in his place of business.

187

3. A practitioner shall act in professional engineering matters for each employer as a faithful agent or trustee and shall regard as confidential information obtained by him as to the business affairs, technical methods or processes of an employer and avoid or disclose a conflict of interest that might influence his actions or judgment.

4. A practitioner must disclose immediately to his client any interest, direct or indirect, that might be construed as prejudicial in any way to the professional judgment of the practitioner in rendering service to the client.

5. A practitioner who is an employee-engineer and is contracting in his own name to perform professional engineering work for other than his employer, must provide his client with a written statement of the nature of his status as an employee and the attendant limitations on his services to the client, must satisfy himself that the work will not conflict with his duty to his employer, and must inform his employer of the work.

6. A practitioner must co-operate in working with other professionals engaged on a project.

7. A practitioner shall,
   i. conduct himself towards other practitioners with courtesy and good faith,
   ii. not accept an engagement to review the work of another practitioner for the same employer except with the knowledge of the other practitioner or except where the connection of the other practitioner with the work has been terminated,
   iii. not maliciously injure the reputation or business of another practitioner,
   iv. not attempt to gain an advantage over other practitioners by paying or accepting a commission in securing professional engineering work, and
   v. give proper credit for engineering work, uphold the principle of adequate compensation for engineering work, provide opportunity for professional development and advancement of his

associates and subordinates, and extend the effectiveness of the profession through the interchange of engineering information and experience.

8. A practitioner shall maintain the honour and integrity of his profession and without fear or favour expose before the proper tribunals unprofessional, dishonest or unethical conduct by any other practitioner.

O. Reg. 538/84, s. 91.

CHAPTER TWENTY-SIX

INDUSTRIAL PROPERTY

Rights that relate generally to patents, trade-marks, copyrights, and industrial designs are sometimes called "industrial-property rights." The federal Patent Act[1], the Trade Marks Act[2], the Copyright Act[3], and the Industrial Design Act[4] govern these rights. The statutes describe such matters as obtaining patents of invention and the registration of trade-marks, copyrights, and industrial designs. Patent applications and trade-mark, industrial design, and copyright registrations are usually effected by professionals who specialize in such matters. This chapter will focus on the basic nature and practical aspects of industrial-property rights.

PATENTS OF INVENTION

Definition and Purpose

As stated in Section 67(3) of the Patent Act, "patents for new inventions are granted not only to encourage invention but to secure that new inventions shall so far as possible be worked on a commercial scale in Canada without undue delay."

The Patent Act defines an invention as "any new and useful art, process, machine, manufacture or composition of matter, or any new and useful improvement in any art, process, machine, manufacture or composition of matter."

What May Be Patented

What constitutes patentable subject matter? The definition

[1] R.S.C. 1970, c. P-4
[2] R.S.C. 1970, c. T-10
[3] R.S.C. 1970, c. C-30
[4] R.S.C. 1970, c. I-8

of "invention" in the Patent Act is a broad one. An idea alone is not patentable: the idea or principle must be reduced to something physical. The need for something tangible was discussed in *Permutit Co.* v. *Borrowman*[5]:

> It is not enough for a man to say that an idea floated through his brain; he must at least have reduced it to a definite and practical shape before he can be said to have invented a process.

In 1929, the Privy Council decided *General Electric Company, Limited* v. *Fada Radio, Limited*[6]. The following excerpt focusses on the idea that patentable inventions must have two characteristics — utility and novelty — that result from the application of ingenuity and skill.

> The law on this subject is, in their Lordships' opinion, accurately summarized by Maclean J. in his judgment. His statement is as follows: "There must be a substantial exercise of the inventive power or inventive genius, though it may in cases be very slight. Slight alterations or improvements may produce important results, and may disclose great ingenuity. Sometimes it is a combination that is the invention; if the invention requires independent thought, ingenuity and skill, producing in a distinctive form a more efficient result, converting a comparatively defective apparatus into a useful and efficient one, rejecting what is bad and useless in former attempts and retaining what is useful, and uniting them all into an apparatus which, taken as a whole, is novel, there is subject matter. A new combination of well known devices, and the application thereof to a new and useful purpose, may require invention to produce it, and may be good subject-matter for a patent."

Discovery alone that an apparatus, for example, may be altered to produce a new result will not qualify for a patent; one must show that ingenuity has been applied to the discovery to produce a novel and useful method or result.

[5] [1926] 43 R.P.C. 356
[6] [1930] A.C. 97

Term of Patent

Once a patent is granted, its term is seventeen years from the date of the grant. If a particular invention has been granted a patent, no other valid patent can be granted with respect to that invention.

Assignment and Licensing of Patent Rights

The value of a patent is enhanced by virtue of the fact that patent rights can be assigned to others. Section 53(1) of the Patent Act provides that:

> Every patent issued for an invention is assignable in law, either as to the whole interest or as to any part thereof, by an instrument in writing.

The owner of a patent can assign part or all of his patent rights, in whole or in part, and for such valuable consideration as may be negotiated with the assignee.

Patent rights may also be licensed, on an exclusive or a non-exclusive basis. Usually a royalty fee is charged based on a percentage of sales of the patented product.

Any assignment of a patent right or grant of exclusive licensing rights must be registered in the Patent Office. Otherwise it will be void and therefore unenforceable against a subsequent assignee or exclusive licensee who does register.

Infringement of Patents

Section 57 of the Patent Act deals with infringement of patents. Infringement of a patent entitles the owner of the patent to claim for all damages he sustains — and any damages sustained by his licensees — by reason of such infringement.

To recover damages, a court action may be brought. The court will have to decide whether the defendant has taken the substance of the plaintiff's invention. If the court decides in favour of the inventor, he may obtain an injunction to restrain the defendant from further infringement. The inventor may then proceed to recover any profits the defendant received as a result of the infringement, based on an accounting thereof. Or he may recover any damages that he can prove were incurred as a result of the infringement. To calculate damages, the general approach is to determine the net profit the plaintiff would have made if he — rather than the infringing defendant — had sold items produced by the infringement of the patent.

Assignment of Patent Rights by Employee Engineer

An engineer may be requested, by his employer, to execute an agreement that assigns to the employer some or all patent rights to which the engineer might otherwise become entitled during the course of his employment.

In general, in the absence of a special contract, the invention of an employee made in the employer's time, with the employer's materials and at the expense of the employer, does not become the property of the employer (*Willard's Chocolates Ltd.* v. *Bardsley*[7]). But there is an exception to this general rule: at times an employee is, by the nature of his employment, expected to apply his ingenuity and inventive faculties. Thus if an engineer produces a patentable invention during the course of his employment, the patent belongs to his employer.

But note that such patent rights extend only to inventions that arise in the course of employment. An excerpt from *British Reinforced Concrete Engineering Co. Limited* v. *Lind*[8] is of interest in this regard:

> In my judgment a draughtsman — I am only dealing with a draughtsman at the moment — in an engineering draughtsman's office, does not do his duty to his employer when he is instructed to prepare a design for the purpose of getting over a known difficulty or for the purpose of arriving at a solution of a problem if he does not exercise among other things such skill and inventive faculty as he may possess. In my judgment it is part of his duty and part of that which he is paid to do, to produce under those circumstances the best design that he is capable of producing. In some cases the employer requires and obtains an express agreement in writing between himself and the employee, providing for inventions that may be made, but in the absence of any agreement of that kind, I desire to guard myself against suggesting that every invention

[7] [1928-29] 35 O.W.N. 92
[8] [1917] 34 R.P.C. 101

which is made by a person, even though he is a draughtsman in an office in an engineering firm, necessarily belongs to the firm. I am not suggesting that for a moment. I can well conceive that such a person might make an invention in respect of something which is outside his work altogether, having nothing to do with the work upon which his employers are engaged, in which case such an invention would be the draughtsman's own property. But in my judgment, if a draughtsman is instructed by his employer to prepare a design for the purpose of solving a particular difficulty or problem, it is his business and his duty to do the best he can to produce the best design, using all the abilities which he may have, and if he does produce a design which solves the problem, as a result of the instructions that he has been given by his employer, then *prima facie* at any rate the design and then invention are the property of the employer and not of the employee.

That being the law as I understand it, in some cases it may seem to work hardly upon the employee. Taking the present case, the Defendant was a person receiving a comparatively small wage, a man of ability, and I have no doubt of some inventive faculty, and it may seem hard that the fruits of his brains and labours should belong to his employer. On the other hand, the position would be an extraordinarily difficult one if it were not so. The position would be, that a person in the position of a draughtsman, being instructed to prepare a design to get over a known difficulty, and preparing that design and thus solving the difficulty, would be entitled to prevent his employer, who had paid him to do the job and in whose time he had done the work, from making use of that design without coming to some agreement with him, the employee, as to the terms upon which it was to be used. It seems to me that that would be a position which would be almost impossible.

TRADE-MARKS

Definition

"Trade-mark" is defined in the Trade Marks Act. Part of the definition states:

> "trade-mark" means
> (a) a mark that is used by a person for the purpose of distinguishing wares or services manufactured, sold, leased, hired or performed by him from those manufactured, sold, leased, hired or performed by others.

A trade-mark may be registered according to the Trade Marks Act; it may be used in connection with wares and/or services. Unless shown to be invalid, the registration of a trade-mark gives the owner the exclusive right to use the trade-mark throughout Canada.

When Trade-Marks Are Registrable

The Trade Marks Act lists certain words and marks that may be registered as trade-marks. Section 12(1) provides, in part:

> Subject to section 13, a trade mark is registrable if it is not
> (a) a word that is primarily merely the name or the surname of an individual who is living or has died within the preceding thirty years;
> (b) whether depicted, written or sounded, either clearly descriptive or deceptively misdescriptive in the English or French languages of the character or quality of the wares or services in association with which it is used or proposed to be used or of the conditions of or the persons employed in their production or of their place of origin;
> (c) the name in any language of any of the wares or services in connection with which it is used or proposed to be used;
> (d) confusing with a registered trade mark.

An essential feature of a registrable trade-mark is its distinctiveness. The trade-mark must distinguish goods of one manufacturer from those of another; manufacturers must not deceive the public. The Trade Marks Act provides:

> "distinctive" in relation to a trade mark means a trade mark that actually distinguishes the wares or services in association with which it is used by its owner from the wares or services of others or is adapted so to distinguish them. . . .

Registered-User Agreements

The owner of a trade-mark may license or authorize another person to use the trade-mark as a registered user. A person who wishes to become a registered user of a trade-mark may apply to the Registrar of Trade Marks. The registered user may acquire the right to use the trade-mark for an indefinite or limited time; his use of the trade-mark is subject to the restrictions set forth in the registered-user agreement.

Duration of Registration

The Trade Marks Act prescribes that registrations are effective for a period of fifteen years; registrations may be renewed for unlimited subsequent periods of fifteen years each.

Infringement

A person who infringes a valid registered trade-mark may be restrained from continuing to use the mark; he may also be liable for damages that resulted from his infringing of the trade-mark. Forgery of a trade-mark with intent to deceive or defraud the public or any person is an offence under the Criminal Code of Canada. The offence is punishable by fine and imprisonment for up to two years.

COPYRIGHT

Definition

Subject to the provisions of the Copyright Act, copyright subsists in every original literary, dramatic, musical and artistic work. "Copyright" generally means the sole right to produce or reproduce the work, or any substantial part thereof in any material form whatever. As well, it conveys

197

sole right to perform — and, in the case of a lecture, to deliver — the work or any substantial part thereof in public. If the work is unpublished, copyright conveys sole right to publish the work, or any substantial part thereof.

Term of Copyright

Except as otherwise expressly provided by the Act, copyright subsists for a term that equals the life of the author and a period of fifty years after his death.

Assignment of Copyright

The first owner of copyright in a work is the author of the work. The owner of the copyright is entitled to assign the copyright in whole or in part. An assignment may be made subject to territorial and timing limitations.

Registration of Copyright

The Copyright Act provides that an author, his legal representatives, or an agent may apply for the registration of a copyright at the Copyright Office. The particulars of any assignment or licence of a copyright may also be registered at the Copyright Office.

Registration by the author is not essential to copyright. However, registration of assignments and licences of copyright are advisable in order to protect assignees and licensees from claims of other subsequent assignees and licensees who may register.

Engineering Plans

Copyright in engineering plans subsists in the engineer who authored the plans. Where an engineer prepares the plans for a client and unless otherwise agreed, the client is precluded from reproducing the engineer's plans or repeating his design in a new structure without the express or implied consent of the engineer. Engineer-client agreements should include a provision that draws attention to this aspect of the engineer's copyright.

INDUSTRIAL DESIGNS

Definition

198   The Industrial Design Act grants protection to originators

of certain industrial designs. The term "industrial design" refers to any sculpture, pattern, shape or configuration of an ornamental nature that is applied to articles of commerce, where the articles are multiplied by an industrial process — printing, painting, embroidery, weaving, sewing, casting, embossing, engraving, staining and so on. Only those industrial designs that are ornamental or aesthetic in nature — as opposed to functional — qualify for protection under the Industrial Design Act. The mechanical construction of an article does not form part of the design; neither does the method of manufacture. Construction and method are functional, and thus are not protected by the Act. (Mechanical constructions or methods of manufacture may qualify for patent protection.)

"Design" may mean the shape or configuration of a part or a portion of an article, or the whole combination, or both.

In order to qualify for protection, a design must meet the tests of novelty and originality.

Term

The proprietor who registers an industrial design is granted an exclusive right to the use of the design for a term of five years. The term is subject to renewal for an additional five years.

Assignment

Designs are freely assignable; the assignment must be made in writing. In addition, a proprietor may licence others to make, use or sell his design during the term of its statutory protection.

Employees

The rights to any designs made by an employee in the course of his employment belong to the employer.

Registration

To register a design under the Industrial Design Act, a proprietor submits a drawing and description of the design in duplicate, together with the prescribed fee, to the appropriate government office. Registration will be refused if it appears that the design is identical with or closely resembles another design currently in use or previously registered.

199

TRADE SECRETS

A patent of invention provides monopoly rights for a limited period; that is, for the seventeen-year term of the patent. Once an invention has been patented, its subject matter is no longer private. Full details of the invention are publicized and become part of the "public domain." When the term of the patent expires, the invention may be freely used by others. The limited term of patent protection causes some concern; as well, it is sometimes difficult to enforce a patent. To avoid these problems, inventors sometimes classify their invention ideas as "trade secrets"; and do not obtain patent protection.

The Nature of a Trade Secret

The subject matter of "trade secrets" or "confidential information" has been defined by the courts[9] as follows:

> A trade secret may consist of a formula, pattern, device or compilation of information which is used in one's business and which gives him an opportunity to obtain an advantage over competitors who do not know or use it. It may be a formula for a chemical compound, a process for manufacturing, treating or preserving materials, a pattern for a machine or other device or a list of customers.

The definition includes what is generally referred to as "industrial know-how." The term describes valuable information acquired by a business enterprise, for example, marketing and manufacturing techniques, organizational methods, and technical data.

Patent law does not effectively protect much of the subject matter of trade secrets. In fact, most elements of "know-how" — such as organizational methods and customer lists — are unpatentable. Trade-secret protection is the only available legal remedy for the unauthorized use of such information.

A person who wishes to succeed in an action for unauthorized disclosure or use of a trade secret must establish two elements. First, it must be shown that the information was indeed "know-how" — the necessary qual-

200   [9] *Seager* v. *Copydex Ltd.* [1967] R.P.C. 349

ity of secrecy must be adduced. Second, it must be shown that the secret information was communicated to the defendant in circumstances that implied a duty of confidence.

Only confidential information — not general knowledge — will qualify for trade-secret protection. If the possessor of a secret voluntarily discloses that secret without restrictions, the protection will be lost. In general, disclosure of the secret must be strictly confined to a limited group of persons, such as employees and potential licensees, or the confidential nature of the secret is lost.

To determine whether certain information possesses the requisite degree of secrecy, the courts have looked at the following factors:

(1) the extent to which the information is known outside the business;

(2) the extent of measures taken to guard the secrecy of the information;

(3) the value of the information to competitors;

(4) the amount of effort or money spent to develop the information.

The common law recognizes the right of an employer to restrain a former employee from making improper use of trade secrets, and the employer's right to damages for profits resulting from any such improper use.

In *Amber Size & Chemical Co., Ltd.* v. *Menzel*[10], the court made several remarks that illustrate the principles a court might apply:

> In my view, after giving the authorities the best attention I can, the law stands thus: — The Court will restrain an ex-servant from publishing or divulging that which has been communicated to him in confidence or under a contract by him, express or implied, not to do so. . . . and generally from making an improper use of information obtained in the course of confidential employment. . . . and, further, from using to his late master's detriment information and knowledge surreptitiously obtained from him during his, the servant's employment. . . .

[10] [1913] 2 Ch. 239

In applying these principles I have to answer four questions of fact:

First, did the plaintiffs in fact possess and exercise a secret process?

Secondly, did the defendant during the course of his employment know that this process was secret?

Thirdly, did the defendant acquire knowledge during his employment of that secret or a material part thereof?

Fourthly, has he since leaving the plaintiff's employ made an improper use of the knowledge so acquired by him?

When a Duty of Confidence Arises   In the relationship of employer and employee, it is an implied contractual term that the employee will not disclose the confidential information of his employer. This obligation continues even after the employment is terminated. But the employee may use any ordinary working knowledge and general experience acquired in one job in any subsequent employment. It is often difficult to distinguish between ordinary working knowledge and protectable trade secrets.

In general, the courts have demonstrated an extreme reluctance to prohibit an employee from using his or her skills in subsequent employment. Clear and convincing evidence of confidentiality is required when an employer alleges breach of confidence by a former employee.

An obligation of confidence also exists where the owner of a trade secret discloses the secret to another enterprise for a specific purpose, such as having a mould or dye made for future production[11]. The recipient of the trade secret must use the information solely for the purpose for which it was entrusted to him. If the recipient discloses it to others or makes use of it for his own purposes, he will be liable to the owner for any damages suffered by the owner as a result.

In the process of negotiating for the licensed use by the recipient of a trade secret, the relationship between two parties will give rise to an obligation of confidence even if

[11] *Saltman* v. *Campbell* [1948] 65 R.P.C. 203

no agreement on the use of the trade secret is ever entered into[12].

[12] *Coco* v. *Clark* [1969] R.P.C. 41

CHAPTER TWENTY-SEVEN

LAWS RELATING TO LABOUR

FEDERAL LAWS

Consistent with the constitutional division of powers between the federal and provincial governments, federal labour legislation governs labour relations and employment matters where industries and undertakings of an interprovincial, national or international nature are concerned. For example, transportation, communications, and any work or undertaking that is for the general advantage of Canada, or for the advantage of two or more of its provinces, are federal matters.

The most significant of the federal statutes is the Canada Labour Code[1]. The Code covers three general areas of employment law. One part of the Code sets out minimum employment standards; it deals with hours of work, overtime pay, minimum wages, holidays, vacations, maternity leave, bereavement leave, notice of termination of employment and unjust dismissal of non-unionized employees. Another portion of the Code deals with safety of employees. (The Code permits an employee to refuse to work where there is an imminent danger to his health and safety; the Code also describes proper procedures to be followed when such refusal occurs.) The third part of the Code covers relations between trade unions and employers. The Code establishes the Canada Labour Relations Board, which administers provisions of the Code relating to the certification of unions as bargaining agents for employees. The Board also investigates claims of unfair labour practice and illegal strikes, and establishes procedures for lawful strikes and lockouts.

[1] R.S.C. 1970, c. L-1

PROVINCIAL LAWS

Each province has enacted provincial labour laws. (A list of certain statutes of the provinces, together with certain federal statutes, is set out at the end of this chapter for reference.) The laws deal with relations between trade unions and employers; labour standards (such as maximum hours of work, overtime, minimum wages, holidays and notice of termination of employment); workmen's compensation, and so on. Provincial labour statutes have established boards to administer labour-relations legislation. In Alberta, for example, the Board of Industrial Relations administers labour standards and labour relations. In Ontario, the Ontario Labour Relations Act[2] is administered by the Labour Relations Board; labour standards are administered by the Employment Standards Branch of the Ministry of Labour.

PROVINCIAL STATUTES – ONTARIO

The Employment Standards Act[3]

The Employment Standards Act establishes minimum terms and conditions of employment. The Act was designed to protect non-union employees; but all employees are covered, with certain limited exceptions. The Act prescribes requirements in many areas: maximum hours of work, payment for overtime, minimum wages, public holidays, vacations with pay, equal pay for male and female employees performing equal work, employee benefit plans, pregnancy leave for female employees and individual and group notice of termination of employment.

The Act also provides that where an employer sells his business or part of his business and the vendor's employees are retained by the purchaser, the employees are not deemed terminated by the sale. The period of employment with the purchaser includes the period of employment with the vendor for purposes of notice of termination, vacations, holidays and pregnancy leave. For example, suppose an employer purchases a business or any part of a business; suppose he retains the employees for only one day, and then

---

[2] R.S.O. 1980, c. 228
[3] R.S.O. 1980, c. 137

decides to terminate them. His notice of termination must be based upon the period of employment with the vendor.

The Act sets out minimum requirements only. Any term or condition of employment included in a written or oral contract of employment that provides a greater right or benefit prevails over the minimum requirement imposed by the Act.

The Act does not affect an employee's civil remedies against an employer. For example, suppose an employee is hired for an indefinite period of time; suppose there is no written contract stipulating the notice period required to terminate the services of the employee. The common law requires that the employer give the employee reasonable notice of termination (or pay instead of reasonable notice) unless the employee is terminated for cause. Common law might provide an employee with a greater period of notice than does the Act. At common law, the period of notice depends upon an employee's position, length of service, age and the availability of similar employment having regard to his experience, training and qualifications. An employer might terminate an employee in accordance with the Act, yet the employee could still sue the employer at common law. He might claim that he was entitled to more notice, or he might ask for pay in lieu of notice.

For an employee with more than ten years' service, the maximum notice of termination required under section 40 of the Act is eight weeks. For an employee who does not exercise supervisory duties and who does not possess any high degree of technical skill, the notice requirements set out in the Act may be sufficient to satisfy the common-law requirement of "reasonable notice." However, for management and professional employees, the period of notice required pursuant to common-law decisions varies. Generally, managers and professional employees are entitled to from three to twenty-one months' notice.

An example is a 1961 Ontario case, *Lazarowicz* v. *Orenda Engines Limited*[4]. A forty-nine-year-old professional engineer with three years' service was awarded the equivalent of three months' salary. A more recent example is the 1979 case, *Blakely* v. *Victaulic Company of Canada*[5].

[4] 26 D.L.R. (2d) 433
[5] [1979] 1 A.C.W.S. 351

A fifty-four-year-old professional engineer, who rose to become the senior officer of a subsidiary of a U.S. company, was asked to move to the United States after twenty-four years of service with the company in Ontario. The employee treated the direction to move as a constructive dismissal. He sued, and recovered twenty-one months' salary in lieu of reasonable notice of termination, the highest award to date in Ontario.

The Workers' Compensation Act[6]

The Workers' Compensation Act provides for an employer-financed accident fund for medical aid and for loss of earnings. As well, the fund compensates permanent or partial disability caused by personal injury, accident, or illness that results from employment. The concept of fault does not apply: Compensation is provided even for injuries sustained by an employee through his own negligence. The rights under the Act replace the common-law right to sue the employer.

For purposes of payment into the fund, employers are divided into classes; the classifications depend upon the hazards in each industry. The Workers' Compensation Board establishes rates of payment for each class annually; rates are based on the cost of accidents occurring in the industries in each class. Some industries are not covered. For example, in industries where all employees work in offices, accidents on the job are infrequent; and coverage is not provided.

When an accident occurs, an employer is required to fill out an accident report. The forms are provided by the Board. The report must be sent to the Board within three days of the accident.

The Workers' Compensation Board, which administers the Act, has very broad jurisdiction. Its decisions are protected from review by any court except on very limited grounds. However, there are several levels of appeal within the Board itself.

The Health Insurance Act[7]

Under the Act, the Ontario government has established a

[6] R.S.O. 1980, c. 539
[7] R.S.O. 1980, c. 197

scheme of health insurance for all residents in Ontario. The scheme is called The Ontario Health Insurance Plan (OHIP). An employer is not obliged to pay OHIP premiums for its employees. An employer with fifteen or more employees must form a group for OHIP purposes; the employer must deduct OHIP premiums from the employees' wages and remit the amounts to OHIP on behalf of the employees.

The Human Rights Code, 1981[8]

The Human Rights Code is of general application to all persons in Ontario.

It establishes that every person has a right to equal treatment with respect to employment, without discrimination because of race, ancestry, place of origin, colour, ethnic origin, citizenship, creed, sex, age, marital status, family status, record of offences or handicap. The Act prohibits any person from infringing the rights of others as established by the Code. The Code further establishes that every employee has the right to be free from sexual harassment in the workplace.

The Occupational Health and Safety Act[9]

Employee safety is covered by the Occupational Health and Safety Act. This statute revised, and consolidated into one Act, earlier legislation: The Employees' Health and Safety Act, 1976; The Construction Safety Act, 1973; The Industrial Safety Act, 1971; The Silicosis Act; and Part IX of The Mining Act.

The Act provides that a health and safety committee is required at most work places where twenty or more workers are employed. The committee must consist of at least two persons; at least half the members of the committee must not exercise managerial functions; and at least half the members must be selected by the workers they represent, or by a trade union. The committee must meet at least once every three months. Where nineteen or fewer workers are employed, the Minister of Labour is authorized to

---

[8] S.O. 1981, c. 53
[9] R.S.O. 1980, c. 321

require an employer, constructor, or group of employers to establish a health and safety committee.

The Occupational Health and Safety Act also contains provisions that give an employee broad powers to refuse to perform work where he has reasonable cause to believe that the machine or device he is using, or the workplace in which he is working, is unsafe.

The Ontario Labour Relations Act

Pursuant to Section 3 of The Ontario Labour Relations Act, every person is free to join a trade union of his own choice and to participate in its lawful activities. The Act provides for the certification of unions; it places constraints upon what an employer may and may not do when faced with a union-organizing campaign. For example, Section 64 of the Act prohibits an employer or persons acting on his behalf from interfering with the selection of a trade union by his employees. The employer may express his views as long as he does not use coërcion, intimidation, threats, promises or undue influence. Once the trade union has signed up sufficient employees, it files an application for certification with the Ontario Labour Relations Board. The Board will then decide what is an appropriate bargaining unit. For example, the Board will exclude persons exercising managerial functions; the Board will determine the number of cards signed by employees in the bargaining unit. The Act provides that professional engineers are entitled to a bargaining unit composed exclusively of professional engineers unless a majority of the engineers wish to be included in a unit with other employees.

Usually, if the union has signed up less than forty-five per cent of the employees in the bargaining unit, the application will be dismissed. If the trade union has signed up more than fifty-five per cent of the employees, the trade union will be certified as the bargaining agent for the employees. If the trade union signs up between forty-five and fifty-five per cent of the employees, the Board will order a vote by secret ballot to determine whether a majority of the employees wish to be represented by the trade union.

Sometimes an employer is found to be in breach of the Act during the organizing campaign. The Board may certify the trade union as bargaining agent for the employees without a vote, even though the trade union has not signed up a majority of the employees.

The Act also provides procedural requirements to effect a collective agreement between the employer and the union. The procedures include conciliation and mediation, if necessary.

Pursuant to Section 63 of the Act, no employees shall strike and no employer shall lock out his employees while a collective agreement is in operation or until the employer and the union have completed the conciliation process.

The Act provides for compulsory arbitration by an independent arbitrator in certain cases: where an employee is disciplined or discharged; where the other party is not complying with the terms of the collective agreement; or where there is disagreement as to the interpretation of the collective agreement.

Section 71(a) of the Act prohibits an employer from engaging in "strike-related" misconduct. This is defined as engaging in unfair conduct intended to interfere with any right, under the Act, during the course of or in anticipation of an unlawful strike or lockout. This section also expressly prohibits an employer from retaining the services of professional strike-breakers.

STATUTES RELATING TO LABOUR
(amendments not cited)

Canada
The Canadian Charter of Rights and Freedoms, Constitution Act, 1982 as enacted by the Canada Act 1982 (U.K.) c.11.
Canada Labour Code, R.S.C. 1970, c.L-1;
Canadian Human Rights Act, S.C. 1976-77, c.33;
Employment Tax Credit Act, S.C. 1977-78, c.4;
Corporations and Labour Unions Returns Act, R.S.C. 1970, c.C-31;
Trade Unions Act, R.S.C. 1970, c.T-11;
Fair Wages and Hours of Labour Act, R.S.C. 1970, c.L-3;
Wages Liability Act, R.S.C. 1970, c.W-1;

Public Service Staff Relations Act, R.S.C.
1970, c.P-35;
Public Service Employment Act, R.S.C.
1970, c.P-32;
Lord's Day Act, R.S.C. 1970, c.L-13;
Holidays Act, R.S.C. 1970, c.H-7;
Canadian Bill of Rights, R.S.C. 1970,
Appendix III;
Unemployment Insurance Act, 1971 S.C.
1970-71-72, c.48;
Canada Pension Plan, R.S.C. 1970, c.C-5.

Alberta   Department of Labour Act, R.S.A. 1980,
c.b-24;
Alberta Bill of Rights, R.S.A. 1980, c.A-16;
The Alberta Lord's Day Act, R.S.A. 1980,
c.A-32;
The Individual's Rights Protection Act,
R.S.A. 1980, c.I-1-2;
The Industrial Wages Security Act, R.S.A.
1980, c.I-3;
The Masters and Servants Act, R.S.A. 1980,
c.M-8;
The Child Welfare Act, R.S.A. 1980, c.C-8;
The Manpower Development Act, R.S.A.
1980, c.M-8;
The Employment Agencies Act, R.S.A.
1980, c.E-10;
The Employment Standards Act, R.S.A.
1980, c.E-10.1;
Labour Relations Act, R.S.A. 1980, c.L-1.1.

British   Ministry of Labour Act, R.S.B.C. 1979,
Columbia   c.276;
Labour Code, R.S.B.C. 1979, c.212;
Essential Services Disputes Act, R.S.B.C.
1979, c.113;
Mining Regulations Act, R.S.B.C. 1979,
c.265;
Employment Standards Act, S.B.C. 1980,
c.10;
Wage (Public Construction) Act, R.S.B.C.
1979, c.426;
Human Rights Code, R.S.B.C. 1979, c.186;

Municipal Act, R.S.B.C. 1979, c.290;
Labour Regulation Act, R.S.B.C. 1979, c.213;
Apprenticeship Act, R.S.B.C. 1979, c.17;
Woodworker Lien Act, R.S.B.C. 1979, c.436.

Manitoba

The Department of Labour Act, R.S.M. 1970, c.L20;
The Labour Relations Act, S.M. 1972, c.75;
The Employment Standards Act, R.S.M. 1970, c.E110;
The Construction Industry Wages Act, R.S.M. 1970, c.C190;
The Vacations With Pay Act, R.S.M. 1970, c.V20;
The Wages Recovery Act, R.S.M. 1970, c.W10;
The Retail Businesses Holiday Closing Act, S.M. 1977, c.26;
The Remembrance Day Act, R.S.M. 1970, c.R80;
The Shops Regulation Act, R.S.M. 1970, c.S110;
The Apprenticeship and Tradesmen's Qualification Act, S.M. 1972, c.45;
The Human Rights Act, S.M. 1974, c.65;
The Lord's Day (Manitoba) Act, R.S.M. 1970, c.L200;
The Payment of Wages Act, S.M. 1975, c.21.

New Brunswick

Industrial Relations Act, R.S.N.B. 1973, c.I-4;
Minimum Employment Standards Act, R.S.N.B. 1973, c.M-12;
Minimum Wage Act, R.S.N.B. 1973, c.M-13;
Occupational Health and Safety Act, S.N.B. 1983, c.O-0.2;
Lord's Day Act, R.S.N.B. 1973, c.L-13;
Human Rights Code, R.S.N.B. 1973, c.H-11;

Industrial Relations Act, R.S.N.B. 1973, c.I-4;
Industrial Standards Act, R.S.N.B. 1973, c.I-6;
Industrial Training and Certification Act, R.S.N.B. 1973, c.I-7;
Public Works Act, R.S.N.B. 1973, c.P-28;
Fair Wages and Hours of Labour Act, R.S.N.B. 1973, c.F-2;
Wage-Earners Protection Act, R.S.N.B. 1973, c.W-1;
Municipalities Act, R.S.N.B. 1973, c.M-22;
Vacation Pay Act, R.S.N.B. 1973, c.V-1;
Closing of Retail Establishments Act, R.S.N.B. 1973, c.C-7;
New Brunswick Day Act, S.N.B. 1975, N-4.1;
Seasonal Employment Act, S.N.B. 1959, c.12.

Newfoundland   The Department of Labour and Manpower Act, S.N. 1973;
The Newfoundland Human Rights Code, R.S.N. 1970, c. 262;
The Industrial Standards Act, R.S.N. 1970, c.170;
The Labour Standards Act, S.N. 1977, c.52;
The Shops Closing Act, S.N. 1977, c.107;
The Child Welfare Act, 1972, S.N. 1972;
The Apprenticeship Act, R.S.N. 1970, c.12;
The Labour Relations Act, 1977, S.N. 1977, c.64.

Nova Scotia   Department of Labour and Manpower Act, S.N.S. 1932, c.3;
Labour Standards Code, S.N.S. 1972, c.10;
Industrial Safety Act, R.S.N.S. 1967, c.141;
Lord's Day (Nova Scotia) Act, R.S.N.S. 1967, c.172;
Trade Union Act, S.N.S. 1972, c.19;
Apprenticeship and Tradesmen's Qualifications Act, R.S.N.S. 197, c.11;
Human Rights Act, S.N.S. 1969, c.11.

Ontario
The Ministry of Labour Act, R.S.O. 1980, c.284;
The Labour Relations Act, R.S.O. 1980, c.228;
The Rights of Labour Act, R.S.O. 1980, c.456;
The Employment Standards Act, R.S.O. 1980, c.137;
The Child Welfare Act, R.S.O. 1980, c.66;
The One Day's Rest in Seven Act, R.S.O. 1980, c.326;
The Lord's Day (Ontario) Act, R.S.O. 1980, c.253;
The Retail Business Holidays Act, R.S.O. 1980, c.453;
The Government Contracts Hours and Wages Act, R.S.O. 1980, c.190;
The Industrial Standards Act, R.S.O. 1980, c.216;
The Apprenticeship and Tradesmen's Qualification Act, R.S.O. 1980, c.24;
The Master and Servant Act, R.S.O. 1980, c.257;
The Wages Act, R.S.O. 1980, c.526;
The Human Rights Code, 1981, S.O. 1981, c.53;
The Hospital Labour Disputes Arbitration Act, R.S.O. 1980, c.205.

Prince Edward Island
Public Departments Act, R.S.P.E.I. 1974, c.P-28;
Human Rights Act, S.P.E.I. 1975, c.72;
Lord's Day (P.E.I.) Act, R.S.P.E.I. 1974, c.L-21;
Store Hours Act, R.S.P.E.I. 1974, c.2-10;
Labour Act, R.S.P.E.I. 1974, c.L-1;
Minimum Age of Employment Act, R.S.P.E.I. 1974, c.M-11;
Apprenticeship and Tradesmen's Qualification Act, R.S.P.E.I. 1974, c.A-13;
Fishermen's Unions Act, R.S.P.E.I. 1974, c.F-10.

Saskatchewan
The Department of Labour Act, R.S.S. 1978, c.D-19;

The Education Act, R.S.S. 1978, c.E-0.1;
The Labour Standards Act, R.S.S. 1978, c.L-1;
The Trade Union Act, R.S.S. 1978, c.T-17;
The Saskatchewan Medical Care Insurance Act, R.S.S. 1978, c.S-29;
The Family Services Act, R.S.S. 1978, c.F-7;
The Lord's Day (Saskatchewan) Act, R.S.S. 1978, c.L-34;
The Urban Municipality Act, R.S.S. 1978, c.U-10;
The Wages Recovery Act, R.S.S. 1978, c.W-1;
The Apprenticeship and Tradesmen's Qualification Act, R.S.S. 1978, c.A-23;
The Saskatchewan Human Rights Code, S.S. 1979, c.S-24.1.

Northwest Territories

Apprentices and Tradesmen's Ordinance, O.N.W.T. 1976 (Third Session), c.1;
Fair Practices Ordinance, R.O.N.W.T., 1974, c.F-2;
Wages Recovery Ordinance, R.O.N.W.T., 1974, c.W-1;
Lord's Day Ordinance, R.O.N.W.T., 1974, c.L-8;
Labour Standards Ordinance, R.O.N.W.T., 1974, c.L-1.

Yukon Territory

Wages Recovery Ordinance, O.Y.T. 1963 (Second Session) c.2;
Fair Practices Ordinance, R.O.Y.T. 1971, c.F-2;
Lord's Day (Yukon) Ordinance, O.Y.T. 1962 (First Session) c.8;
Labour Standards Ordinance, R.O.Y.T. 1971, c.L1;
Apprentice Training Ordinance, R.O.Y.T. 1971, c.A-1.

APPENDIX

Statutes of Ontario, 1984.

Chapter 13

The Professional Engineers Act, 1984

CONTENTS

Section

1. Interpretation
2. Association continued
3. Council of Association
4. Annual meetings
5. Membership
6. Powers of Minister
7. Regulations
8. By-laws
9. Official publication
10. Establishment of committees
11. Executive Committee
12. Licence or limited licence required
13. Corporation
14. Issuance of licence
15. Issuance of certificate of authorization
16. Issuance of licence or certificate of authorization on direction of Council
17. Supervision by professional engineer
18. Issuance of temporary licence or limited licence
19. Hearing by Registration Committee
20. Fiduciary relationship between corporation and client
21. Registers
22. Continuation of memberships
23. Cancellation for default of fees
24. Complaints Committee
25. Duties of Complaints Committee

Section

26. Complaints Review Councillor
27. Examination by Complaints Review Councillor
28. Discipline Committee
29. Duties of Discipline Committee
30. Stay of decision on appeal
31. Discipline proceedings
32. Appeal to court
33. Fees Mediation Committee
34. Registrar's investigation
35. Liability insurance
36. Information re insurance claims
37. Surrender of revoked licence or certificate
38. Application for licence, etc., after revocation
39. Confidentiality
40. Order directing compliance
41. Penalties
42. Falsification of documents
43. Onus of proof respecting licensing
44. Service of notice or document
45. Registrar's certificate as evidence
46. Immunity of Association
47. Limitation of action
48. Joint Practice Board
49. Annual report
50. Application of *Corporations Act*
51. Repeal
52. Commencement
53. Short title

217

HER MAJESTY, by and with the advice and consent of the Legislative Assembly of the Province of Ontario, enacts as follows:

Interpretation

1. In this Act,

   (a) "Academic Requirements Committee" means the Academic Requirements Committee appointed pursuant to the regulations;

   (b) "architect" means a person who is licensed or who holds a certificate of practice or a temporary licence under the *Architects Act, 1984*;

1984, c. 12

   (c) "Association" means Association of Professional Engineers of Ontario;

   (d) "by-laws" means by-laws made under this Act;

   (e) "certificate of authorization" means certificate of authorization issued under this Act to engage in the business of providing services that are within the practice of professional engineering;

   (f) "Complaints Review Councillor" means Complaints Review Councillor appointed under this Act;

   (g) "Council" means Council of the Association;

   (h) "Experience Requirements Committee" means the Experience Requirements Committee appointed pursuant to the regulations;

   (i) "Joint Practice Board" means Joint Practice Board established under the *Architects Act, 1984*;

   (j) "licence" means licence to engage in the practice of professional engineering issued under this Act;

   (k) "limited licence" means limited licence to engage in the practice of professional engineering issued under this Act;

   (l) "Minister" means the Attorney General or such other member of the Executive Council as is designated by the Lieutenant Governor in Council;

   (m) "practice of professional engineering" means any act of designing, composing, evaluating, advising, reporting, directing or supervising wherein the safeguarding of life, health, property or the public welfare is concerned and that requires the application of engineering principles, but does not include practising as a natural scientist;

(n) "professional engineer" means a person who holds a licence or a temporary licence;

(o) "Registrar" means Registrar of the Association;

(p) "regulations" means regulations made under this Act;

(q) "temporary licence" means temporary licence to engage in the practice of professional engineering issued under this Act.

2. – (1) The Association of Professional Engineers of the Province of Ontario, a body corporate, is continued as a corporation without share capital under the name of "Association of Professional Engineers of Ontario". *Association continued*

(2) The head office of the Association shall be at The Municipality of Metropolitan Toronto. *Head office*

(3) The principal object of the Association is to regulate the practice of professional engineering and to govern its members, holders of certificates of authorization, holders of temporary licences and holders of limited licences in accordance with this Act, the regulations and the by-laws in order that the public interest may be served and protected. *Principal object*

(4) For the purpose of carrying out its principal object, the Association has the following additional objects: *Additional objects*

1. To establish, maintain and develop standards of knowledge and skill among its members.

2. To establish, maintain and develop standards of qualification and standards of practice for the practice of professional engineering.

3. To establish, maintain and develop standards of professional ethics among its members.

4. To promote public awareness of the role of the Association.

5. To perform such other duties and exercise such other powers as are imposed or conferred on the Association by or under any Act.

(5) For the purpose of carrying out its objects, the Association has the capacity and the powers of a natural person. *Capacity and powers of Association*

3. – (1) The Council of the Association is continued and shall be the governing body and board of directors of the Association and shall manage and administer its affairs. *Council of Association*

(2) The Council shall be composed of, *Composition of Council*

(a) not fewer than fifteen and not more than twenty persons who are members of the Association and who are elected by the members of the Association as provided by the regulations;

(b) not fewer than five and not more than seven persons who are members of the Association and who are appointed by the Lieutenant Governor in Council;

(c) not fewer than three and not more than five persons who are not members of the governing body of a self-regulating licensing body under any other Act or licensed under this Act and who are appointed by the Lieutenant Governor in Council; and

(d) the holders of offices prescribed by the regulations who are not members of the Council under clause (a), (b) or (c).

Idem

(3) No person shall be elected or appointed to the Council unless he is a Canadian citizen resident in Ontario.

Remuneration of lay members

(4) The persons appointed under clause (2) (c) shall be paid, out of the moneys appropriated therefor by the Legislature, such expenses and remuneration as is determined by the Lieutenant Governor in Council.

Term of office of appointed members

(5) In each year, the persons to be appointed by the Lieutenant Governor in Council shall be appointed for one year, two year or three year terms in order that one-third, or as near thereto as possible, shall be appointed in each year.

Qualifications to vote

(6) Every member of the Association who is not in default of payment of an annual fee prescribed by the by-laws is qualified to vote at an election of members of the Council.

Officers

(7) The Association shall have the officers provided for by the regulations.

Registrar and staff

(8) The Council shall appoint during pleasure a Registrar and may appoint one or more deputy registrars who shall have the powers of the Registrar for the purposes of this Act, and may appoint such other persons as are from time to time necessary or desirable in the opinion of the Council to perform the work of the Association.

Quorum

(9) A majority of the members of the Council constitutes a quorum.

Vacancies

(10) Where one or more vacancies occur in the membership of the Council, the members remaining in office constitute the Council so long as their number is not fewer than a quorum.

Filling of vacancy

(11) A vacancy on the Council caused by the death, resignation, removal or incapacity to act of an elected member of the

Council shall be filled as soon as practicable by a member of the Association,

  (a) where a quorum of the Council remains in office, appointed by the majority of the Council, and the member so appointed shall be deemed to be an elected member of the Council; or

  (b) where no quorum of the Council remains in office, elected in accordance with the regulations,

and the member so appointed or elected shall hold office for the unexpired portion of the term of office of the member whose office he is elected or appointed to fill.

(12) The Council shall meet at least four times a year.

Meetings of Council

(13) The members of the Council of the Association of Professional Engineers of the Province of Ontario who were elected or appointed and in office immediately before this Act comes into force shall continue in office and shall be deemed to be elected or appointed, as the case requires, under subsection (2) until the expiration of the term for which they were elected or appointed or until the office otherwise becomes vacant.

Continuation of Council members

4. The Association shall hold an annual meeting of the members of the Association not more than fifteen months after the holding of the last preceding annual meeting.

Annual meetings

5. – (1) Every person who holds a licence is a member of the Association subject to any term, condition or limitation to which the licence is subject.

Membership

(2) A member may resign his membership by filing with the Registrar his resignation in writing and his licence is thereupon cancelled, subject to the continuing jurisdiction of the Association in respect of any disciplinary action arising out of his professional conduct while a member.

Resignation of membership

6. In addition to his other powers and duties under this Act, the Minister may,

Powers of Minister

  (a) review the activities of the Council;

  (b) request the Council to undertake activities that, in the opinion of the Minister, are necessary and advisable to carry out the intent of this Act;

  (c) advise the Council with respect to the implementation of this Act and the regulations and with respect to the methods used or proposed to be used by the Council to implement policies and to enforce its regulations and procedures.

7. — (1) Subject to the approval of the Lieutenant Governor in Council and with prior review by the Minister, the Council may make regulations,

1. fixing the number of members to be elected to the Council under clause 3 (2) (a) and defining constituencies, and prescribing the number of representatives;

2. respecting and governing the qualifications, nomination, election and term or terms of office of the members to be elected to the Council, and controverted elections;

3. prescribing the conditions disqualifying elected members from sitting on the Council and governing the filling of vacancies on the Council;

4. prescribing positions of officers of the Association and providing for their election or appointment;

5. respecting the composition of the committees required by this Act, other than the Complaints Committee and the Discipline Committee, the mechanism of the appointment of members of the committees and procedures ancillary to those specified in this Act in respect of any committee;

6. respecting matters of practice and procedure before committees required under this Act that do not conflict with the *Statutory Powers Procedure Act*;

R.S.O. 1980, c. 484

7. prescribing the quorums of the committees required by this Act other than the Complaints Committee and the Discipline Committee;

8. prescribing classes of persons whose interest are related to those of the Association and the privileges of members of the classes in relation to the Association;

9. respecting any matter ancillary to the provisions of this Act with regard to the issuing, suspension and revocation of licences, certificates of authorization, temporary licences and limited licences, including but not limited to regulations respecting,

   i. the scope, standards and conduct of any examination set or approved by the Council as a licensing requirement,

   ii. the curricula and standards of professional training programs offered by the Council,

   iii. the academic, experience and other requirements for admission into professional training programs,

    iv. classes of licences,

    v. the academic and experience requirements for the issuance of a licence or any class of licence, and

    vi. classes of certificates of authorization, temporary licences and limited licences, including prescribing requirements and qualifications for the issuance of specified classes of certificates of authorization, temporary licences and limited licences, and terms and conditions that shall apply to specified classes of certificates of authorization, temporary licences and limited licences;

10. prescribing forms of applications for licences, certificates of authorization, temporary licences and limited licences and requiring their use;

11. requiring the making of returns of information in respect of the holdings of shares and the officers and directors of corporations that apply for or hold certificates of authorization and in respect of the interests of partners that apply for or hold certificates of authorization and prescribing and requiring the use of forms of such returns;

12. requiring and governing the signing and sealing of documents and designs by members of the Association, holders of temporary licences and holders of limited licences, specifying the forms of seals and respecting the issuance and ownership of seals;

13. requiring the making of returns of information by members of the Association and holders of certificates of authorization, temporary licences and limited licences in respect of names, addresses, telephone numbers, professional associates, partners, employees and professional liability insurance, and prescribing and requiring the use of forms of such returns;

14. requiring and governing the disclosure of the identity of holders of certificates of authorization on documents and designs involving the practice of professional engineering issued by such holders and specifying the form and manner of such disclosure;

15. governing the use of names and designations in the practice of professional engineering by members of the Association and holders of certificates of authorization, temporary licences and limited licences;

16. providing for the maintenance and inspection of registers of members of the Association, holders of temporary licences, holders of limited licences and holders of certificates of authorization;

17. prescribing and governing standards of practice and performance standards for the profession;

18. providing for the setting of schedules of suggested fees for professional engineering services and for the publication of the schedules;

19. respecting the advertising of the practice of professional engineering;

20. prescribing a code of ethics;

21. defining professional misconduct for the purposes of this Act;

22. providing for the designation of members of the Association and holders of temporary licences as specialists, prescribing the qualifications and requirements for designation as a specialist, providing for the suspension or revocation of such a designation and for the regulation and prohibition of the use of the designation by members of the Association, a holder of a temporary licence or a certificate of authorization;

23. providing for the designation of members of the Association as consulting engineers, prescribing the qualifications and requirements for designation as a consulting engineer, providing for the suspension or revocation of such a designation and for the regulation and prohibition of the use of the designation by members of the Association, a holder of a temporary licence or a certificate of authorization;

24. prescribing the minimum requirements for professional liability insurance, requiring the delivery to the Registrar of proof of such insurance and prescribing the form of such proof and the manner and time of the delivery;

25. prescribing the amount of and requiring the payment of annual fees by holders of certificates of authorization, temporary and limited licences and by students and members of related classes recognized by the Association, and fees for temporary licences, limited licences, certification, registration, designations, examinations and continuing education, including penalties for late

payment, and fees for anything the Registrar is required or authorized to do, and prescribing the amounts thereof;

26. providing for the entering into of arrangements by the Association for its members and holders of certificates of authorization, temporary licences and limited licences respecting indemnity for professional liability and requiring the payment and remittance of premiums in connection therewith and prescribing levies to be paid by members and holders of certificates of authorization, temporary licences and limited licences in respect of such indemnity for professional liability;

27. providing for continuing education of members;

28. respecting the duties and authority of the Registrar;

29. prescribing qualifications and requirements that shall be complied with to obtain the reinstatement of a licence, certificate of authorization, temporary licence or limited licence that was cancelled by the Registrar;

30. classifying and exempting any class of holders of licences, certificates of authorization, temporary licences or limited licences from any provision of the regulations under such special circumstances in the public interest as the Council considers advisable;

31. exempting any act within the practice of professional engineering from the application of this Act;

32. specifying acts within the practice of professional engineering that are exempt from the application of this Act when performed or provided by a member of a prescribed class of persons, and prescribing classes of persons for the purpose of the exemption.

(2) A copy of each regulation made under subsection (1),   Distribution of regulations

    (a) shall be forwarded to each member of the Association and to each holder of a certificate of authorization, temporary licence or limited licence; and

    (b) shall be available for public inspection in the office of the Association.

8. − (1) The Council may pass by-laws relating to the administrative and domestic affairs of the Association not inconsistent with this Act and the regulations and, without limiting the generality of the foregoing,   By-laws

    1. prescribing the seal and other insignia of the Association and providing for their use;

225

2. providing for the execution of documents by the Association;

3. respecting banking and finance;

4. fixing the financial year of the Association and providing for the audit of the accounts and transactions of the Association;

5. respecting the calling, holding and conducting of meetings of the Council and the duties of members of Council;

6. providing for meetings of the Council and committees, except in a proceeding in respect of a membership, certificate of authorization, temporary licence or limited licence, by means of conference telephone or other communications equipment by means of which all persons participating in the meeting can hear each other, and a member of the Council or committee participating in a meeting in accordance with such by-law shall be deemed to be present in person at the meeting:

7. providing that the Council or a committee may act upon a resolution consented to by the signatures of all members of the Council or the committee except in a proceeding in respect of a licence, certificate of authorization, temporary licence or limited licence, and a resolution so consented to in accordance with such a by-law is as valid and effective as if passed at a meeting of the Council or the committee duly called, constituted and held for that purpose;

8. respecting the calling, holding and conducting of meetings of the membership of the Association;

9. authorizing voting by mail by the general membership of the Association on any of the business of the Association and prescribing procedures for such voting;

10. prescribing the duties of officers of the Association;

11. prescribing forms and providing for their use;

12. providing procedures for the making, amending and revoking of the by-laws;

13. respecting management of the property of the Association;

14. providing for the appointment, composition, powers, duties and quorums of additional or special committees;

15. respecting the application of the funds of the Association and the investment and reinvestment of any of its funds not immediately required, and for the safekeeping of its securities;

16. prescribing the amount and requiring the payment of annual fees by members of the Association;

17. respecting the borrowing of money by the Association and the giving of security therefor;

18. respecting membership of the Association in other organizations the objects of which are not inconsistent with and are complementary to those of the Association, the payment of annual assessments and provision for representatives at meetings;

19. providing for the establishment and dissolution and governing the operation of groups of members of the Association and respecting grants by the Association to any such groups;

20. authorizing the making of grants for any purpose that may tend to advance knowledge of professional engineering education, or maintain or improve the standards of practice in professional engineering or support and encourage public information and interest in the past and present role of professional engineering in society;

21. respecting scholarships, bursaries and prizes related to the study of professional engineering;

22. respecting the establishment and operation and use of publications of the Association;

23. providing for an employment advisory service and for the continuance of the retirement savings plans in which members of the Association may participate on a voluntary basis;

24. regarding such other matters as are entailed in carrying on the business of the Association and are not included in section 7.

(2) A by-law passed by the Council is not effective until confirmed by the members of the Association.

When by-laws come into force

(3) A by-law passed by the Council may be confirmed by the members of the Association only by means of a vote conducted by mail.

Confirmation of by-laws

(4) A copy of the by-laws made under subsection (1) and amendments thereto,

Distribution of by-laws

227

(a) shall be forwarded to the Minister;

(b) shall be forwarded to each member of the Association; and

(c) shall be available for public inspection in the office of the Association.

Official publication

9. The Council shall establish and designate an official publication of the Association.

Establishment of committees

10. − (1) The Council shall establish and appoint the following committees:

(a) Executive Committee:

(b) Academic Requirements Committee;

(c) Experience Requirements Committee;

(d) Registration Committee;

(e) Complaints Committee;

(f) Discipline Committee;

(g) Fees Mediation Committee,

and may establish such other committees as the Council from time to time considers necessary.

Vacancies

(2) Where one or more vacancies occur in the membership of a committee, the members remaining in office constitute the committee so long as their number is not fewer than the prescribed quorum.

Executive Committee

11. The Council may delegate to the Executive Committee the authority to exercise any power or perform any duty of the Council other than to make, amend or revoke a regulation or a by-law.

Licence or limited licence required

12. − (1) No person shall engage in the practice of professional engineering or hold himself out as engaging in the practice of professional engineering unless the person is the holder of a licence, a temporary licence or a limited licence.

Certificate of authorization

(2) No person shall offer to the public or engage in the business of providing to the public services that are within the practice of professional engineering except under and in accordance with a certificate of authorization.

Exceptions

(3) Subsections (1) and (2) do not apply to prevent a person,

(a) from doing an act that is within the practice of professional engineering in relation to machinery or equipment, other than equipment of a structural nature, for use in the facilities of the person's employer in the production of products by the person's employer;

(b) from doing an act that is within the practice of professional engineering where a professional engineer assumes responsibility for the services within the practice of professional engineering to which the act is related;

(c) from designing or providing tools and dies;

(d) from doing an act that is within the practice of professional engineering but that is exempt from the application of this Act when performed or provided by a member of a class of persons prescribed by the regulations for the purpose of the exemption, if the person is a member of the class;

(e) from doing an act that is exempt by the regulations from the application of this Act.

(4) Subsections (1) and (2) do not apply to the preparation or provision of a design for the construction, enlargement or alteration of a building, Idem

(a) that is not more than three storeys and not more than 600 square metres in gross area as constructed, enlarged or altered;

(b) that is used or intended for one or more of residential occupancy, business occupancy, personal services occupancy, mercantile occupancy or industrial occupancy; and

(c) is not designed to house and is not part of an apparatus, process, facility or works the design of which is within the practice of professional engineering.

(5) Subsections (1) and (2) do not apply to, Idem

(a) the preparation or provision of a design for the construction, enlargement or alteration of a building that is not more than three storeys and that is used or intended for residential occupancy and,

(i) that contains one dwelling unit or two attached dwelling units each of which is constructed directly on grade, or

(ii) that is not more than 600 square metres in building area as constructed, enlarged or altered and contains three or more attached dwelling units, each of which is constructed directly on grade, with no dwelling unit constructed above another dwelling unit; or

229

(b) the preparation or provision of a design for alterations within a dwelling unit that will not affect or are not likely to affect fire separations, firewalls, the strength or safety of the building or the safety of persons in the building.

(6) The following rules govern the relationship between professional engineers and architects and subsections (1) and (2) do not apply to prevent an architect from preparing or providing a design for and carrying out the general review of the construction, enlargement or alteration of a building in accordance with these rules:

1. Only an architect may prepare or provide a design for the construction, enlargement or alteration of a building,

    i. used or intended for residential occupancy,

    ii. that exceeds 600 square metres in gross area, and

    iii. that does not exceed three storeys,

    and carry out the general review of the construction, enlargement or alteration of the building but an architect who prepares or provides such a design may engage a professional engineer to provide services within the practice of professional engineering in connection with the design and the professional engineer may provide the services.

2. A professional engineer or an architect may prepare or provide a design for the construction, enlargement or alteration of a building,

    i. that exceeds 600 square metres in gross area or three storeys, and

    ii. that is used or intended for,

        A. industrial occupancy, or

        B. mixed occupancy consisting of industrial occupancy and one or more other occupancies, where none of the other occupancies exceeds 600 square metres of the gross area,

    but only a professional engineer may provide services within the practice of professional engineering in connection with the design.

3. Subject to rules 4 and 5, a professional engineer shall provide services that are within the practice of professional engineering and an architect shall provide services that are within the practice of architecture related to the

construction, enlargement or alteration of a building used or intended for,

    i. assembly occupancy,

    ii. institutional occupancy,

    iii. business occupancy or personal services occupancy that exceeds 600 square metres in gross area or three storeys,

    iv. Mercantile occupancy that exceeds 600 square metres in gross area or three storeys,

    v. residential occupancy that exceeds three storeys,

    vi. mixed occupancy consisting of industrial occupancy and one or more other occupancies, where one of the other occupancies exceeds 600 square metres in gross area,

    vii. mixed occupancy consisting of a combination of,

        A. assembly occupancy and any other occupancy, except industrial occupancy,

        B. institutional occupancy and any other occupancy, except industrial occupancy,

        C. one or more of,

            1. business occupancy,

            2. personal services occupancy, or

            3. mercantile occupancy,

        and any other occupancy, except assembly occupancy, institutional occupancy or industrial occupancy,

        where the building as constructed, enlarged or altered exceeds 600 square metres in gross area or three storeys,

        D. residential occupancy that exceeds three storeys and any other occupancy, where the building as constructed, enlarged or altered exceeds 600 square metres in gross area, or

    viii. any other occupancy where the building as constructed, enlarged or altered exceeds 600 square metres in gross area or three storeys,

but a professional engineer may provide a design for the industrial occupancy of a mixed occupancy described in subparagraph vi.

4. An architect may perform or provide services that are within the practice of professional engineering in preparing or providing a design for and carrying out the general review of the construction, enlargement or alteration of a building described in rule 2 or 3 where to do so does not constitute a substantial part of the services within the practice of professional engineering related to the construction, enlargement or alteration of the building and is necessary,

    i. for the construction, enlargement or alteration of the building and is incidental to other services provided as part of the practice of architecture by the architect in respect of the construction, enlargement or alteration of the building, or

    ii. for co-ordination purposes.

5. A professional engineer may perform or provide services that are within the practice of architecture in preparing or providing a design for and carrying out the general review of the construction, enlargement or alteration of a building described in rule 1 or 3 where to do so does not constitute a substantial part of the services within the practice of architecture related to the construction, enlargement or alteration of the building and is necessary,

    i. for the construction, enlargement or alteration of the building and is incidental to other services provided as part of the practice of professional engineering by the professional engineer in respect of the construction, enlargement or alteration of the building, or

    ii. for co-ordination purposes.

6. Only an architect may carry out or provide the general review of the construction, enlargement or alteration of a building,

    i. that is constructed, enlarged or altered in accordance with a design prepared or provided by an architect, or

    ii. in relation to services that are provided by an architect in connection with the design in accordance with which the building is constructed, enlarged or altered.

7. Only a professional engineer may carry out or provide the general review of the construction, enlargement or alteration of a building,

      i. that is constructed, enlarged or altered in accordance with a design prepared or provided by a professional engineer, or

     ii. in relation to services that are provided by a professional engineer in connection with the design in accordance with which the building is constructed, enlarged or altered.

  8. A professional engineer or an architect may act as prime consultant for the construction, enlargement or alteration of a building.

  9. A reference in these rules to the provision of a design or services by a professional engineer applies equally to a holder of a certificate of authorization.

(7) Subsections (1) and (2) do not apply to prevent a person from carrying out a general review of the construction, enlargement or alteration of a building that does not or is not intended to take the place of a general review required to be done by a professional engineer. Idem

(8) In this section, Interpretation

  (a) "assembly occupancy" means occupancy for gatherings of persons for civic, educational, political, recreational, religious, social, travel or other similar purpose, or for the consumption of food or drink;

  (b) "building" means a structure consisting of a wall, roof and floor, or any one or more of them;

  (c) "building area" means the greatest horizontal area of a building within the outside surface of exterior walls or, where a firewall is to be constructed, within the outside surface of exterior walls and the centre line of firewalls;

  (d) "business occupancy" means occupancy for the transaction of business;

  (e) "construction" means the doing of anything in the erection, installation, extension or repair of a building and includes the installation of a building unit fabricated or moved from elsewhere, and "constructed" has a corresponding meaning;

  (f) "design" means a plan, sketch, drawing, graphic representation or specification intended to govern the construction, enlargement or alteration of a building or a part of a building;

  (g) "dwelling unit" means a room or suite of rooms used

233

or intended to be used as a domicile by one or more persons and usually containing cooking, eating, living, sleeping and sanitary facilities;

(h) "fire separation" means a construction assembly that acts as a barrier against the spread of fire and that may or may not have a fire-resistance rating or a fire-protection rating;

(i) "firewall" means a type of fire separation of non-combustible construction that subdivides a building or separates adjoining buildings to resist the spread of fire and that has a fire-resistance rating as prescribed in Ontario Regulation 583/83 (known as the Building Code), as amended from time to time, and has structural stability to remain intact under fire conditions for the fire-resistance time for which it is rated;

(j) "general review", in relation to the construction, enlargement or alteration of a building, means an examination of the building to determine whether the construction, enlargement or alteration is in general conformity with the design governing the construction, enlargement or alteration, and reporting thereon;

(k) "grade" means the lowest of the average levels of finished ground adjoining each exterior wall of a building, but does not include localized depressions such as for vehicle or pedestrian entrances;

(l) "graphic representation" means a representation produced by electrical, electronic, photographic or printing methods and includes a representation produced on a video display terminal;

(m) "gross area" means the total area of all floors above grade measured between the outside surfaces of exterior walls or, where no access or building service penetrates a firewall, between the outside surfaces of exterior walls and the centre line of firewalls but in a residential occupancy where access or a building service penetrates a firewall, the measurement may be taken to the centre line of the firewall;

(n) "industrial occupancy" means occupancy for assembling, fabricating, manufacturing, processing, repairing or storing of goods or materials or for producing, converting, processing or storing of energy, waste or natural resources;

(o) "institutional occupancy" means occupancy for the

harbouring, housing or detention of persons who require special care or treatment on account of their age or mental or physical limitations or who are involuntarily detained;

(p) "mercantile occupancy" means occupancy or use for displaying or selling retail goods, wares or merchandise;

(q) "personal services occupancy" means occupancy for the rendering or receiving of professional or personal services;

(r) "residential occupancy" means occupancy for providing sleeping accommodation for persons, but does not include institutional occupancy.

(9) For the purposes of this section, proof of the performance of one act in the practice of professional engineering on one occasion is sufficient to establish engaging in the practice of professional engineering.

Proof of practice

13. A corporation that holds a certificate of authorization may provide services that are within the practice of professional engineering.

Corporation

14. − (1) The Registrar shall issue a licence to a natural person who applies therefor in accordance with the regulations and,

Issuance of licence

(a) is a citizen of Canada or has the status of a permanent resident of Canada;

(b) is not less than eighteen years of age;

(c) has complied with the academic requirements specified in the regulations for the issuance of the licence and has passed such examinations as the Council has set or approved in accordance with the regulations or is exempted therefrom by the Council;

(d) has complied with the experience requirements specified in the regulations for the issuance of the licence; and

(e) is of good character.

(2) The Registrar may refuse to issue a licence to an applicant where the Registrar is of the opinion, upon reasonable and probable grounds, that the past conduct of the applicant affords grounds for belief that the applicant will not engage in the practice of professional engineering in accordance with the law and with honesty and integrity.

Grounds for refusal to issue licence

235

related to the services provided by the holder of a certificate of authorization, the certificate of authorization is subject to the same terms and conditions prescribed by the regulations that apply to the temporary licence.

(5) A holder of a certificate of authorization ceases to be entitled to offer to the public or to provide to the public services that are within the practice of professional engineering as soon as there is no holder of a licence or a temporary licence who assumes responsibility for and supervises the practice of professional engineering provided by the holder of the certificate of authorization. *Suspension of effect of certificate of authorization*

(6) The holder of a certificate of authorization must give notice to the Registrar when there ceases to be a holder of a licence or a temporary licence who assumes responsibility for and supervises the practice of professional engineering by the holder of the certificate of authorization and when the holder of the certificate of authorization designates another holder of a licence or a temporary licence to assume such responsibility and carry out such supervision. *Notice to Registrar by holder of certificate of authorization*

(7) A holder of a licence or a temporary licence who ceases to be responsible for and to supervise the practice of professional engineering by a holder of a certificate of authorization as the person so designated by the holder of the certificate of authorization shall give notice of the cessation forthwith to the Registrar. *Notice to Registrar by person in position of professional responsibility*

(8) The Registrar may refuse to issue or may suspend or revoke a certificate of authorization where the Registrar is of the opinion, upon reasonable and probable grounds, *Past conduct*

   (a) that the past conduct of a person who is in a position of authority or responsibility in the operation of the business of the applicant for or the holder of the certificate of authorization affords grounds for the belief that the applicant or holder will not engage in the business of providing services that are within the practice of professional engineering in accordance with the law and with honesty and integrity;

   (b) that the holder of the certificate of authorization does not meet the requirements or the qualifications for the issuance of the certificate of authorization set out in the regulations; or

   (c) that there has been a breach of a condition of the certificate of authorization.

16. The Registrar shall issue a licence or a certificate of authorization upon a direction of the Council made in accordance with a recommendation by the Joint Practice Board. *Issuance of licence or certificate of authorization on direction of Council*

Supervision by professional engineer

17. − (1) It is a condition of every certificate of authorization that the holder of the certificate shall provide services that are within the practice of professional engineering only under the personal supervision and direction of a member of the Association or the holder of a temporary licence.

Professional responsibility of supervising professional engineer

(2) A member of the Association or a holder of a temporary licence who personally supervises and directs the providing of services within the practice of professional engineering by a holder of a certificate of authorization or who assumes responsibility for and supervises the practice of professional engineering related to the providing of services by a holder of a certificate of authorization is subject to the same standards of professional conduct and competence in respect of the services and the related practice of professional engineering as if the services were provided or the practice of professional engineering was engaged in by the member of the Association or the holder of the temporary licence.

Issuance of temporary licence or limited licence

18. − (1) The Registrar shall issue a temporary licence or a limited licence to a natural person who applies therefor in accordance with the regulations and who meets the requirements and qualifications for the issuance of the temporary licence or the limited licence set out in the regulations, provided that, in the case of a limited licence, the applicant is a Canadian citizen or has the status of a permanent resident of Canada.

Grounds for refusal, suspension or revocation

(2) The Registrar may refuse to issue or may suspend or revoke a temporary licence or a limited licence where the Registrar is of the opinion, upon reasonable and probable grounds,

(a) that the past conduct of the applicant for or the holder of the temporary licence or the limited licence affords grounds for the belief that the applicant or holder will not engage in the practice of professional engineering in accordance with the law and with honesty and integrity;

(b) that the holder of the temporary licence or the limited licence does not meet the requirements or the qualifications for the issuance of the temporary licence or the limited licence set out in the regulations; or

(c) that there has been a breach of a condition of the temporary licence or the limited licence.

Referral to committee

(3) Subsections 14 (3) to (6) (which relate to the Academic Requirements Committee and the Experience Requirements Committee) apply with necessary modifications in respect of an applicant for a temporary licence or a limited licence.

(4) Subsection (1) does not apply in respect of a member of the Association or a holder of a certificate of authorization. Application of subs. (1)

(5) A holder of a temporary licence or a limited licence is not a member of the Association. Membership

19. – (1) Where the Registrar proposes, Hearing by Registration Committee

    (a) to refuse to issue a licence; or

    (b) to refuse to issue, to suspend or to revoke a temporary licence, a limited licence or a certificate of authorization,

the Registrar shall serve notice of his proposal, together with written reasons therefor, on the applicant.

(2) Subsection (1) does not apply in respect of a proposal to refuse to issue a licence, a temporary licence or a limited licence where, Exceptions

    (a) the Academic Requirements Committee has determined that the applicant has not met the academic requirements set out in the regulations for the issuance of the licence, the temporary licence or the limited licence;

    (b) the Experience Requirements Committee has determined that the applicant has not met the experience requirements set out in the regulations for the issuance of the licence, the temporary licence or the limited licence; or

    (c) the applicant previously held a licence, a certificate of authorization, a temporary licence or a limited licence that was suspended or revoked as a result of a decision of the Discipline Committee.

(3) A notice under subsection (1) shall state that the applicant is entitled to a hearing by the Registration Committee if the applicant mails or delivers, within thirty days after the notice under subsection (1) is served on the applicant, notice in writing requiring a hearing by the Registration Committee and the applicant may so require such a hearing. Notice

(4) Where the applicant does not require a hearing by the Registration Committee in accordance with subsection (3), the Registrar may carry out the proposal stated in the notice under subsection (1). Power of Registrar where no hearing

(5) Where an applicant requires a hearing by the Registration Committee in accordance with subsection (3), the Registration Committee shall appoint a time for, give notice of and shall hold the hearing. Hearing by Registration Committee

239

Continuation on expiry of committee membership

(6) Where a proceeding is commenced before the Registration Committee and the term of office on the Council or on the committee of a member sitting for the hearing expires or is terminated other than for cause before the proceeding is disposed of but after evidence is heard, the member shall be deemed to remain a member of the Registration Committee for the purpose of completing the disposition of the proceeding in the same manner as if the member's term of office had not expired or been terminated.

Powers of Registration Committee

(7) Following upon a hearing under this section in respect of a proposal by the Registrar, the Registration Committee may, by order,

(a) where the committee is of the opinion upon reasonable grounds that the applicant meets the requirements and qualifications of this Act and the regulations and will engage in the practice of professional engineering or in the business of providing services that are within the practice of professional engineering with competence and integrity, direct the Registrar to issue a licence, certificate of authorization, temporary licence or limited licence, as the case may be, to the applicant;

(b) where the committee is of the opinion upon reasonable grounds that the applicant does not meet the requirements and qualifications of this Act and the regulations,

   (i) direct the Registrar to refuse to issue a licence, certificate of authorization, temporary licence or limited licence, or to suspend or revoke the certificate of authorization issued to the applicant, as the case may be, or

   (ii) where the committee is of the opinion upon reasonable grounds that the applicant will engage in the practice of professional engineering with competence and integrity, exempt the applicant from any of the requirements of this Act and the regulations and direct the Registrar to issue a licence, certificate of authorization, temporary licence or limited licence, as the case may be; or

(c) where the committee is of the opinion upon reasonable grounds that it is necessary in order to ensure that the applicant will engage in the practice of professional engineering or in the business of providing services that are within the practice of professional engineering with competence and integrity, direct the Registrar to issue a licence, certificate of authorization, temporary licence or limited licence, as the case may be, subject to such terms, conditions or limitations as the Registration Committee specifies.

(8) The Registration Committee may extend the time for the giving of notice requiring a hearing by an applicant under this section before or after the expiration of such time where it is satisfied that there are apparent grounds for granting relief to the applicant following upon a hearing and that there are reasonable grounds for applying for the extension, and the Registration Committee may give such directions as it considers proper consequent upon the extension.

Extension of time for requiring hearing

(9) The Registrar and the applicant who has required the hearing are parties to proceedings before the Registration Committee under this section.

Parties

(10) The applicant shall be given a reasonable opportunity to show or to achieve compliance before the hearing with all lawful requirements for the issue of the licence, the certificate of authorization, the temporary licence or the limited licence.

Opportunity to show compliance

(11) A party to proceedings under this section shall be afforded an opportunity to examine before the hearing any written or documentary evidence that will be produced or any report the contents of which will be given in evidence at the hearing.

Examination of documentary evidence

(12) Members of the Registration Committee holding a hearing shall not have taken part before the hearing in any investigation or consideration of the subject-matter of the hearing and shall not communicate directly or indirectly in relation to the subject-matter of the hearing with any person or with any party or his representative except upon notice to and opportunity for all parties to participate, but the Registration Committee may seek legal advice from an adviser independent from the parties and, in such case, the nature of the advice shall be made known to the parties in order that they may make submissions as to the law.

Members holding hearing not to have taken part in investigation, etc.

(13) The oral evidence taken before the Registration Committee at a hearing shall be recorded and, if so required, copies of a transcript thereof shall be furnished upon the same terms as in the Supreme Court.

Recording of evidence

(14) No member of the Registration Committee shall participate in a decision of the Registration Committee following upon a hearing unless he or she was present throughout the hearing and heard the evidence and argument of the parties.

Only members at hearing to participate in decision

(15) Documents and things put in evidence at a hearing shall, upon the request of the person who produced them, be released to

Release of documentary evidence

241

the person by the Registration Committee within a reasonable time after the matter in issue has been finally determined.

Applicant (16) In this section, "applicant" means applicant for a licence or applicant for or holder of a temporary licence, a limited licence or a certificate of authorization.

Fiduciary, etc., relationship between corporation and client **20.** A corporation that holds a certificate of authorization has the same rights and is subject to the same obligations in respect of fiduciary, confidential and ethical relationships with each client of the corporation that exist at law between a member of the Association and his client.

Registers **21.** − (1) The Registrar shall maintain one or more registers in which is entered every person who is licensed under this Act and every holder of a certificate of authorization, temporary licence or limited licence, identifying the terms, conditions and limitations attached to the licence, certificate of authorization, temporary licence or limited licence, and shall note on the register every revocation, suspension and cancellation or termination of a licence, certificate of authorization, temporary licence or limited licence and such other information as the Registration Committee or Discipline Committee directs.

Inspection (2) Any person has the right, during normal business hours, to inspect the registers maintained by the Registrar.

Copies (3) The Registrar shall provide to any person, upon payment of a reasonable charge therefor, a copy of any part of the registers mentioned in subsection (1) maintained by the Registrar.

Continuation of memberships **22.** − (1) Every person who is a member of the Association immediately before this Act comes into force shall be deemed to be the holder of a licence and is a member of the Association.

Continuation of licences and certificates (2) Every licence or certificate of authorization issued under the *Professional Engineers Act*, being chapter 394 of the Revised Statutes of Ontario, 1980, or a predecessor thereof, and in effect immediately before this Act comes into force continues in the same manner as if issued as a temporary licence or a standard certificate of authorization, as the case requires, under this Act.

Cancellation for default of fees **23.** − (1) The Registrar may cancel a licence, certificate of authorization, temporary licence or limited licence for non-payment of any fee prescribed by the regulations or the bylaws after giving the member or the holder of the certificate of authorization, temporary licence or limited licence at least two months notice of the default and intention to cancel, subject to the continuing jurisdiction of the Association in respect of any disciplinary action arising out of his professional conduct while a member or holder.

(2) A person who was a member of the Association or a holder of a certificate of authorization, temporary licence or limited licence whose licence, certificate of authorization, temporary licence or limited licence was cancelled by the Registrar under subsection (1) is entitled to have the licence, certificate of authorization, temporary licence or limited licence reinstated upon compliance with the requirements and qualifications prescribed by the regulations.

24. − (1) The Complaints Committee shall be composed of not fewer than three members of the Association appointed to the Committee by the Council, including at least one member of the Council who was appointed to the Council by the Lieutenant Governor in Council.

(2) No person who is a member of the Discipline Committee shall be a member of the Complaints Committee.

(3) The Council shall name one member of the Complaints Committee to be chairman.

(4) Three members of the Complaints Committee, of whom one shall be a person appointed to the Council by the Lieutenant Governor in Council, constitute a quorum.

25. − (1) The Complaints Committee shall consider and investigate complaints made by members of the public or members of the Association regarding the conduct or actions of a member of the Association or holder of a certificate of authorization, a temporary licence or a limited licence, but no action shall be taken by the Committee under subsection (2) unless,

(a) a written complaint in a form that shall be provided by the Association has been filed with the Registrar and the member or holder whose conduct or actions are being investigated has been notified of the complaint and given at least two weeks in which to submit in writing to the Committee any explanations or representations the member or holder may wish to make concerning the matter; and

(b) the Committee has examined or has made every reasonable effort to examine all records and other documents relating to the complaint.

(2) The Committee in accordance with the information it receives may,

(a) direct that the matter be referred, in whole or in part, to the Discipline Committee;

(b) direct that the matter not be referred under clause (a); or

243

(c) take such action as it considers appropriate in the circumstances and that is not inconsistent with this Act or the regulations or by-laws.

Decision
and
reasons

(3) The Committee shall give its decision in writing to the Registrar for the purposes of subsection (4) and, where the decision is made under clause (2) (b), its reasons therefor.

Notice

(4) The Registrar shall send to the complainant and to the person complained against by prepaid first class mail a copy of the written decision made by the Complaints Committee and its reasons therefor, if any, together with notice advising the complainant of his right to apply to the Complaints Review Councillor under section 27.

Hearing

(5) The Committee is not required to hold a hearing or to afford to any person an opportunity for a hearing or an opportunity to make oral submissions before making a decision or giving a direction under this section.

Complaints
Review
Councillor

26. — (1) There shall be a Complaints Review Councillor who shall be appointed by and from among the members of the Council appointed by the Lieutenant Governor in Council under clause 3 (2) (c).

Idem

(2) The Complaints Review Councillor is not eligible to be a member of the Complaints Committee or the Fees Mediation Committee.

Examination
by
Complaints
Review
Councillor

27. — (1) The Complaints Review Councillor may examine from time to time the procedures for the treatment of complaints by the Association.

Review
by
Complaints
Review
Councillor

(2) Where a complaint respecting a member of the Association or a holder of a certificate of authorization, a temporary licence or a limited licence has not been disposed of by the Complaints Committee within ninety days after the complaint is filed with the Registrar, upon application by the complainant or on his own initiative the Complaints Review Councillor may review the treatment of the complaint by the Complaints Committee.

Application
to
Complaints
Review
Councillor

(3) A complainant who is not satisfied with the handling by the Complaints Committee of his complaint to the Committee may apply to the Complaints Review Councillor for a review of the treatment of the complaint after the Committee has disposed of the complaint.

Complaints
Review
Councillor
not to
inquire
into merit
of complaint

(4) In an examination or review in respect of the Association, the Complaints Review Councillor shall not inquire into the merits of any particular complaint made to the Association.

(5) The Complaints Review Councillor in his discretion may decide in a particular case not to make a review or not to continue a review in respect of the Association where, Discretionary power of Complaints Review Councillor

   (a) the review is or would be in respect of the treatment of a complaint that was disposed of by the Association more than twelve months before the matter came to the attention of the Complaints Review Councillor; or

   (b) in the opinion of the Complaints Review Councillor,

      (i) the application to the Complaints Review Councillor is frivolous or vexatious or is not made in good faith, or

      (ii) the person who has made application to the Complaints Review Councillor has not a sufficient personal interest in the subject-matter of the particular complaint.

(6) Before commencing an examination or review in respect of the Association, the Complaints Review Councillor shall inform the Association of his intention to commence the examination or review. Notice

(7) The Council shall provide to the Complaints Review Councillor such accommodation and support staff in the offices of the Association as are necessary to the performance of the powers and duties of the Complaints Review Councillor. Office accommodation

(8) Every examination or review by the Complaints Review Councillor in respect of the Association shall be conducted in private. Privacy

(9) In conducting an examination or review in respect of the Association, the Complaints Review Councillor may hear or obtain information from any person and may make such inquiries as he thinks fit. Receipt of information

(10) The Complaints Review Councillor is not required to hold or to afford to any person an opportunity for a hearing in relation to an examination, review or report in respect of the Association. Hearing not required

(11) Every person who is, Duty to furnish information

   (a) a member of the Council;

   (b) an officer of the Association;

   (c) a member of a committee of the Association; or

   (d) an employee of the Association,

shall furnish to the Complaints Review Councillor such information regarding any proceedings or procedures of the Association in respect of the treatment of complaints made to the Association as the Complaints Review Councillor from time to time requires, and shall give the Complaints Review Councillor access to all records, reports, files and other papers and things belonging to or under the control of the Association or any of such persons and that relate to the treatment by the Association of complaints or any particular complaint.

Report by
Complaints
Review
Councillor

(12) The Complaints Review Councillor shall make a report following upon each examination or review by him in respect of the Association.

Report
following
upon
examination

(13) Where the report follows upon an examination of the procedure for the treatment of complaints by the Association, the Complaints Review Councillor shall transmit the report to the Council.

Report
following
upon
review

(14) Where the report follows upon a review of the treatment of a complaint by the Association, the Complaints Review Councillor shall transmit the report to the Council, to the complainant and to the person complained against.

Report to
Minister

(15) The Complaints Review Councillor may transmit a report following upon an examination or review to the Minister where, in the opinion of the Complaints Review Councillor, the report should be brought to the attention of the Minister.

Recommen-
dations

(16) The Complaints Review Councillor may include in a report following upon an examination or review his recommendations in respect of the procedures of the Association, either generally or with respect to the treatment of a particular complaint.

Consideration
by Council

(17) The Council shall consider each report, and any recommendations included in the report, transmitted to it by the Complaints Review Councillor and shall notify the Complaints Review Councillor of any action it has taken in consequence.

Discipline
Committee

28. – (1) The Discipline Committee shall be composed of,

(a) at least one person appointed to the Discipline Committee by the Council from among the members of the Council elected to the Council;

(b) at least one person who is a member of the Association and who is a member of the Council appointed by the Lieutenant Governor in Council; and

(c) the persons appointed to the Committee by the Council from among the members of the Association who have not less than ten years experience in the practice of professional engineering.

(2) Five members of the Discipline Committee, of whom one shall be a person appointed to the Council by the Lieutenant Governor in Council and one shall be a person elected to the Council, constitute a quorum, and all disciplinary decisions require the vote of a majority of the members of the Discipline Committee present at the meeting. Quorum and votes

(3) Where the Discipline Committee commences a hearing and the member or members thereof who are appointed to the Council by the Lieutenant Governor in Council or who are elected members of the Council become unable to continue to act, the remaining members may complete the hearing notwithstanding the absence of the member or members and may render a decision as effectually as if all members of the Discipline Committee were present throughout the hearing, notwithstanding the absence of a quorum of the Committee. Disability of member

(4) The members of the Discipline Committee shall name one of them to be chairman of the Discipline Committee. Chairman

(5) The Council or the Executive Committee, by resolution, may direct the Discipline Committee to hold a hearing and determine any allegation of professional misconduct or incompetence on the part of a member of the Association or a holder of a certificate of authorization, a temporary licence or a limited licence specified in the resolution. Reference by Council or Executive Committee

29. — (1) The Discipline Committee shall, Duties of Discipline Committee

   (a) when so directed by the Council, the Executive Committee or the Complaints Committee, hear and determine allegations of professional misconduct or incompetence against a member of the Association or a holder of a certificate of authorization, a temporary licence or a limited licence;

   (b) hear and determine matters referred to it under section 25, 28 or 38; and

   (c) perform such other duties as are assigned to it by the Council.

(2) A member of the Association or a holder of a certificate of authorization, a temporary licence or a limited licence may be found guilty of professional misconduct by the Committee if, Professional misconduct

   (a) the member or holder has been found guilty of an offence relevant to suitability to practise, upon proof of such conviction;

   (b) the member or holder has been guilty in the opinion of the Discipline Committee of professional misconduct as defined in the regulations.

247

(3) The Discipline Committee may find a member of the Association or a holder of a temporary licence or a limited licence to be incompetent if in its opinion,

(a) the member or holder has displayed in his professional responsibilities a lack of knowledge, skill or judgment or disregard for the welfare of the public of a nature or to an extent that demonstrates the member or holder is unfit to carry out the responsibilities of a professional engineer; or

(b) the member or holder is suffering from a physical or mental condition or disorder of a nature and extent making it desirable in the interests of the public or the member or holder that the member or holder no longer be permitted to engage in the practice of professional engineering or that his practice of professional engineering be restricted.

Powers of
Discipline
Committee

(4) Where the Discipline Committee finds a member of the Association or a holder of a certificate of authorization, a temporary licence or a limited licence guilty of professional misconduct or to be incompetent it may, by order,

(a) revoke the licence of the member or the certificate of authorization, temporary licence or limited licence of the holder;

(b) suspend the licence of the member or the certificate of authorization, temporary licence or limited licence of the holder for a stated period, not exceeding twenty-four months;

(c) accept the undertaking of the member or holder to limit the professional work of the member or holder in the practice of professional engineering to the extent specified in the undertaking;

(d) impose terms, conditions or limitations on the licence or certificate of authorization, temporary licence or limited licence, of the member or holder, including but not limited to the successful completion of a particular course or courses of study, as are specified by the Discipline Committee;

(e) impose specific restrictions on the licence or certificate of authorization, temporary licence or limited licence, including but not limited to,

(i) requiring the member or the holder of the certificate of authorization, temporary licence or limited

248

licence to engage in the practice of professional engineering only under the personal supervision and direction of a member,

(ii) requiring the member to not alone engage in the practice of professional engineering,

(iii) requiring the member or the holder of the certificate of authorization, temporary licence or limited licence to accept periodic inspections by the Committee or its delegate of documents and records in the possession or under the control of the member or the holder in connection with the practice of professional engineering,

(iv) requiring the member or the holder of the certificate of authorization, temporary licence or limited licence to report to the Registrar or to such committee of the Council as the Discipline Committee may specify on such matters in respect of the member's or holder's practice for such period of time, at such times and in such form, as the Discipline Committee may specify;

(f) require that the member or the holder of the certificate of authorization, temporary licence or limited licence be reprimanded, admonished or counselled and, if considered warranted, direct that the fact of the reprimand, admonishment or counselling be recorded on the register for a stated or unlimited period of time;

(g) revoke or suspend for a stated period of time the designation of the member or holder by the Association as a specialist, consulting engineer or otherwise;

(h) impose such fine as the Discipline Committee considers appropriate, to a maximum of $5,000, to be paid by the member of the Association or the holder of the certificate of authorization, temporary licence or limited licence to the Treasurer of Ontario for payment into the Consolidated Revenue Fund;

(i) subject to subsection (5) in respect of orders of revocation or suspension, direct that the finding and the order of the Discipline Committee be published in detail or in summary and either with or without including the name of the member or holder in the official publication of the Association and in such other manner or medium as the Discipline Committee considers appropriate in the particular case;

249

(j) fix and impose costs to be paid by the member or the holder to the Association;

(k) direct that the imposition of a penalty be suspended or postponed for such period and upon such terms or for such purpose, including but not limited to,

    (i) the successful completion by the member or the holder of the temporary licence or the limited licence of a particular course or courses of study,

    (ii) the production to the Discipline Committee of evidence satisfactory to it that any physical or mental handicap in respect of which the penalty was imposed has been overcome,

or any combination of them.

(5) The Discipline Committee shall cause an order of the Committee revoking or suspending a licence or certificate of authorization, temporary licence or limited licence to be published, with or without the reasons therefor, in the official publication of the Association together with the name of the member or holder of the revoked or suspended licence or certificate of authorization, temporary licence or limited licence.

Publication on request

(6) The Discipline Committee shall cause a determination by the Committee that an allegation of professional misconduct or incompetence was unfounded to be published in the official publication of the Association, upon the request of the member of the Association or the holder of the certificate of authorization, temporary licence or limited licence against whom the allegation was made.

Costs

(7) Where the Discipline Committee is of the opinion that the commencement of the proceedings was unwarranted, the Committee may order that the Association reimburse the member of the Association or the holder of the certificate of authorization, temporary licence or limited licence for his costs or such portion thereof as the Discipline Committee fixes.

Stay of decision on appeal, incompetence

30. – (1) Where the Discipline Committee revokes, suspends or restricts a licence, temporary licence or limited licence on the grounds of incompetence, the decision takes effect immediately notwithstanding that an appeal is taken from the decision, unless the court to which the appeal is taken otherwise orders, and, where the court is satisfied that it is appropriate in the circumstances, the court may so order.

Stay of decision on appeal, professional misconduct

(2) Where the Discipline Committee revokes, suspends or restricts a licence or a certificate of authorization, temporary licence or limited licence on grounds other than for incompe-

tence, the order does not take effect until the time for appeal from the order has expired without an appeal being taken or, if taken, the appeal has been disposed of or abandoned, unless the Discipline Committee otherwise orders, and, where the Committee considers that it is appropriate for the protection of the public, the Committee may so order.

31. — (1) In proceedings before the Discipline Committee, the Association and the member of the Association or the holder of a certificate of authorization, a temporary licence or a limited licence whose conduct is being investigated in the proceedings are parties to the proceedings.

Discipline proceedings, parties

(2) A member or holder of a certificate of authorization, a temporary licence or a limited licence whose conduct is being investigated in proceedings before the Discipline Committee shall be afforded an opportunity to examine before the hearing any written or documentary evidence that will be produced or any report the contents of which will be given in evidence at the hearing.

Examination of documentary evidence

(3) Members of the Discipline Committee holding a hearing shall not have taken part before the hearing in any investigation of the subject-matter of the hearing other than as a member of the Council considering the referral of the matter to the Discipline Committee or at a previous hearing of the Committee, and shall not communicate directly or indirectly in relation to the subject-matter of the hearing with any person or with any party or his representative except upon notice to and opportunity for all parties to participate, but the Committee may seek legal advice from an adviser independent from the parties and, in such case, the nature of the advice shall be made known to the parties in order that they may make submissions as to the law.

Members holding hearing not to have taken part in investigation, etc.

(4) Notwithstanding anything in the *Statutory Powers Procedure Act*, hearings of the Discipline Committee shall be held *in camera*, but, if the party whose conduct is being investigated requests otherwise by a notice delivered to the Registrar before the day fixed for the hearing, the committee shall conduct the hearing in public except where,

In camera R.S.O. 1980, c. 484

    (a) matters involving public security may be disclosed; or

    (b) the possible disclosure of intimate financial or personal matters of a person other than the person whose conduct is being investigated outweighs the desirability of holding the hearing in public.

(5) The oral evidence taken before the Discipline Committee shall be recorded and, if so required, copies of a transcript thereof shall be furnished only to the parties upon the same terms as in the Supreme Court.

Recording of evidence

Evidence
R.S.O. 1980,
c. 484

(6) Notwithstanding the *Statutory Powers Procedure Act*, nothing is admissible in evidence before the Discipline Committee that would be inadmissible in a court in a civil case and the findings of the Discipline Committee shall be based exclusively on evidence admitted before it.

Only
members
at hearing to
participate
in decision

(7) No member of the Discipline Committee shall participate in a decision of the Committee following upon a hearing unless he was present throughout the hearing and heard the evidence and argument of the parties.

Release of
documentary
evidence

(8) Documents and things put in evidence at a hearing of the Discipline Committee shall, upon the request of the party who produced them, be returned by the Committee within a reasonable time after the matter in issue has been finally determined.

Continuation
of expiry of
Committee
membership

(9) Where a proceeding is commenced before the Discipline Committee and the term of office on the Council or on the Committee of a member sitting for the hearing expires or is terminated, other than for cause, before the proceeding is disposed of but after evidence has been heard, the member shall be deemed to remain a member of the Discipline Committee for the purpose of completing the disposition of the proceeding in the same manner as if his term of office had not expired or been terminated.

Service of
decision of
Discipline
Committee

(10) Where the Discipline Committee finds a member of the Association or a holder of a certificate of authorization, temporary licence or limited licence guilty of professional misconduct or incompetence, a copy of the decision shall be served upon the person complaining in respect of the conduct or action of the member or holder.

Appeal
to court

32. – (1) A party to proceedings before the Registration Committee or the Discipline Committee may appeal to the Divisional Court, in accordance with the rules of court, from the decision or order of the committee.

Certified
copy of
record

(2) Upon the request of a party desiring to appeal to the Divisional Court and upon payment of the fee therefor, the Registrar shall furnish the party with a certified copy of the record of the proceedings, including the documents received in evidence and the decision or order appealed from.

Powers of
court on
appeal

(3) An appeal under this section may be made on questions of law or fact or both and the court may affirm or may rescind the decision of the committee appealed from and may exercise all powers of the committee and may direct the committee to take any action which the committee may take and as the court considers proper, and for such purposes the court may substitute its opinion for that of the committee or the court may refer the matter

back to the committee for rehearing, in whole or in part, in accordance with such directions as the court considers proper.

33. − (1) No person who is a member of the Complaints Committee or the Discipline Committee shall be a member of the Fees Mediation Committee.

(2) The Fees Mediation Committee,

(a) shall, unless the Committee considers it inappropriate to do so, mediate any written complaint by a client of a member of the Association or of a holder of a certificate of authorization, a temporary licence or limited licence in respect of a fee charged for professional engineering services provided to the client; and

(b) shall perform such other duties as are assigned to it by the Council.

(3) The Fees Mediation Committee, with the written consent of all parties to the dispute, may arbitrate a dispute in respect of a fee between a client and a member of the Association or a holder of a certificate of authorization, temporary licence or limited licence and in that case the decision of the Fees Mediation Committee is final and binding on all parties to the dispute.

(4) Where the Fees Mediation Committee acts as arbitrator under subsection (3), the *Arbitrations Act* does not apply.

(5) A decision by the Fees Mediation Committee under subsection (3), exclusive of the reasons therefor, certified by the Registrar, may be filed with the Supreme Court or a county or district court and when filed the decision may be enforced in the same manner as a judgment of the court.

34. − (1) Where the Registrar believes on reasonable and probable grounds that a member of the Association or a holder of a certificate of authorization, a temporary licence or limited licence has committed an act of professional misconduct or incompetence or that there is cause to refuse to issue or to suspend or revoke a certificate of authorization, the Registrar by order may appoint one or more persons to investigate whether such act has occurred or there is such cause, and the person or persons appointed shall report the result of the investigation to the Registrar.

(2) For purposes relevant to the subject-matter of an investigation under this section, the person appointed to make the investigation may inquire into and examine the practice of the member or holder of the certificate of authorization, temporary licence or limited licence in respect of whom the investigation is being made and may, upon production of his appointment, enter at any

reasonable time the business premises of the member or holder and examine books, records, documents and things relevant to the subject-matter of the investigation and, for the purposes of the inquiry, the person making the investigation has the powers of a commission under Part II of the *Public Inquiries Act*, which Part applies to such inquiry as if it were an inquiry under that Act.

R.S.O. 1980, c. 411

Obstruction of investigator

(3) No person shall obstruct a person appointed to make an investigation under this section or withhold from him or conceal or destroy any books, records, documents or things relevant to the subject-matter of the investigation.

Order by provincial judge

(4) Where a provincial judge is satisfied on evidence upon oath,

(a) that the Registrar had grounds for appointing and by order has appointed one or more persons to make an investigation; and

(b) that there is reasonable ground for believing there are in any building, dwelling, receptacle or place any books, records, documents or things relating to the member of the Association or holder of a certificate of authorization, a temporary licence or a limited licence whose affairs are being investigated and to the subject-matter of the investigation,

the provincial judge may issue an order authorizing the person or persons making the investigation, together with such police officer or officers as they call upon to assist them, to enter and search, by force if necessary, such building, dwelling, receptacle or place for such books, records, documents or things and to examine them.

Execution of order

(5) An order issued under subsection (4) shall be executed at reasonable times as specified in the order.

Expiry of order

(6) An order issued under subsection (4) shall state the date on which it expires, which shall be a date not later than fifteen days after the order is issued.

Ex parte application

(7) A provincial judge may receive and consider an application for an order under subsection (4) without notice to and in the absence of the member of the Association or holder of a certificate of authorization, temporary licence or a limited licence whose affairs are being investigated.

Removal of books, etc.

(8) Any person making an investigation under this section may, upon giving a receipt therefor, remove any books, records, documents or things examined under this section relating to the member or holder whose practice is being investigated and to the subject-matter of the investigation for the purpose of making

copies of such books, records or documents, but such copying shall be carried out with reasonable dispatch and the books, records or documents in question shall be promptly thereafter returned to the member or holder whose practice is being investigated.

(9) Any copy made as provided in subsection (8) and certified to be a true copy by the person making the investigation is admissible in evidence in any action, proceeding or prosecution as proof in the absence of evidence to the contrary of the original book, record or document and its contents.

Admissibility of copies

(10) The Registrar shall report the results of the investigation to the Council or such committee as the Registrar considers appropriate.

Report of Registrar

35. It is a condition of every certificate of authorization that the holder of the certificate shall not offer or provide to the public services that are within the practice of professional engineering unless the holder is insured in respect of professional liability in accordance with the regulations.

Liability insurance

36. − (1) In this section, "insurer" means a person offering insurance in respect of liability incurred in the practice of professional engineering.

Interpretation

(2) Upon the request of the Registrar, an insurer shall furnish to the Registrar all documents that relate to a claim for indemnity in respect of the practice of professional engineering and that are in the possession or under the control of the insurer and have been prepared by a professional engineer and relate to engineering matters.

Information re insurance claims

(3) Subsection (2) does not apply in respect of a document prepared by an insured person related to a claim for indemnity in respect of the practice of professional engineering by the insured person.

Exception

(4) The Registrar may forward any information referred to in subsection (2) to the Council or to such committee as the Registrar considers appropriate.

Transmittal of information

37. Where a licence, certificate of authorization, temporary licence or limited licence is revoked or cancelled, the former holder thereof shall forthwith deliver the licence, certificate of authorization, temporary licence or limited licence and related seal to the Registrar.

Surrender of revoked licence or certificate

38. − (1) A person whose licence, certificate of authorization, temporary licence or limited licence has been revoked for cause under this Act, or whose membership has been cancelled for cause under a predecessor of this Act, may apply in writing to the

Application for licence, etc., after revocation

Registrar for the issuance of a licence, certificate of authorization, temporary licence or limited licence, but such application shall not be made sooner than two years after the revocation.

Removal of suspension

(2) A person whose licence, certificate of authorization, temporary licence or limited licence has been suspended for cause under this Act, or whose membership has been suspended for cause under a predecessor of this Act, may apply in writing to the Registrar for the removal of the suspension, but, where the suspension is for more than one year, the application shall not be made sooner than one year after the commencement of the suspension.

Reference to Discipline Committee

(3) The Registrar shall refer an application under subsection (1) or (2) in respect of a licence or a certificate of authorization, a temporary licence or a limited licence to the Discipline Committee which shall hold a hearing respecting and decide upon the application, and shall report its decision and reasons to the Council and the applicant.

Procedures

(4) The provisions of this Act applying to hearings by the Registration Committee, except section 32, apply with necessary modifications to proceedings of the Discipline Committee or the Registration Committee under this section.

Confidentiality

39. − (1) Every person engaged in the administration of this Act, including any person making an examination or review under section 27 or an investigation under section 34, shall preserve secrecy with respect to all matters that come to his knowledge in the course of his duties, employment, examination, review or investigation and shall not communicate any such matters to any other person except,

(a) as may be required in connection with the administration of,

(i) this Act and the regulations and by-laws, or

1984, c. 12

(ii) the *Architects Act, 1984* and the regulations and by-laws under that Act,

or any proceedings under,

(iii) this Act or the regulations, or

1984, c. 12

(iv) the *Architects Act, 1984* or the regulations under that Act;

(b) to his counsel; or

(c) with the consent of the person to whom the information relates.

256

(2) No person to whom subsection (1) applies shall be required

to give testimony or to produce any book, record, document or thing in any action or proceeding with regard to information obtained by him in the course of his duties, employment, examination, review or investigation except in a proceeding under this Act or the regulations or by-laws or a proceeding under the *Architects Act, 1984* or the regulations or by-laws under that Act.

40. — (1) Where it appears to the Association that any person does not comply with any provision of this Act or the regulations, notwithstanding the imposition of any penalty in respect of such non-compliance and in addition to any other rights it may have, the Association may apply to a judge of the High Court for an order directing the person to comply with the provision, and upon the application the judge may make the order or such other order as the judge thinks fit.

(2) An appeal lies to the Court of Appeal from an order made under subsection (1).

41. — (1) Every person who contravenes section 12 is guilty of an offence and on conviction is liable for the first offence to a fine of not more than $15,000 and for each subsequent offence to a fine of not more than $30,000.

(2) Every person who is not a holder of a licence or a temporary licence and who,

(a) uses the title "professional engineer" or an abbreviation or variation thereof as an occupational or business designation;

(b) uses a term, title or description that will lead to the belief that the person may engage in the practice of professional engineering; or

(c) uses a seal that will lead to the belief that the person is a professional engineer,

is guilty of an offence and on conviction is liable for the first offence to a fine of not more than $5,000 and for each subsequent offence to a fine of not more than $15,000.

(3) Every person who is not acting under and in accordance with a certificate of authorization and who,

(a) uses a term, title or description that will lead to the belief that the person may provide to the public services that are within the practice of professional engineering; or

(b) uses a seal that will lead to the belief that the person may provide to the public services that are within the practice of professional engineering,

Testimony in civil action

Order directing compliance

Appeal

Penalties

Idem, use of term "professional engineer", etc.

Idem, services of professional engineer

257

is guilty of an offence and on conviction is liable for the first offence to a fine of not more than $5,000 and for each subsequent offence to a fine of not more than $15,000.

(4) Any person who obstructs a person appointed to make an investigation under section 34 in the course of his or her duties is guilty of an offence and on conviction is liable to a fine of not more than $5,000.

(5) Where a corporation is guilty of an offence under subsection (1), (2), (3) or (4), every director or officer of the corporation who authorizes, permits or acquiesces in the offence is guilty of an offence and on conviction is liable to a fine of not more than $30,000.

(6) Where a person who is guilty of an offence under subsection (1), (2), (3) or (4) is a member or an employee of a partnership, every member of the partnership who authorizes, permits or acquiesces in the offence is guilty of an offence and on conviction is liable to a fine of not more than $30,000.

(7) Proceedings shall not be commenced in respect of an offence under subsection (1), (2), (3), (4), (5) or (6) after two years after the date on which the offence was, or is alleged to have been, committed.

(8) Subsection (2) does not apply to a holder of a limited licence who uses a term, title or description authorized or permitted by the regulations.

42. – (1) Any person who makes or causes to be made a wilful falsification in a matter relating to a register or issues a false licence, certificate, temporary licence, limited licence or document with respect to registration is guilty of an offence and on conviction is liable to a fine of not more than $5,000.

(2) Every person who wilfully procures or attempts to procure the issuance of a licence, a certificate of authorization, a temporary licence or a limited licence under this Act by knowingly making a false representation or declaration or by making a fraudulent representation or declaration, either orally or in writing, is guilty of an offence and on conviction is liable to a fine of not more than $5,000, and every person knowingly aiding and assisting such person therein is guilty of an offence and on conviction is liable to a fine of not more than $5,000.

(3) Proceedings to obtain a conviction for an offence under subsection (1) or (2) shall not be commenced after the expiration of six months after the date on which the offence was, or is alleged to have been, committed.

43. Where licensing or the holding of a certificate of authorization, a temporary licence or a limited licence or acting under and in accordance with a certificate of authorization under this Act is required to permit the lawful doing of an act or thing, if in any prosecution it is proven that the defendant has done the act or thing, the burden of proving that he was so licensed or that he held a subsisting certificate of authorization, temporary licence or limited licence or that he acted under and in accordance with a certificate of authorization under this Act rests upon the defendant.

Onus of proof respecting licensing

44. — (1) A notice or document under this Act or the regulations is sufficiently given, served or delivered if delivered personally or by mail.

Service of notice or document

(2) Where a notice or document under this Act or the regulations is sent to a person by mail addressed to the person at the last address of the person in the records of the Association, there is a rebuttable presumption that the notice or document is delivered to the person on the tenth day after the day of mailing.

Idem

45. Any statement containing information from the records required to be kept by the Registrar under this Act, purporting to be certified by the Registrar under the seal of the Association, is admissible in evidence in all courts as proof in the absence of evidence to the contrary of the facts stated therein without proof of the appointment or signature of the Registrar and without proof of the seal.

Registrar's certificate as evidence

46. — (1) No action or other proceeding for damages shall be instituted against the Association, a committee of the Association or a member of the Association or committee of the Association, or an officer, employee, agent or appointee of the Association for any act done in good faith in the performance or intended performance of a duty or in the exercise or the intended exercise of a power under this Act, a regulation or a by-law, or for any neglect or default in the performance or exercise in good faith of such duty or power.

Immunity of Association

(2) Every member of the Council, a committee of the Association and every officer and employee of the Association, and his heirs, executors and administrators, and estate and effects, respectively, may, with the consent of the Association, given by the members of the Association, from time to time and at all times, be indemnified and saved harmless out of the funds of the Association, from and against,

Councillor indemnified in suits respecting execution of his office

(a) all costs, charges and expenses whatsoever that he sustains or incurs in or about any action, suit or proceeding

259

that is brought, commenced or prosecuted against him, for or in respect of any act, deed, matter or thing whatsoever, made, done or permitted by him, in or about the execution of the duties of his office; and

(b) all other costs, charges and expenses that he sustains or incurs in or about or in relation to the affairs thereof, except such costs, charges or expenses as are occasioned by his own wilful neglect or default.

Limitation
of action

47. − (1) Proceedings shall not be commenced against a member of the Association or a holder of a certificate of authorization, a temporary licence or a limited licence for damages arising from the provision of a service that is within the practice of professional engineering after twelve months after the date on which the service was, or ought to have been, performed.

Extension
of time

(2) The court in which an action mentioned in subsection (1) has been or may be brought may extend the limitation period specified in subsection (1) before or after the expiration of the period if the court is satisfied that there are apparent grounds for the proceedings and that there are reasonable grounds for applying for the extension.

Application

(3) Subsections (1) and (2) do not apply to proceedings under any other section of this Act.

Joint
Practice
Board

48. − (1) The Council shall appoint to the Joint Practice Board (composed of a chairman, three members representing the Ontario Association of Architects and three members representing the Association of Professional Engineers of Ontario) the three members of the Joint Practice Board representing the Association and shall prescribe the term of each appointment.

recommendation

(2) The Joint Practice Board may recommend to the Council that the Council direct the Registrar to issue a licence or a certificate of authorization to a holder of a certificate of practice issued under the *Architects Act, 1984*.

1984, c. 12

Direction
by Council

(3) The Council, upon the recommendation of the Joint Practice Board, may direct the Registrar to issue a licence or a certificate of authorization to a holder of a certificate of practice under the *Architects Act, 1984* and, if the Council does not direct the issuance of the licence or the certificate of authorization, the Council shall give its reasons therefor in writing to the Joint Practice Board and to the applicant for the licence or the certificate of authorization.

Referral of
dispute to
Joint
Practice
Board

(4) Where a dispute arises between an architect and a professional engineer or a holder of a certificate of authorization as to jurisdiction in respect of professional services, the Registrar may

refer the matter to the Joint Practice Board and the Joint Practice Board shall consider the matter and assist the architect and the professional engineer or the holder of the certificate of authorization to resolve the dispute in accordance with the rules in section 12.

(5) Proceedings shall not be commenced under this Act in respect of a matter mentioned in subsection (4) except upon the certificate of the chairman of the Joint Practice Board that the Board has considered the matter and has been unable to resolve the dispute. Commencement of proceedings

(6) The certificate of the chairman is admissible in evidence in all courts as proof in the absence of evidence to the contrary of the facts stated therein without proof of the appointment or signature of the chairman. Certificate

49. − (1) The Council shall make a report annually to the Minister containing such information as the Minister requires. Annual report

(2) The Minister shall submit the report to the Lieutenant Governor in Council and shall then lay the report before the Assembly if it is in session or, if not, at the next ensuing session. Idem

50. − (1) The *Corporations Act* does not apply in respect of the Association except for the following sections of that Act which shall apply with necessary modifications in respect of the Association: Application of R.S.O. 1980, c. 95

1. Section 81 (which relates to liability for wages).

2. Section 94 (which relates to auditors) and, for the purpose, the Minister shall be deemed to be the Minister referred to in the section.

3. Subsection 95 (1) (which relates to the auditor's qualifications) and, for the purpose, the subsection shall be deemed not to include,

    i. the exception as provided in subsection 95 (2), and

    ii. the reference to an affiliated company.

4. Section 96 (which relates to the auditor's functions).

5. Subsection 97 (1), exclusive of clause 97 (1) (b), (which relates to the auditor's report) and, for the purpose, the Association shall be deemed to be a private company.

6. Subsection 97 (3) (which relates to the auditor's report).

7. Section 122 (which relates to the liability of members).

8. Section 276 (which relates to the holding of land) and, for the purpose, the Minister shall be deemed to be the Minister referred to in the section.

9. Section 280 (which relates to making contracts).

10. Section 281 (which relates to power of attorney).

11. Section 282 (which relates to authentication of documents) except in respect of information from the records required to be kept by the Registrar.

12. Section 292 (which relates to validity of acts of directors).

13. Section 297 (which relates to directions by a court as to holding a meeting).

14. Section 299 (which relates to minutes of meetings).

15. Section 302 (which relates to books of account).

16. Section 303 (which relates to untrue entries) and, for the purpose, the section shall be deemed not to refer to section 41 of that Act.

17. Section 304 (which relates to the place of keeping and the inspection of records) and, for the purpose,

    i. the section shall be deemed not to refer to sections 41 and 43 of that Act, and

    ii. the Minister shall be deemed to be the Minister referred to in the section.

18. Section 305 (which relates to inspection of records) and, for the purpose, the section shall be deemed not to refer to section 41 of that Act.

19. Section 310 (which relates to investigations and audits).

20. Section 323 (which relates to evidence of by-laws and certificates of amounts due).

21. Section 329 (which relates to removal of proceedings into the Supreme Court).

22. Section 330 (which relates to appeals).

23. Section 331 (which relates to untrue statements) and, for the purpose,

    i. the section shall be deemed not to refer to regulations made under that Act, and

    ii. the Minister and the Deputy Minister to the Minister shall be deemed to be the Minister and the Deputy Minister referred to in the section.

24. Section 333 (which relates to orders by the court) and, for the purpose, the section shall be deemed not to refer to creditors.

(2) For the purposes of subsection (1), a member of the Association shall be deemed to be a shareholder.

51. — (1) The *Professional Engineers Act*, being chapter 394 of the Revised Statutes of Ontario, 1980, is repealed.

(2) Any reference in any Act or regulation to the *Professional Engineers Act* shall be deemed to be a reference to this Act.

(3) Any reference in any Act or regulation to a professional engineer as a member of the Association under the *Professional Engineers Act* shall be deemed to be a reference to a professional engineer licensed under this Act.

52. This Act comes into force on a day to be named by proclamation of the Lieutenant Governor.

53. The short title of this Act is the *Professional Engineers Act, 1984*.

Interpretation

Repeal

References
R.S.O. 1980,
c. 394

Idem

Commence-
ment

Short title

CHAPTER E-11.1

The Engineering, Geological and Geophysical Professions Act
(*Assented to June 2, 1981*)

HER MAJESTY, by and with the advice and consent of the Legislative Assembly of Alberta, enacts as follows:

Definitions   **1** In this Act,

(a)   "Association" means the Association of Professional Engineers, Geologists and Geophysicists of Alberta;

(b)   "Board of Examiners" means the Board of Examiners established under section 29;

(c)   "certificate holder" means
(i)   a joint firm, and
(ii)   a restricted practitioner;

(d)   "Council" means the Council of the Association;

(e)   "Court" means the Court of Queen's Bench;

(f)   "Discipline Committee" means the Discipline Committee established under section 44;

(g)   "Joint Board" means the Joint Board of Practice established under *The Department of Housing and Public Works Act*;

(h)   "joint firm" means a firm to which a certificate of authorization has been issued under section 34;

(i)   "licensee" means an individual who holds a licence under this Act;

(i.1)   "member of the public" means a person who is
(i)   a Canadian citizen or who is lawfully admitted to Canada for permanent residence.
(ii)   a resident of Alberta, and
(iii)   not a member of the Association;

(j)   "member-in-training" means engineer-in-training, geologist-in-training or geophysicist-in-training, as the case may be;

(k)   "Minister" means the Minister of Housing and Public Works;

(l)   "permit holder" means a partnership or other association of persons or a corporation that holds a permit under this Act;

(m) "practice of engineering" means

    (i) reporting on, advising on, evaluating, designing, preparing plans and specifications for or directing the construction, technical inspection, maintenance or operation of any structure, work or process

        (A) that is aimed at the discovery, development or utilization of matter, materials or energy or in any other way designed for the use and convenience of man, and

        (B) that requires in the reporting, advising, evaluating, designing, preparation or direction the professional application of the principles of mathematics, chemistry, physics or any related applied subject, or

    (ii) teaching engineering at a university;

(n) "practice of geology" means

    (i) reporting, advising, evaluating, interpreting, geological surveying, sampling or examining related to any activity

        (A) that is aimed at the discovery or development of oil, natural gas, coal, metallic or non-metallic minerals, precious stones, other natural resources or water or that is aimed at the investigation of geological conditions, and

        (B) that requires in that reporting, advising, evaluating, interpreting, geological surveying, sampling or examining, the professional application of the principles of the geological sciences, or

    (ii) teaching geology at a university;

(o) "practice of geophysics" means

    (i) reporting on, advising on, acquiring, processing, evaluating or interpreting geophysical data, or geophysical surveying that relates to any activity

        (A) that is aimed at the discovery or development of oil, natural gas, coal, metallic or non-metallic minerals or precious stones or other natural resources or water or that is aimed at the investigation of sub-surface conditions in the earth, and

        (B) that requires in that reporting, advising, eva-

265

luating, interpreting, or geophysical surveying, the professional application of the
principles of the geophysical sciences, or

(ii) teaching geophysics at a university;

(p) "Practice Review Board" means the Practice Review
Board established under section 15;

(q) "profession" means the profession of engineering,
geology or geophysics, as the case may be;

(r) "professional engineer" means an individual who
holds a certificate of registration to engage in the
practice of engineering under this Act;

(s) "professional geologist" means an individual who
holds a certificate of registration to engage in the
practice of geology under this Act;

(t) "professional geophysicist" means an individual who
holds a certificate of registration to engage in the
practice of geophysics under this Act;

(u) "professional member" means a professional engineer,
professional geologist or professional geophysicist
registered as a member of the Association pursuant to
this Act;

(v) "Registrar" means the Registrar appointed under section 13;

(w) "restricted practitioner" means a registered architect
under *The Architects Act, 1980* who holds a certificate
of authorization under this Act.

PART 1
SCOPE OF PRACTICE

Exclusive
scope of the
practice of
engineering

2(1) Except as otherwise provided in this Act, no individual,
corporation, partnership or other entity, except a professional
engineer, a licensee so authorized in his licence, a permit holder
so authorized in its permit or a certificate holder so authorized in
his certificate shall engage in the practice of engineering.

(2) No individual, corporation, partnership or other entity,
may engage in both the practice of engineering and the practice
of architecture as defined in *The Architects Act, 1980*, or hold out
that it is entitled to engage in both the practice of engineering and
the practice of architecture unless it holds a certificate of authorization under this Act or *The Architects Act, 1980* permitting it to do
so.

(3) A professional engineer, licensee, permit holder or joint firm may engage in the practice of surveying other than land surveying as defined in *The Land Surveyors Act, 1981.*

(4) Subsection (1) does not apply to the following:

(a) a person engaged in the execution or supervision of the construction, maintenance, operation or inspection of any process, system, work, structure or building in the capacity of contractor, superintendent, foreman or inspector or in any similar capacity, when the process, system, work, structure or building has been designed by and the execution or supervision is being carried out under the supervision and control of a professional engineer or licensee;

(b) a person engaged in the practice of engineering as an engineer-in-training, technician or technologist in the course of his being employed or engaged and supervised and controlled by a professional engineer, licensee, permit holder or certificate holder;

(c) a member of a class of persons designated in the regulations as a technician or technologist as defined in the regulations;

(d) a person who in accordance with an Act or regulation in respect of mines, minerals, pipelines, boilers and pressure vessels, building codes or safety codes for building is engaged in any undertaking or activity required under or pursuant to that Act or the regulations under that Act;

(e) a person who, on his own property and for his sole use or the use of his domestic establishment, carries out any work that does not involve the safety of the general public;

(f) a member of the Canadian Forces while actually employed on duty with the Forces.

(5) A restricted practitioner is not authorized by the operation of subsection (1) to engage in the practice of engineering beyond the scope of the practice that is specified in the register.

(6) Subsection (1) does not apply to a person if he engages in

(a) planning, designing or giving advice on the design of or on the erection, construction or alteration of or addition to,

(b) preparing plans, drawings, detail drawings, specifications or graphic representations for the design of or for the erection, construction or alteration of or addition to, or

(c) inspecting work or assessing the performance of work under a contract for the erection, construction or alteration of or addition to

a building that is a building in a category or type of building described in *The Alberta Uniform Building Standards Act* as set out in subsection (7).

(7) The categories or types of buildings referred to in subsection (6) are the following:

(a) a building, 3 storeys or less in height, for assembly occupancy or institutional occupancy that,
   (i) in the case of a single storey building, has a gross area of 300 square metres or less,
   (ii) in the case of a 2 storey building, has a gross area of 150 square metres or less on each floor, or
   (iii) in the case of a 3 storey building, has a gross area of 100 square metres or less on each floor;

(b) a building for residential occupancy that
   (i) is a single family dwelling, or
   (ii) is a multiple family dwelling, containing 4 dwelling units or less;

(c) a building, 3 storeys or less in height, for residential occupancy as a hotel, motel or similar use that,
   (i) in the case of a single storey building, has a gross area of 400 square metres or less,
   (ii) in the case of a 2 storey building, has a gross area of 200 square metres or less on each floor, or
   (iii) in the case of a 3 storey building, has a gross area of 130 square metres or less on each floor;

(d) a building, 3 storeys or less in height, for warehouse, business and personal services occupancy, for mercantile occupancy or for industrial occupancy that
   (i) in the case of a single storey building has a gross area of 500 square metres or less,
   (ii) in the case of a 2 storey building has a gross area of 250 square metres or less on each floor, or
   (iii) in the case of a 3 storey building has a gross area of 165 square metres or less on each floor;

(e) a building that is a farm building not for public use;

(f) a relocatable industrial camp building.

3 No individual, corporation, partnership or other entity, except a professional engineer, licensee, permit holder or joint firm entitled to engage in the practice of engineering, shall

    (a)   use
-     (i)   the title "professional engineer" or any abbreviation of that title, or
-     (ii)   the word "engineer" in combination with any other name, title, description, letter, symbol or abbreviation that represents expressly or by implication that he is a professional engineer, licensee or permit holder,

    (b)   represent or hold out, expressly or by implication, that
-     (i)   he is entitled to engage in the practice of engineering, or
-     (ii)   he is a professional engineer, licensee, permit holder or joint firm,

    or

    (c)   affix the stamp or seal of a professional engineer, licensee or permit holder or permit that stamp to be affixed, to a plan, drawing, detail drawing, specification or other document or a reproduction of any of them unless
-     (i)   that plan, drawing, detail drawing, specification, other document or reproduction was prepared by or under the supervision and control of, and
-     (ii)   the stamp is affixed with the knowledge and consent or in accordance with the direction of

the professional engineer or licensee to whom or the permit holder or joint firm to which the stamp or seal was issued.

4 A joint firm

    (a)   may hold itself out as "engineers and architects" or "architects and engineers" only if it has both professional engineers and registered architects as partners or shareholders in an arrangement that is satisfactory to the Council and the council of The Alberta Association of Architects;

    (b)   shall not hold itself out as "engineers and architects" or "architects and engineers" if the registered architects or professional engineers are employees only and not partners or shareholders, or if the partnership or shareholding arrangement is not satisfactory to the

Council or the council of The Alberta Association of Architects.

Exclusive
scope of the
practice of
geology

5(1) Subject to subsection (2), no individual, corporation, partnership of other entity, except a professional geologist, a licensee so authorized in his licence and a permit holder so authorized in the permit, shall engage in the practice of geology.

(2) Subsection (1) does not apply to the following:

(a) a person engaged in the practice of geology as a geologist-in-training, geological technician or technologist in the course of his being employed or engaged and supervised and controlled by a professional geologist, licensee or permit holder;

(b) a member of a class of persons designated in the regulations as a geological technician or technologist as defined in the regulations;

(c) a person who, as a prospector, is engaged in any activities that are normally associated with the business of prospecting;

(d) a member of the Canadian Forces while actually employed on duty with the Forces.

Exclusive
use of name
geologists

6 No individual, corporation, partnership or other entity, except a professional geologist or a licensee or permit holder entitled to engage in the practice of geology shall

(a) use
  (i) the title "professional geologist" or any abbreviation of that title, or
  (ii) the word "geologist" in combination with any other name, title, description, letter, symbol or abbreviation that represents expressly or by implication that he is a professional geologist, licensee or permit holder, or

(b) represent or hold out, expressly or by implication, that
  (i) he is entitled to engage in the practice of geology, or
  (ii) he is a professional geologist, licensee or permit holder.

Exclusive
scope of the
practice of
geophysics

7(1) Subject to subsection (2), no individual, corporation, partnership or other entity, except a professional geophysicist, a licensee so authorized in his licence or a permit holder so authorized in the permit, shall engage in the practice of geophysics.

(2) Subsection (1) does not apply to the following:

(a) a person engaged in the practice of geophysics as a geophysicist-in-training, geophysical technician or technologist in the course of his being employed or engaged and supervised and controlled by a professional geophysicist, licensee or permit holder;

(b) a member of a class of persons designated in the regulations as a geophysical technician or technologist as defined in the regulations;

(c) a person who is engaged in the routine maintenance of geophysical equipment, or if carried out under the supervision and control of a professional geophysicist, the routine operation, reduction or plotting of geophysical observations;

(d) a member of the Canadian Forces while actually employed on duty with the Forces.

8 No individual, corporation, partnership or other entity, except a professional geophysicist or a licensee or permit holder entitled to engage in the practice of geophysics shall

Exclusive use of name geophysicist

(a) use
    (i) the title "professional geophysicist" or any abbreviation of that title, or
    (ii) the word "geophysicist" in combination with any other name, title, description, letter, symbol or abbreviation, that represents expressly or by implication that he is a professional geophysicist, licensee or permit holder,

(b) represent or hold out, expressly or by implication, that
    (i) he is entitled to engage in the practice of geophysics, or
    (ii) he is a professional geophysicist, licensee or permit holder.

9 The Court, on application by the Council by way of originating notice, may grant an injunction enjoining any person from doing any act or thing that contravenes this Part, notwithstanding any penalty that may be provided by this Act or the regulations in respect of that act or thing.

Injunction

PART 2
ASSOCIATION

Association of Professional Engineers, Geologists and Geophysicists

10(1) The Association of Professional Engineers, Geologists and Geophysicists of Alberta is continued as a corporation.

(2) The abbreviated form of the name of the Association shall be A.P.E.G.G.A. or APEGGA.

(3) No person other than the Association shall use the abbreviated form of the name of the Association or any other abbreviation alone or in combination with any other word or name in a way that represents expressly or by implication that he is a member of or connected in any way with the Association.

Powers of
Association

11 In addition to the powers vested in it by this Act, the Association has the power expressed in section 16 of *The Interpretation Act, 1980* and the power to

    (a)   acquire and hold real property and sell, lease or otherwise dispose of it, and

    (b)   borrow money for the purposes of the Association and mortgage or charge real or personal property of the Association or its sources of funds as security.

Council

12(1) There is hereby established a governing body of the Association called the Council.

(2) The Council shall manage and conduct the business and affairs of the Association and exercise the powers of the Association in the name of and on behalf of the Association.

(3) The Council shall submit annually to the Minister in a form satisfactory to him a report on those matters of the business and affairs of the Association that the Minister requires.

(4) The Minister shall, upon receipt of the annual report of the Association, lay it before the Legislative Assembly if it is then sitting, and if it is not then sitting, within 15 days after the commencement of the next ensuing sitting.

Registrar

13 The Council shall appoint a Registrar for the purposes of this Act.

Council
members

14(1) Subject to subsection (2), the Council shall include the president, 2 vice-presidents, the immediate past-president and at least 12 other professional members, the number of which shall be prescribed by the by-laws, each of whom shall be elected by the professional members at the time, in the manner and for the period provided for in the by-laws.

(2) The Council shall consist of

    (a)   at least 16 professional members among whom there shall be not less than
        (i)   2 professional engineers,
        (ii)   2 professional geologists, and
        (iii)   1 professional geophysicist, and

(b) when the total number of elected professional members does not exceed 20, 2 members of the public, or when the total number of elected professional members is more than 20 but not more than 30, 3 members of the public, who shall be appointed by the Minister, after consultation with the Association, for a 1 year term of office.

(3) A member of the Council appointed under subsection (2)(b) continues to hold office after the expiry of his term of office until he is reappointed or his successor is appointed.

(4) The Minister may, after consultation with the Council, revoke the appointment of a member of the Council made under subsection (2)(b).

(5) The Minister may pay to a member of the Council appointed under subsection (2)(b) travelling and living expenses incurred by that member for his attendance at any meeting of the Council while away from his usual place of residence and fees in an amount prescribed by the Minister.

(6) The powers, duties and operations of the Council under this Act, the regulations and the by-laws are not affected by

(a) the fact that no member of the public is appointed as a member of the Council pursuant to subsection (2)(b),

(b) the revocation of the appointment of a member of the public, or

(c) the resignation from the Council of a member of the public.

(7) The failure of a member of the public appointed pursuant to subsection (2)(b) to attend a meeting of the Council shall not be construed to affect or restrict the Council from exercising at that meeting any powers or performing any duties under this Act, the regulations or the by-laws.

15(1) There is hereby established a board called the Practice Review Board consisting of not less than 5 members as follows:

Practice Review Board

(a) the Council shall appoint not less than 4 professional members who have a combination of knowledge and experience suitable for determining the academic qualifications and experience necessary for a person to continue to engage in the practice of the profession of engineering, geology or geophysics;

(b) the Minister shall appoint 1 member of the public nominated by the Council.

(2) If the Council fails, within a reasonable period of time after being requested to do so by the Minister, to make a nomination for the purposes of subsection (1)(b), the Minister may appoint a member of the public to the Practice Review Board without the Council's nomination.

(3) The Minister may pay to the member of the Board appointed under subsection (1)(b) travelling and living expenses incurred by that member for attendance at a hearing of the Board away from his usual place of residence and fees in an amount prescribed by the Minister.

(4) The Minister may, after consultation with the Council, revoke the appointment under subsection (1)(b) of a member of the public.

(5) The powers, duties and operations of the Board under this Act, the regulations and by-laws are not affected by

- (a) the fact that no member of the public is appointed as a member of the Board pursuant to subsection (1)(b),
- (b) the revocation under subsection (4) of the appointment of a member of the public, or
- (c) the resignation as a member of the Board of a member of the public.

(6) The failure of a member of the public appointed under subsection (1)(b) to attend a meeting of the Board shall not be construed to affect or restrict the Board from exercising any powers or performing any duties under this Act, the regulations or the by-laws at that meeting.

Powers of
the Practice
Review
Board

16(1) The Practice Review Board

- (a) shall, on its own initiative or at the request of the Council, inquire into
  - (i) the assessment of existing and the development of new educational standards and experience requirements that are conditions precedent to obtaining and continuing registration under this Act,
  - (ii) the evaluation of desirable standards of competence of professional members, licensees, permit holders and certificate holders generally,
  - (iii) the practice of the profession by professional members, licensees, permit holders or certificate holders generally, and
  - (iv) any other matter that the Council from time to time considers necessary or appropriate in connection with the exercise of its powers and the

performance of its duties in relation to competence in the practice of the profession under this Act and the regulations, and

(b) may, with the approval of the Council, conduct a review of the practice of a professional member, licensee, permit holder or certificate holder in accordance with this Act and the regulations.

(2) The Board shall report to and advise the Council with respect to any matter dealt with by it pursuant to subsection (1).

(3) A person requested to appear at an inquiry under this section by the Board is entitled to be represented by counsel.

(4) The Board may, after a review under this section with respect to an individual practitioner, make any order that the Discipline Committee may make under section 60 or 61.

(5) The provisions of Part 5 with respect to an investigation and hearing by the Discipline Committee apply to a review of an individual practitioner by the Practice Review Board.

(6) The Board may at any time during an inquiry or review under this section recommend to the Discipline Committee that the inquiry or review be conducted by the Discipline Committee pursuant to Part 5.

(7) On receiving a recommendation under subsection (6) the Discipline Committee may proceed with an investigation and hearing under Part 5 as if the recommendation were a written complaint.

(8) After each inquiry under this section the Board shall make a written report to the Council on the inquiry and may make any recommendations to the Council that the Board considers appropriate in connection with the matter inquired into, with reasons for the recommendations.

(9) The Council may, if it considers it to be in the public interest to do so, direct that the whole or any portion of an inquiry by the Board under this section shall be held in camera.

17 A professional member, licensee, permit holder or certificate holder who is the subject of a hearing or a review by the Practice Review Board may appeal any decision or order of the Board to the Council as if it were a decision or order of the Discipline Committee under Part 5.

Appeal to Council

275

PART 3
REGULATIONS AND BY-LAWS

18(1) The Council may make regulations

(a) respecting the establishment of categories of and conditions respecting the enrolment of engineers-in-training, geologists-in-training, geophysicists-in-training, examination candidates and students;

(b) respecting the academic qualifications of and experience requirements for applicants for registration as professional engineers, geologists or geophysicists;

(c) governing the evaluation by the Council, the Board of Examiners, the Practice Review Board or a committee established by any of them of the academic qualifications of and experience requirements for applicants for registration to engage in the practice of engineering, geology or geophysics and the examination of those applicants with respect to those qualifications or requirements;

(d) respecting the eligibility of applicants generally for registration to engage in the practice of engineering, geology or geophysics;

(e) respecting the powers, duties and functions of the Practice Review Board, including but not limited to the referral of matters by that Board to the Council or the Discipline Committee and appeals from decisions of that Board;

(e.1) prescribing the number of members that constitutes a quorum of the Council, the Practice Review Board, the Board of Examiners or the Discipline Committee;

(f) governing the establishment of boards or committees of professional members and respecting the delegation of powers of the Council to those boards or committees or the Practice Review Board;

(g) prescribing technical standards for the practice of the profession;

(h) establishing and providing for the publication of a code of ethics respecting the practice of the profession, the maintenance of the dignity and honour of the profession and the protection of the public interest;

(i) governing the names under which professional members, licensees, permit holders and certificate holders may engage in the practice of the profession;

(j) governing, subject to this Act, the operation and proceedings of the Board of Examiners and the Practice Review Board, the designation of chairman and vice-chairman, the appointment of acting members and the procedures for filling vacancies in the offices of chairman and vice-chairman and in the membership of either Board, and the appointment of ex officio members of either Board and prescribing their powers, duties and functions;

(k) respecting the procedures of the Discipline Committee, of the Practice Review Board and of the Council in matters relating to the conduct or practice of professional members, licensees, permit holders or certificate holders, whether or not a complaint has been made;

(l) respecting the establishment by the Council of a compulsory continuing education program for professional members and licensees;

(m) governing the publication of a notice of the suspension or cancellation of the registration of a professional member, licensee, permit holder or certificate holder in a form and manner prescribed by the Council;

(n) respecting committees of inquiry for reinstatement under Part 5;

(n.1) for the purposes of sections 2(4), 5(2) and 7(2),
  (i) designating a class of persons as technicians or technologists, and
  (ii) defining technician and technologist;

(o) establishing classes or categories of professional engineers, geologists or geophysicists and licensees or permit holders and prescribing the restrictions of practice and the privileges and obligations of the classes or categories so established;

(p) respecting the use of stamps and seals;

(q) governing the eligibility for registration of persons, firms, partnerships and other entities as permit holders or certificate holders;

(r) governing the operation of permit holders or certificate holders;

(s) governing the publication of information with respect to the profession including but not limited to the publication of surveys of fees;

277

(t) respecting registration, licensing, the issuing of permits and certificates, disciplinary matters and the practice of engineering, geology and geophysics generally.

(2) A regulation under subsection (1) does not come into force unless it has been approved by

(a) a majority of the professional members
 (i) present and voting at a general meeting, or
 (ii) voting in a mail vote conducted in accordance with the by-laws,

and

(b) the Lieutenant Governor in Council.

19(1) The Council may make by-laws

(a) for the government of the Association and the management and conduct of its affairs;

(b) determining the location of the head office of the Association;

(c) respecting the calling of and conduct of meetings of the Association and the Council;

(d) respecting the nomination, election, number and term of office of Council members and officers of the Association and the appointment of individuals as ex officio members of the Council, the Discipline Committee, the Practice Review Board, the Board of Examiners and any other committee established by the Council and prescribing their powers, duties and functions;

(d.1) prescribing those areas of the professions of engineering, geology and geophysics from which members of the Board of Examiners shall be appointed by the Council;

(e) respecting the appointment, functions, duties and powers of an Executive Director of the Association;

(f) respecting the establishment of divisions and sections of the Association and their operation;

(g) providing for the division of Alberta into electoral districts and prescribing the number of Council members to be elected from each district;

(h) providing for the appointment of an Acting Registrar who has all of the powers and can perform all of the duties of the Registrar under this Act, the regulations and the by-laws when the Registrar is absent, or unable to act or when there is a vacancy in the office of Registrar;

(i) establishing classes or categories of membership in the Association in addition to professional engineers, professional geologists and professional geophysicists and prescribing the rights, privileges and obligations of the classes or categories of membership so established;

(j) providing for the appointment of acting members of the Council and procedures for the election or appointment of professional members to fill vacancies on the Council;

(k) prescribing the number of professional members that constitutes a quorum at meetings of the Association;

(l) governing the establishment, operation and proceedings of committees, the appointment of members of committees, the appointment of acting members and procedures for filling vacancies on committees and the delegation of any powers or duties of the Council under the Act, regulations or by-laws to a committee established by the Council or under this Act;

(m) prescribing fees and expenses payable to members of the Association for attending to the business of the Association;

(n) respecting the establishment and payment of sums of money for scholarships, fellowships and any other educational incentive or benefit program that the Council considers appropriate;

(o) governing the information to be engraved on stamps and seals by professional members, licensees, permit holders and certificate holders;

(p) respecting the fixing of fees, dues and levies payable to the Association;

(q) respecting the costs payable by any person on the conclusion of a hearing or review by the Practice Review Board or under Part 5;

(r) respecting the establishment, content and maintenance of registers of professional members, licensees, permit holders and certificate holders and of records of other classes or categories of membership to be kept by the Registrar;

279

(s) respecting the removal from the registers and records of any memorandum or entry made in them under this Act or the by-laws;

(t) requiring professional members, licensees, permit holders and certificate holders to inform the Registrar in writing of their current mailing addresses and of any change of address forthwith after the change occurs;

(u) prescribing the form of a certificate of registration, a licence, a permit, a certificate of authorization and an annual certificate.

(2) The Council may make by-laws respecting the holding of mail votes on any matter relating to the Association, but a by-law under this subsection does not come into force unless it is approved by a majority of professional members of the Association present and voting at a general meeting.

(3) A by-law under subsection (1) does not come into force unless it is approved by a majority of the professional members

(a) present and voting at a general meeting, or

(b) voting by a mail vote conducted in accordance with the by-laws.

(4) *The Regulations Act* does not apply to by-laws of the Association made under this section.

PART 4
REGISTRATION

Registers and membership records

20(1) The Registrar shall maintain, in accordance with the by-laws and subject to the direction of the Council, a register for each of the following:

(a) professional engineers;

(b) professional geologists;

(c) professional geophysicists;

(d) licensees to engage in the practice of
(i) professional engineering,
(ii) professional geology, or
(iii) professional geophysics;

(e) permit holders to engage in the practice of
(i) professional engineering,
(ii) professional geology, or
(iii) professional geophysics;

(f)   joint firms;

(g)   restricted practitioners.

(2) The Registrar shall enter in the appropriate register the name of a person who has paid the fee prescribed under the by-laws, and

(a)   whose registration to engage in the practice of
(i)   engineering, as a professional engineer or licensee,
(ii)   geology, as a professional geologist or licensee, or
(iii) geophysics, as a professional geophysicist or licensee

has been approved by the Board of Examiners,

(b)   whose registration to engage in the practice of the profession as a permit holder has been approved by the Council, or

(c)   whose registration to engage in the practice of engineering has been approved
(i)   in the case of a joint firm, by the Council, or
(ii)   in the case of a restricted practitioner, in accordance with section 36.

(3) The Registrar shall maintain, in accordance with the by-laws and subject to the direction of the Council, a membership record of the members in each class or category of membership established under the regulations and the by-laws.

21 The Board of Examiners shall approve for registration as a professional engineer, professional geologist or professional geophysicist an individual who has applied to the Board and is eligible in accordance with this Act and the regulations to become a professional engineer, geologist or geophysicist, as the case may be. Registration as professional member

22 The Board of Examiners shall approve the registration as a licensee of an individual who has applied to the Board of Examiners and is eligible in accordance with this Act and the regulations to become registered to engage in the practice of engineering, geology or geophysics as a licensee. Registration as licensee

23(1) The Council shall approve the registration as a permit holder of a partnership or other association of persons, or of a corporation incorporated or registered under *The Companies Act*, that has applied to the Council and is eligible under this section and the regulations to become registered to engage in the practice of engineering, geology or geophysics as a permit holder. Registration of permit holders

(2) A partnership or other association of persons or a corporation that applies to the Council is eligible to become registered as a permit holder entitled to engage in the practice of engineering, geology or geophysics if it satisfies the Council that it complies with the Act and the regulations.

24(1) On entering the name of a professional engineer, geologist or geophysicist in the register, the Registrar shall issue to him

(a) a certificate of registration, and

(b) a stamp or seal engraved as prescribed in the by-laws.

(2) On entering the name of a licensee in the register, the Registrar shall issue to him

(a) a licence to engage in the practice of engineering, geology or geophysics as a licensee as authorized in the licence, and

(b) a stamp or seal engraved as prescribed in the by-laws.

(3) On entering the name of a permit holder in the register, the Registrar shall issue to it

(a) a permit to engage in the practice of engineering, geology or geophysics as a permit holder as authorized in the permit, and

(b) a stamp or seal engraved as prescribed in the by-laws.

(4) On entering the name of a joint firm in the register, the Registrar shall issue to it

(a) a certificate of authorization to engage in the practice of engineering and architecture, and

(b) a stamp engraved as prescribed in the by-laws.

(5) On entering the name of a restricted practitioner in the register, the Registrar shall issue to that individual a certificate of authorization to engage in the restricted scope of the practice of engineering that is specified in the certificate.

(6) A certificate of registration, a licence, a permit or a certificate of authorization issued under this section entitles the holder to engage in the practice of engineering, geology or geophysics, as the case may be, subject to this Act, the regulations and by-laws.

25(1) A professional member, licensee, permit holder or certificate holder engaged in the practice of engineering, geology or geophysics shall pay to the Association the annual fee prescribed under the by-laws.

(2) The Registrar shall issue an annual certificate in accord-

ance with the by-laws to a professional member, licensee, permit holder or certificate holder

(a) whose registration is not under suspension, and

(b) who has paid the annual fee.

(3) Subject to this Act, an annual certificate entitles the professional member, licensee, permit holder or certificate holder to engage in the practice of engineering, geology or geophysics, as the case may be, during the year for which the annual certificate is issued.

(4) An annual certificate expires on December 31 of the year for which it is issued.

26(1) The registration of a professional member, licensee, permit holder or certificate holder is suspended when the decision to suspend the registration is made in accordance with this Act.

Entries in registers

(2) The Registrar shall enter a memorandum of suspension of a registration in the appropriate register indicating

(a) the duration of the suspension, and

(b) the reason for the suspension.

(3) The registration of a professional member, licensee, permit holder or certificate holder is cancelled when the decision to cancel the registration is made in accordance with this Act.

(4) The Registrar shall enter a memorandum of cancellation of registration in the appropriate register.

(5) The Registrar shall not remove from the registers any memorandum made by him under this section, except in accordance with the by-laws.

27 The Registrar shall maintain and, during regular office hours, permit any person to inspect a list of all the professional members, licensees, permit holders and certificate holders in good standing.

List of registrants open to the public

28(1) The Registrar shall not cancel the registration of a professional member, licensee, permit holder or certificate holder at his request unless the request for the cancellation has been approved by the Council.

Cancellation on request

(2) When the request for cancellation of a registration is approved by the Council

(a) the Registrar shall cancel that registration, and

(b) the professional member, licensee, permit holder or

283

certificate holder requesting the cancellation shall, on being notified of the approval, surrender to the Registrar the certificate of registration, licence, permit, annual certificate and the stamp or seal issued by the Registrar.

Board of
Examiners

29(1) The Council shall establish a Board of Examiners in accordance with the regulations.

(2) The Board of Examiners shall consider applications for the registration of applicants as professional members or licensees in accordance with this Part, the regulations and by-laws and may

    (a)   approve the registration,

    (b)   refuse the registration, or

    (c)   defer the approval of registration until it is satisfied that the applicant has complied with a requirement made under this section.

(3) The Board of Examiners may, in its discretion, require an applicant for registration

    (a)   to pass 1 or more examinations set by the Board,

    (b)   to obtain more experience of a kind satisfactory to the Board for a period set by the Board, or

    (c)   to pass 1 or more examinations and obtain more experience

before approving the registration.

Approval by
the Board of
Examiners

30(1) The Board of Examiners shall approve the registration as a professional member of a person who proves to the satisfaction of the Board that

    (a)   he is of good character and reputation,

    (b)   he is a resident of Alberta,

    (c)   he is a Canadian citizen or lawfully admitted to Canada for permanent residence, and

    (d)   his education and his experience meet the requirements of the regulations and by-laws.

(2) The Board of Examiners shall approve the registration as a licensee of a person who proves to the satisfaction of the Board that he is

    (a)   a resident of Alberta but is not a Canadian citizen or lawfully admitted to Canada for permanent residence, or

    (b)   a resident outside Alberta

and otherwise complies with the provisions of subsection (1).

31(1) The Board of Examiners shall send a written notice of any decision made by it under this Part to the applicant.

Review by
the Council

(2) If the decision made by the Board is to refuse or defer registration of the applicant, reasons for the decision shall be sent in writing to the applicant.

(3) If the decision made by the Board is to approve the registration, the Registrar shall publish a notice of approval in accordance with the by-laws.

(4) An applicant whose application for registration has been refused by the Board of Examiners may, within 30 days of receiving a notice of refusal and the reasons for the refusal, request the Council to review the application by serving on the Registrar a written request for review by the Council setting out the reasons why, in his opinion, his registration as a professional member or licensee should be approved.

(5) The Council shall, after receipt of a request for review under this section, review the application.

(6) The applicant for registration

(a) shall be notified in writing by the Council of the date, place and time that it will consider the matter, and

(b) is entitled to appear with counsel and make representations to the Council when it considers the matter.

(7) A member of the Board of Examiners who is also a member of the Council may participate at a review by the Council under this section but shall not vote in a decision of the Council at a review under this section.

(8) On hearing a review under this section, the Council may make any decision the Board of Examiners may make under this Part.

32(1) In this section and sections 33 and 34,

Joint firms

(a) "Architects Association" means The Alberta Association of Architects under *The Architects Act, 1980*;

(b) "architects firm" means a partnership or corporation
  (i) that
    (A) confines its practice to providing architectural consulting services, or
    (B) if it does not confine its practice to providing architectural consulting services, engages in a practice satisfactory to the Joint Board,

285

and

    (ii) in which registered architects

        (A) hold a majority interest, and

        (B) control the partnership or corporation,

and that is otherwise entitled to engage in the practice of architecture under *The Architects Act, 1980*;

  (c)   "engineers firm" means a partnership or corporation

    (i)   that

        (A) confines it practice to providing engineering consulting services, or

        (B) if it does not confine its practice to providing engineering consulting services, engages in a practice satisfactory to the Joint Board,

and

    (ii) in which professional engineers

        (A) hold a majority interest, and

        (B) control the partnership or corporation,

and that is otherwise entitled to engage in the practice of engineering under this Act;

  (d)   "proposed engineers and architects firm" means a partnership or corporation

    (i)   that

        (A) proposes to confine its practice to providing engineering consulting services and architectural consulting services, or

        (B) if it does not propose to confine its practice to providing engineering consulting services and architectural consulting services, proposes to engage in a practice satisfactory to the Joint Board,

and

    (ii) in which professional engineers and registered architects

        (A) hold a majority interest, and

        (B) control the partnership or corporation,

and that is otherwise entitled to engage in the practice of engineering under this Act or the practice of architecture under *The Architects Act, 1980*.

(2) An application for a certificate of authorization may be made by the following:

  (a)   a professional engineer;

  (b)   a registered architect;

(c)　　an engineers firm;

(d)　　an architects firm;

(e)　　a proposed engineers and architects firm;

(f)　　a partnership or corporation that is not referred to in clauses (c), (d) or (e) that the Joint Board considers a suitable applicant for a certificate of authorization.

(3) An applicant under subsection (2) shall

(a)　　if its prime activity is the provision of engineering consulting services, apply to the Council, and

(b)　　if its prime activity is the provision of architectural consulting services, apply to the council of the Architects Association.

33(1) Every application under section 32 shall be referred to the Joint Board by the council to which it was made, with or without comment from that council.

Approval by
Joint Board

(2) The Joint Board shall consider with respect to each application referred to it whether

(a)　　the applicant is eligible to apply under section 32(2);

(b)　　the applicant has at least 1 full time employee who is a professional engineer who shall take responsibility for the engineering work of the applicant and at least 1 full time employee who is a registered architect who shall take reponsibility for the architectural work of the applicant;

(c)　　the presence of any ownership interests in the applicant will give rise to conflicts with the professional responsibilities of the firm;

(d)　　the granting of a certificate of authorization to the applicant will give rise to unauthorized practice or otherwise lead to circumvention of this Act or *The Architects Act, 1980*;

(e)　　any detriment to the public would result from the applicant becoming entitled to engage in the practice of both engineering and architecture.

(3) After considering an application for a certificate of authorization referred to it, the Joint Board shall recommend

(a)　　in the case of an application by a registered architect or architects firm, to the Council,

(b)　　in the case of an application by a professional engineer or an engineers firm, to the council of the Architects Association, or

287

(c)　in the case of an application by a proposed engineers and architects firm or other applicant, to the Council and to the council of the Architects Association,

whether or not to grant a certificate of authorization, based on the criteria considered by it under subsection (2).

Registration of joint firm

34(1) On receipt of a recommendation of the Joint Board under section 33 the Council may approve the registration of a proposed engineers and architects firm if that firm is eligible to become registered under the regulations.

(2) When recommendations are made by the Joint Board to both the Council and the council of the Architects Association with respect to an application for a certificate of authorization, both councils must agree that the certificate should be issued and both shall sign the certificate before it is issued.

(3) Subject to subsection (2), an applicant is entitled to be registered as a joint firm when the Council approves its registration.

Duties of joint firm

35(1) A joint firm may engage in the practice of both engineering and architecture in

(a)　the names of the individuals who are its partners,

(b)　its corporate name, or

(c)　any other name that is approved by the Council pursuant to the by-laws.

(2) A joint firm shall advise the Registrar in writing of

(a)　the names of the individual shareholders, directors and officers of the firm,

(b)　the names of the employees who are professional engineers and registered architects, and

(c)　of any change in those shareholders, directors, officers or employees forthwith after the change occurs.

(3) When a joint firm causes plans, drawings, detail drawings and specifications prepared in its practice of engineering to be signed by its proper officers and imprinted with the stamp issued to the firm, it shall also cause them to be signed by and imprinted with the stamp or seal of the professional engineer who had supervision and control over their preparation.

Restricted practitioner

36(1) The Joint Board may recommend to the Council that a certificate of authorization be issued to an individual who is a registered architect who

(a)　has historically competently provided a service in the

practice of professional engineering in Alberta, and

(b) applies for the certificate within 1 year after the date of the coming into force of section 21.1 of *The Department of Housing and Public Works Act.*

(2) On receipt of a recommendation under subsection (1) the Council may approve the registration of an individual who has applied to the Council and is eligible under the by-laws to become registered as a restricted practitioner.

(3) If the Council approves the registration of an individual as a restricted practitioner, it shall specify in the certificate and in the register the restricted scope of the practice of engineering in which the individual is permitted to engage.

37 On the recommendation of the Joint Board, the Council may authorize an individual who is a registered architect under *The Architects Act, 1980* to apply for a permit under *The Alberta Uniform Building Standards Act* for a building of a type described in section 4.4 of *The Alberta Uniform Building Standards Act* without the final design drawings and specifications of the building having the seal of a professional engineer.

Exemption from seal requirement

38(1) The Council may direct the Registrar to cancel the registration of

Cancellation

(a) a professional member, licensee or permit holder who is in default of payment of annual fees or any other fees, dues or levies payable under this Act, or

(b) a permit holder if it no longer has employees in compliance with this Act

after the expiration of 30 days following the service on the professional member, licensee or permit holder of a written notice by the Council pursuant to subsection (2), unless the professional member, licensee or permit holder on whom the notice is served complies with the notice.

(2) The notice under subsection (1) shall state that the Registrar may cancel the registration unless

(a) the fees, due or levies are paid as indicated in that notice, or

(b) evidence satisfactory to the Council has been received by it within the time prescribed in the notice indicating that the permit holder has employees in compliance with this Act.

(3) The Council may direct the Registrar to cancel the regis-

tration of a professional member, licensee or permit holder that was entered in error in the register.

(4) If the registration of a professional member, licensee or permit holder has been cancelled under this section, he shall forthwith surrender to the Registrar any certificate of registration, licence, permit, stamp or seal issued to him.

(5) If a registration has been cancelled pursuant to subsection (1), the Council may direct the Registrar, subject to any conditions that the Council may prescribe, to reinstate that registration in the applicable register and reissue the certificate of registration, licence or permit and the stamp or seal.

(6) Notwithstanding subsection (5), if a person applies to the Council to be reinstated more than 7 years after the date on which his registration was cancelled, the Council shall not direct the Registrar to reinstate him.

(7) Notwithstanding subsection (6), a person whose registration has been cancelled under this section may make an application to the Board of Examiners for registration as a professional member or licensee.

Cancellation of a joint firm

39(1) The Council may direct the Registrar to cancel the registration of a joint firm that

    (a)   is in default of payment of annual fees or any other fees, dues or levies payable under this Act, or

    (b)   ceases to have at least 1 professional engineer and at least 1 registered architect to take the reponsibility referred to in section 33(2)(b)

after the expiration of 1 month following the service on the joint firm of a written notice that the Council intends to cancel the registration, unless the joint firm on which the notice is served complies with the notice.

(2) The notice under subsection (1) shall state that the Registrar may cancel the registration unless

    (a)   the fees, dues or levies are paid as indicated in the notice, or

    (b)   the joint firm has at least 1 professional engineer and at least 1 registered architect to take the responsibility referred to in section 33(2)(b).

(3) If the registration of a joint firm has been cancelled under this section, the joint firm shall forthwith surrender to the Registrar the certificate of authorization and stamp issued to it.

(4) The Council may direct the Registrar, subject to any

conditions that the Council may prescribe, to reinstate the joint firm in the applicable register and to reissue the certificate of authorization and stamp.

40(1) The Council may direct the Registrar to cancel the registration of a restricted practitioner who

(a) is in default of payment of annual fees or any other fees, dues or levies payable under this Act, or

(b) who is not a registered architect in good standing under *The Architects Act, 1980*,

after the expiration of 1 month following the service on the restricted practitioner of a written notice that the Council intends to cancel the registration unless the restricted practitioner on whom the notice is served complies with the notice.

(2) The notice under subsection (1) shall state that the Registrar may cancel the registration unless

(a) the fees, dues or levies are paid as indicated in the notice, or

(b) the restricted practitioner is a registered architect in good standing under *The Architects Act, 1980*.

(3) If registration of a restricted practitioner has been cancelled under this section, the restricted practitioner shall forthwith surrender to the Registrar the certificate of authorization and the stamp issued to it.

(4) The Council may direct the Registrar, subject to any condition that the Council may prescribe, to reinstate the restricted practitioner in the applicable register and to reissue the certificate of authorization and the stamp.

PART 5
DISCIPLINE

41 In this Part,

(a) "conduct" includes an act or omission;

(b) "investigated person" means a professional member, licensee, permit holder, certificate holder or member-in-training with respect to whose conduct an investigation is held under this Part, and

(c) "practice of the profession" means practice of engineering practice of geology or practice of geophysics, as the case may be.

291

42(1) A person may complain to the Registrar about the conduct of a professional member, licensee, permit holder, certificate holder or member-in-training, and the complaint shall be dealt with in accordance with this Part and the regulations.

(2) A complaint respecting the conduct of a professional member, licensee, permit holder or certificate holder whose registration was cancelled pursuant to this Act may, notwithstanding the cancellation, be dealt with within 2 years following the date of cancellation of the registration as if the cancellation had not occurred.

(3) Notwithstanding section 45, a person designated by the Registrar as a mediator may assist in settling a complaint if the complainant and the person about whose conduct the complaint was made agree, but if within 30 days from the date of receipt of the complaint or a longer period agreed to by those persons a settlement of the complaint between those persons does not occur, or in the mediator's opinion is not likely to occur, the complaint shall be referred forthwith by the mediator to the Discipline Committee.

Determination of unprofessional conduct and unskilled practice

43(1) Any conduct of a professional member, licensee, permit holder, certificate holder or member-in-training that in the opinion of the Discipline Committee or the Council

(a) is detrimental to the best interests of the public,

(b) contravenes a code of ethics of the profession as established under the regulations,

(c) harms or tends to harm the standing of the profession generally,

(d) displays a lack of knowledge of or lack of skill or judgment in the practice of the profession, or

(e) displays a lack of knowledge of or lack of skill or judgment in the carrying out of any duty or obligation undertaken in the practice of the profession,

whether or not that conduct is disgraceful or dishonourable, constitutes either unskilled practice of the profession or unprofessional conduct, whichever the Discipline Committee finds.

(2) If an investigated person fails to comply with or contravenes this Act, the regulations or the by-laws, and the failure or contravention is, in the opinion of the Discipline Committee, of a serious nature, the failure or contravention may be found by the Discipline Committee to be unprofessional conduct whether or not it would be so found under subsection (1).

44(1) The Council shall establish a Discipline Committee the members of which shall be appointed in accordance with the regulations.

(2) The Council shall make regulations governing, subject to this Part, the operation and proceedings of the Discipline Committee, the designation of a chairman, the appointment of acting members and the procedures of filling vacancies in the offices of chairman and the membership and the appointment of ex officio members, and prescribing their powers, duties and functions.

(3) A regulation made under subsection (2) does not come into force unless it has been approved by the Lieutenant Governor in Council.

45 The Discipline Committee or a person appointed by it shall forthwith upon the receipt of a complaint appoint a person to conduct a preliminary investigation with respect to the matter.

46 The Registrar shall forthwith send notice in writing to the investigated person that a preliminary investigation is being conducted.

47(1) A person conducting a preliminary investigation may

(a) require the investigated person to produce to him any plans, drawings, detailed drawings, specifications, reports, books, papers or other documents or records in the investigated person's possession or under his control, and

(b) copy and keep copies for the purposes of this Part of any of the documents or records that are produced to him.

(2) A person conducting a preliminary investigation into the conduct of a professional member, licensee, permit holder, certificate holder or member-in-training may investigate any other matter regarding the conduct of the investigated person that arises in the course of the investigation.

48 The person conducting a preliminary investigation shall, forthwith on concluding the preliminary investigation, report his findings to the Discipline Committee.

49(1) The Discipline Committee may terminate the investigation at any time if it is of the opinion that the complaint is frivolous or vexatious.

(2) On terminating an investigation the Discipline Committee shall direct the Registrar to serve on the investigated person and

on the complainant, if any, a notice in accordance with the by-laws that the investigation has been terminated.

(3) A complainant who is served with a notice under subsection (2) informing him that the investigation has been terminated may, by notice in writing to the Registrar within 30 days of receipt of the notice under subsection (2), appeal that decision to the Council.

(4) On an appeal under subsection (3), the Council shall determine whether the complaint

(a)   is frivolous or vexatious, or

(b)   should be referred to the Discipline Committee for a hearing in accordance with this Part,

and shall notify the complainant, the investigated person and the Discipline Committee in writing of its decision.

Duty of Discipline Committee

50(1) If the investigation is not terminated under section 49, the Discipline Committee shall hold a hearing into the complaint forthwith.

(2) The Registrar shall serve on the investigated person and on the complainant, if any, a notice of hearing stating the date, time and place at which the Discipline Committee will hold the hearing and giving reasonable particulars of the conduct or complaint in respect of which the hearing will be held.

Further investigation

51(1) The Discipline Committee may also investigate and hear any other matter concerning the conduct of the investigated person that arises in the course of the hearing, but in that event the Committee shall declare its intention to investigate and hear the further matter and shall permit the person sufficient opportunity to prepare his answer to the further matter.

(2) Sections 53 to 59 apply to an investigation and hearing of a further matter under subsection (1).

Suspension pending investigation and hearing

52 Notwithstanding anything in this Act, the Discipline Committee may suspend the registration of a professional member, licensee, permit holder, certificate holder or member-in-training pending a preliminary investigation of his conduct and a decision by the Discipline Committee as to that conduct.

Right to counsel and to appearance

53 The Association, the investigated person and the complainant, if any, may appear and be represented by counsel at a hearing before the Discipline Committee.

Proceedings in camera

294

54 All proceedings under this Part except those before the Court or the Court of Appeal shall be held in camera.

55(1) Evidence may be given before the Discipline Committee in any matter that the Committee considers appropriate, and the Committee is not bound by the rules of law respecting evidence applicable to judicial proceedings.

Evidence

(2) For the purposes of an investigation, hearing or review under this Act, the Registrar or any member of the Council, the Discipline Committee or the Practice Review Board is conferred with the power of a commissioner of oaths under *The Commissioners for Oaths Act*.

56(1) The investigated person and any other person who in the opinion of the Discipline Committee has knowledge of the complaint or any conduct being investigated is a compellable witness in any proceeding under this Part.

Witnesses and documents

(2) A witness may be examined on oath on all matters relevant to the investigation or hearing and shall not be excused from answering any question on the ground that the answer might

    (a)   tend to incriminate him,

    (b)   subject him to punishment under this Part, or

    (c)   tend to establish his liability
        (i)   to a civil proceeding at the instance of the Crown or of any other person, or
        (ii) to prosecution under any Act or regulations under any Act,

but if the answer so given tends to incriminate him, subjects him to punishment or tends to establish his liability, it shall not be used or received against him in any civil proceedings or in any proceedings under any other Act.

(3) For the purpose of obtaining the testimony of a witness who is out of Alberta, a judge of the Court on an application ex parte by the Association may direct the issuing of a commission for the obtaining of the evidence of the witness, and the commission shall be issued and the evidence taken pursuant to the Alberta Rules of Court.

57(1) The attendance of witnesses before the Discipline Committee and the production of plans, drawings, detail drawings, specifications, reports, books, papers and other documents or records may be enforced by a notice issued by the Registrar requiring the witness to attend and stating the date, time and place at which the witness is to attend and the plans, drawings, detail drawings, specifications, books, papers and other documents or records, if any, he is required to produce.

Enforcement of attendance and production of documents

(2) On the written request of the investigated person or of his

counsel or agent, the Registrar shall without charge issue and deliver to that person or his counsel or agent any notices that he may require for the attendance of witnesses or the production of documents or records.

(3) A witness other than the investigated person who has been served with a notice to attend or a notice for the production of documents or records under subsection (1) or (2) is entitled to be paid the same fees as are payable to witnesses in an action in the Court.

Failure to give evidence **58**(1) Proceedings for civil contempt of court may be brought against a witness

(a) who fails
(i)   to attend before the Discipline Committee in compliance with a notice to attend,
(ii) to produce any books, papers or other documents or records in compliance with a notice to produce them, or
(iii) in any way to comply with either notice,

or

(b) who refuses to be sworn or to answer any question directed to be answered by the Discipline Committee.

(2) If the witness referred to in subsection (1) is the investigated person, his failure or refusal may be held to be unprofessional conduct.

(3) The Discipline Committee, on proof of service of the notice of investigation on the investigated person and the complainant, if any, may

(a) proceed with the investigation in the absence of either or both of those persons, and

(b) act on the matter being investigated in the same way as though either or both of those persons were in attendance.

Finding by the Discipline Committee **59**(1) The Discipline Committee may find that the conduct of an investigated person constitutes neither unskilled practice of the profession nor unprofessional conduct.

(2) The Discipline Committee may find that the conduct of an investigated person constitutes unskilled practice of the profession or unprofessional conduct or both and shall deal with the investigated person in accordance with this Part.

Powers of the Discipline Committee **60** If the Discipline Committee finds that the conduct of the investigated person is unprofessional conduct or unskilled prac-

296

tice of the profession or both, the Discipline Committee may make any one or more of the following orders:

(a)   reprimand the investigated person;

(b)   suspend the registration of the investigated person for a specified period;

(c)   suspend the registration of the investigated person either generally or from any field of practice until
   (i)   he has completed a specified course of studies or obtained supervised practical experience, or
   (ii)   the Discipline Committee is satisfied as to the competence of the investigated person generally or in a specified field of practice;

(d)   accept in place of a suspension the investigated person's undertaking to limit his practice;

(e)   impose conditions on the investigated person's entitlement to engage in the practice of the profession generally or in any field of the practice, including the conditions that he
   (i)   practise under supervision,
   (ii)   not engage in sole practice,
   (iii)   permit periodic inspections by a person authorized by the Discipline Committee, or
   (iv)   report to the Discipline Committee on specific matters;

(f)   direct the investigated person to pass a particular course of study or satisfy the Discipline Committee as to his practical competence generally or in a field of practice;

(g)   direct the investigated person to satisfy the Discipline Committee that a disability or addiction can be or has been overcome, and suspend the person until the Discipline Committee is so satisfied;

(h)   require the investigated person to take counselling or to obtain any assistance that in the opinion of the Discipline Committee is appropriate;

(i)   direct the investigated person to waive, reduce or repay a fee for services rendered by the investigated person that, in the opinion of the Discipline Committee, were not rendered or were improperly rendered;

(j)   cancel the registration of the investigated person;

(k)   any other order that it considers appropriate in the circumstances.

297

Order to pay
costs or a
fine

61(1) The Discipline Committee may, in addition to or instead of dealing with the investigated person in accordance with section 60, order that the investigated person pay

(a) the costs of the hearing in accordance with the by-laws,

(b) a fine not exceeding $10 000 to the Association, or

(c) both the costs under clause (a) and a fine under clause (b),

within the time fixed by the order.

(2) If the investigated person ordered to pay a fine, costs or both under subsection (1) fails to pay the fine, costs or both within the time ordered, the Discipline Committee may suspend the registration of that person until he has paid the fine, costs or both.

(3) A fine or costs ordered to be paid to the Association under this section is a debt due to the Association and may be recovered by the Association by civil action for debt.

62(1) The Discipline Committee shall, within a reasonable time after the conclusion of a hearing, make a written decision on the matter, in which it shall

(a) describe each finding made in accordance with this Part,

(b) state the reasons for each finding made, and

(c) state any order made under this Part.

(2) The Discipline Committee shall immediately forward to the Registrar

(a) the decision, and

(b) the record of the hearing, consisting of all evidence presented before it, including
(i) all exhibits,
(ii) all documents and records, and
(iii) a transcript of all testimony given before it, whether recorded electronically, mechanically or in handwritten form.

(3) The Registrar shall, immediately on receiving the decision and the record of the hearing referred to in subsection (2), serve

(a) a copy of the decision on the investigated person, and

(b) a notice of the nature of the decision on the complain-ant, if any

(4) The investigated person or his counsel or agent may examine the record or any part of the record of the proceedings and hear any recording or examine any mechanical or handwritten form of record of any testimony.

63(1) Notwithstanding an appeal under this Part, the Discipline Committee may order that its decision remain in effect until the time that the Council, the Court or the Court of Appeal, as the case may be, makes its decision on the appeal.

Suspension or cancellation pending appeal

(2) An investigated person may, by filing an originating notice with the Court and serving a copy on the Registrar, apply for an order of the Court staying the decision of the Discipline Committee pending the determination of the appeal.

(3) The Court may hear an application made under this section not less than 10 days after the originating notice has been served on the Registrar.

(4) On hearing an application made under this section the Court may, subject to any conditions that it considers proper, stay the decision of the Discipline Committee pending the determination of the appeal.

64(1) An investigated person may appeal to the Council

Appeal to Council

    (a)   a finding made by a Discipline Committee in accordance with section 59,

    (b)   any order of the Discipline Committee under section 60 or 61, or

    (c)   a finding referred to in clause (a) and an order referred to in clause (b).

(2) An appeal under subsection (1) shall be commenced by a written notice of appeal that shall

    (a)   describe the finding or order appealed from,

    (b)   state the reasons for the appeal, and

    (c)   be served on the Registrar not more than 30 days after the date that the decision of the Discipline Committee was served on the investigated person.

(3) The Registrar shall, on receiving a notice of appeal under subsection (2), give the Council a copy of the notice of appeal and make the record of the hearing available to each member of the Council.

65(1) The Council, on receiving a notice of appeal under section 64, shall serve on the investigated person a notice of

Time of appeal

hearing of an appeal stating the date, time and place that the Council will hear the matters appealed.

(2) The Council shall hear an appeal forthwith.

Powers of the Council on appeal

66(1) A member of the Discipline Committee who is also a member of the Council may participate in an appeal before the Council but shall not vote in a decision of the Council on the appeal.

(2) The Council on an appeal may do any or all of the following:

    (a)   grant adjournments of the proceedings or reserve the determination of the matters before it for a future meeting of the Council;

    (b)   receive further evidence on granting special leave for that purpose;

    (c)   draw inferences of fact and make a determination or finding that in its opinion ought to have been made by the Discipline Committee;

    (d)   order that the matter be referred back to the Discipline Committee.

(3) Sections 53 to 59, 62 and 63 apply to the hearing of an appeal by the Council.

(4) The Council shall forthwith after the date of the conclusion of all proceedings before it,

    (a)   make any findings as to the conduct of the investigated person that in its opinion ought to have been made by the Discipline Committee,

    (b)   quash, vary or confirm the finding or order of the Discipline Committee or substitute or make a finding or order of its own, or

    (c)   refer the matter back to the Discipline Committee for further consideration in accordance with any direction that the Council may make.

(5) The Council may order the investigated person to pay the costs of the appeal determined in accordance with the by-laws.

Appeal to the Court

67(1) An investigated person may appeal to the Court on mixed questions of law and fact relating to any finding or order made by the Council under section 66.

(2) The Association shall be the respondent in an appeal under subsection (1) and may make representations to the Court.

(3) An appeal under this section shall be commenced.

    (a)   by filing an originating notice with the clerk of the Court, and

    (b)   by serving a copy of the originating notice on the Registrar,

both within 30 days from the date that the decision of the Council is served on the investigated person.

(4) An appeal under this section shall be dealt with by the Court as a new trial.

68(1) An investigated person may appeal to the Court of Appeal on a question of law relating to any finding or order made by the Council under section 66.

(2) The Association shall be the respondent in an appeal under subsection (1) and may make representations to the Court of Appeal.

(3) An appeal under this section shall be commenced

    (a)   by filing a notice of appeal with the Registrar of the Court of Appeal in Edmonton or Calgary, and

    (b)   by serving a copy of the notice of appeal on the Registrar,

both within 30 days from the date on which the decision of the Council is served on the investigated person.

69 The appellant may, after commencing an appeal and on notice to the Registrar, apply to the Court or the Court of Appeal, as the case may be, for an order staying all or any part of the order or decision of the Council appealed.

70(1) An appeal under section 67 or 68 shall be supported by copies, certified by the Registrar, of the decision of the Council and the record of the appeal before the Council.

(2) The Registrar, on being paid any disbursements and expenses in connection with a request made by the appellant or his solicitor or agent, shall furnish to the appellant or his solicitor or agent the number of copies so requested of the documents mentioned in subsection (1).

71(1) The Court or the Court of Appeal on hearing the appeal may do any or all of the following:

    (a)   make any finding that in its opinion ought to have been made;

(b) quash, confirm or vary the order or decision of the Council or any part of it;

(c) refer the matter back to the Council for further consideration in accordance with any direction of the Court or the Court of Appeal.

(2) The Court or the Court of Appeal may make any awards as to the costs of an appeal to it that it considers appropriate.

Fraudulent registration **72**(1) If the Council is satisfied, after a hearing on the matter, that a person whose registration is entered in the register obtained registration by means of any false or fraudulent representation or declaration, either oral or written, the Council shall order that his registration be cancelled.

(2) The provisions of this Part respecting the procedures of the Discipline Committee apply to a hearing held by the Council under subsection (1).

Surrender of certificates **73**(1) If the registration of a professional member, licensee, permit holder or certificate holder has been cancelled or suspended under this Part, he shall forthwith surrender to the Registrar any certificate, licence, permit, stamp or seal issued to him.

(2) If the registration of a professional member, licensee, permit holder or certificate holder has been cancelled under this Part, the registration shall not be reinstated in the register except by order of the Council, the Court or the Court of Appeal.

(3) No order shall be made under subsection (2) within 1 year after

(a) the date on which the registration was cancelled, or

(b) if an order was granted staying the imposition of a punishment imposed by the Council and the punishment is later confirmed by the Court or the Court of Appeal, the date on which the Court or the Court of Appeal made its order confirming the punishment.

(4) A member of the Council who is a member of a committee of inquiry appointed pursuant to the regulations to consider an application under this Part for reinstatement of registration may participate in or vote at any proceedings of the Council under this section, and the Registrar and the Association's solicitor may participate in those proceedings.

Misrepresentation of status **74** The conduct of a person who is or was registered as a professional member, licensee, permit holder or certificate holder who represents or holds out that he is registered and in good standing while his registration is suspended or cancelled may be dealt with as being unprofessional conduct in accordance with this Part.

75 After a finding or order is made by the Discipline Committee, the Council, the Court or the Court of Appeal under this Part, the name of the investigated person may be published in accordance with regulations.

Publication

PART 6
GENERAL

76(1) A professional member, licensee or restricted practitioner shall sign and stamp or seal all documents or records in accordance with the regulations.

Use of stamp or seal

(2) No person other than a professional member, licensee, permit holder or certificate holder shall use a stamp or seal issued by the Registrar under this Act.

77(1) The relationship between a permit holder or certificate holder engaged in the practice of engineering, geology or geophysics and a person receiving the professional services of the permit holder or certificate holder is subject to this Act, the regulations and any other law applicable to the relationship between a professional member and his client.

Liability to others

(2) The relationship of a professional member or licensee to a permit holder, whether as member, shareholder or employee of the permit holder, does not affect, modify or diminish the application of this Act, the regulations and by-laws

    (a)   to him personally as a professional member or licensee, or

    (b)   to the relationship between the professional member and his client.

78(1) A certificate purporting to be signed by the Registrar and stating that a named person was or was not, on a specified day or during a specified period,

Registrar's certificate

    (a)   a professional member, licensee or certificate holder, or

    (b)   an officer of the Association or a member of the Council

shall be admitted in evidence as prima facie proof of the facts stated in it without proof of the Registrar's appointment or signature.

(2) A certificate purporting to be signed by the Registrar and stating that a named corporation, partnership or other association of persons was or was not, on a specified day or during a specified period, a permit holder or certificate holder shall be admitted in evidence as prima facie proof of the facts stated in it without proof of the Registrar's appointment or signature.

Protection
from liability

79(1) No action lies against

(a)   any person conducting a preliminary investigation, a member of the Discipline Committee, the Practice Review Board, the Council or the Board of Examiners, the Registrar, the Association or any person acting on the instructions of any of them, or

(b)   any member, officer or employee of the Association

for anything done by him in good faith and in purporting to act under this Act, the regulations or the by-laws.

(2) No action for defamation may be founded on a communication that consists of or pertains to a complaint regarding the conduct of a professional member, licensee, permit holder, certificate holder or member-in-training, if the communication is published to or by

(a)   the Association,

(b)   a member of the Council, the Discipline Committee, the Practice Review Board or the Board of Examiners,

(c)   a person conducting a preliminary investigation,

(d)   an officer or employee of the Association, or

(e)   a person acting on the instructions of any of them

in good faith in the course of investigating the complaint or in the course of any proceedings under Part 5 relating to the complaint.

PART 7
PROHIBITIONS AND PENALTIES

Practice
prohibitions

80(1)A person whose registration as a professional engineer, professional geologist, professional geophysicist, licensee, permit holder or certificate holder is cancelled or suspended under this Act shall not, without the consent of the Council, engage in the practice of engineering, geology or geophysics, as the case may be, or directly or indirectly associate himself or itself in the practice of engineering, geology or geophysics with any other professional member, licensee, permit holder or certificate holder.

(2) No professional engineer, professional geologist, profes-

sional geophysicist, licensee, permit holder or certificate holder shall, except with the consent of the Council, associate in the practice of engineering, geology or geophysics, as the case may be, directly or indirectly with or employ in connection with his practice a person whose registration has been cancelled or suspended under this Act.

(3) The Council may permit a professional member, licensee, permit holder or certificate holder to employ in connection with his practice a person whose registration has been cancelled or suspended under this Act, but the employment shall be in the capacity and subject to the terms and conditions that are prescribed by the Council.

Penalties

81(1) Every person and every member, officer, employee or agent of a firm, partnership or other association of persons and of a corporation who contravenes Part 1, sections 28(2)(b), or 38(4) or this Part is guilty of an offence and liable on summary conviction

    (a)   for the 1st offence, to a fine of not more than $2000,

    (b)   for the 2nd offence, to a fine of not more than $4000, and

    (c)   for the 3rd and each subsequent offence, to a fine of not more than $6000 or to imprisonment for a term of not more than 6 months or to both a fine and imprisonment.

(2) A prosecution under this section may be commenced within 2 years after the commission of the alleged offence, but not afterwards.

Onus of proof

82 In a prosecution under this Act, the burden of proving that a person is a professional engineer, professional geologist, professional geophysicist, licensee, permit holder or certificate holder is on the accused.

PART 8
TRANSITIONAL AND CONSEQUENTIAL

Registration continued

83(1) In this Part, "former Act" means *The Engineering and Related Professions Act*, being chapter 124 of the Revised Statutes of Alberta 1970.

(2) An individual who holds a certificate of registration as a registered member under section 23 of the former Act is deemed to be a professional engineer, professional geologist or professional geophysicist, as the case may be, and the holder of an annual certificate under this Act.

305

(3) A permit holder that holds a permit under section 22 of the former Act is deemed to be a permit holder and the holder of a permit under this Act.

(4) An individual who holds a certificate of registration as a licensee under section 23 of the former Act is deemed to be a licensee and the holder of a licence under this Act.

(5) A joint firm that holds a certificate of authorization under section 20.4 of the former Act is deemed to be a certificate holder under this Act.

(6) A restricted practitioner who holds a certificate of authorization under section 20.7 of the former Act is deemed to be a certificate holder under this Act.

(7) The Registrar shall, in the appropriate register established pursuant to this Act,

> (a) register the names of those individuals referred to in subsection (2) and the names of those permit holders referred to in subsection (3), and
>
> (b) unless the Council otherwise directs in a particular case, register the names of those individuals and firms referred to in subsections (4), (5) and (6).

Council
members
continued

84 The members of the council of the Association elected under the former Act are deemed to be members of the Council under this Act, elected for the same periods and holding the same offices.

Applications
for
registration
continued

85 An application for registration made but not concluded before the coming into force of this Act shall be dealt with under the former Act.

Discipline
proceedings
continued

86 Any complaints or discipline proceedings that were commenced but not concluded before the coming into force of this Act shall be concluded under the former Act as though this Act had not come into force.

Amends
1980 c58

87 *The Architects Act, 1980 is amended by striking out "The Engineering and Related Professions Act" wherever it occurs in the following provisions and substituting "The Engineering, Geological and Geophysical Professions Act":*

section 3(1), (2) and (3);
section 17(1);
section 18(2).

Amends
RSA 1970
c62

88 *The Condominium Property Act is amended in section 8(1)(b)*

306

> (a)   *by striking out "The Engineering and Related Professions*

Act" wherever it appears and substituting "The Engineering, Geological and Geophysical Professions Act", and

(b) *in subclause (iv) by striking out* "professional engineering" *and substituting* "the practice of engineering".

89 *The Department of Housing and Public Works Act is amended in section 21.1(1) as enacted by section 78 of The Architects Act, 1980 by striking out "The Engineering and Related Professions Act" and substituting "The Engineering, Geological and Geophysical Professions Act".*

Amends
1975(2) c13

90 *The Drainage Districts Act is amended in section 27(3) by striking out "The Engineering and Related Professions Act" and substituting "The Engineering, Geological and Geophysical Professions Act".*

Amends
RSA 1970
c115

91 *The Irrigation Act is Amended in section 39(5) by striking out "The Engineering and Related Professions Act" and substituting "The Engineering, Geological and Geophysical Professions Act".*

Amends
RSA 1970
c192

92 *The Licensing of Trades and Businesses Act is amended in section 3(b) by striking out "The Engineering and Related Professions Act" and substituting "The Engineering, Geological and Geophysical Professions Act".*

Amends
RSA 1970
c207

93 *The Municipal Government Act is amended by adding the following between sections 214 and 215:*

Amends
RSA 1970
c246

214.3 Section 214 does not empower a council to make a by-law that has the effect of requiring a professional engineer, licensee, permit holder or certificate holder under *The Engineering, Geological and Geophysical Professions Act* to obtain a licence to engage in the practice of engineering or to carry on the practice or profession of a professional engineer in the municipality.

94 *The Alberta Uniform Building Standards Act is amended in sections 4.3 and 4.4. as enacted by section 80 of The Architects Act, 1980*

Amends
1973 c85

(a) *by striking out "The Engineering and Related Professions Act" wherever it occurs and substituting "The Engineering, Geological and Geophysical Professions Act", and*

(b) *by adding* "or licensee" *after* "professional engineer" *wherever it occurs.*

Amends
RSA 1970
c388

95 *The Water Resources Act is amended in section 2(1), clause 9.1 by striking out "The Engineering and Related Professions Act" and substituting "The Engineering, Geological and Geophysical Professions Act".*

Repeals
RSA 1970
c124

96 *The Engineering and Related Professions Act is repealed on Proclamation.*

Coming into
force

97 This Act comes into force on Proclamation.

TABLE OF ABBREVIATIONS TO CASE AND STATUTE CITATIONS THROUGHOUT TEXT

CANADA:

Reports
C.C.L.T.   Canadian Cases on the Law of Torts
C.P.R.   Canadian Patent Reports
D.L.R.   Dominion Law Reports
Ex. C.R.   Exchequer Court Reports
O.L.R.   Ontario Law Reports
O.R.   Ontario Reports
O.W.N.   Ontario Weekly Notes
S.C.R.   Supreme Court Reports
W.W.R.   Western Weekly Reports
A.C.W.S.   All Canada Weekly Summaries

(Revised) Statutes
R.S.A.   Alberta
R.S.B.C.   British Columbia
R.S.C.   Canada
R.S.M.   Manitoba
R.S.Nfld.   Newfoundland
R.S.N.S.   Nova Scotia
R.S.O.   Ontario
R.S.P.E.I.   Prince Edward Island
R.S.S.   Saskatchewan
R.S.N.B.   New Brunswick
R.O.N.W.T.   Northwest Territories
R.O.Y.T.   Yukon

UNITED KINGDOM:
App. Cas.   Appeal Cases
All E.R.   All England Reports
E.R.   English Reports
A.C.   Appeal Cases
W.L.R.   Weekly Law Reports
C.A.   Court of Appeal
K.B.   King's Bench Division
P.D.   Probate Division
Exch.   Exchequer
R.P.C.   Reports of Patent Case
Ch.   Chancery Division

309

SELECTED REFERENCES

Laidlaw, Young & Dick: Engineering law, Fifth Edition, 1958. 1958.

Waddams: Products Liability. 1974.

Smyth/Soberman: The Law and Business Administration in Canada, Third Edition, 1976

Goldsmith: Canadian Building Contracts, Second Edition, 1976.

Macklem and Bristow: Mechanics' Liens in Canada, Fourth Edition, 1978.

Hudson's Building and Engineering Contracts, Tenth Edition. London, 1970.

Keating: Building Contracts. London, 1978.

Creswell: The Law Relating to Building and Engineering Contracts, Sixth Edition. 1957.

Fox: Canadian Patent Law and Practice, Fourth Edition. 1969.

Fox: The Canadian Law of Trade Marks and Unfair Competition, Third Edition. 1972.

Fox: The Canadian Law of Copyright and Industrial Designs, Second Edition. 1967.

SAMPLE
CASE
STUDIES

The following hypothetical cases are included for study purposes only.

1   Creative Developments Ltd. ("Creative") entered into a contract with Sharp & Associates, Architects, for the design and preparation of contract documentation necessary to construct a twenty-storey office building of unique design. Sharp & Associates also agreed to perform inspection services during the construction of the office building.

Sharp & Associates prepared a conceptual design, and Jason Biggar's engineering consulting firm agreed to prepare the detailed structural design for the project.

Jason Biggar's firm was retained. However, it appeared that the firm's very busy schedule would not permit Jason Biggar sufficient time to attend to the design personally. Biggar turned the matter over to one of his employee engineers, John Abel, a recent engineering graduate in whom Jason Biggar had great confidence.

Abel completed his design and Biggar reviewed it. Although he had not checked all of Abel's calculations in detail, Biggar concluded that the design appeared satisfactory. Biggar then affixed his professional engineer's stamp to the design drawings and submitted them to Sharp & Associates. Sharp & Associates included Biggar's structural-design drawings in the contract documents for the construction of the project.

Creative entered into a construction contract with Sound Construction Ltd. to erect the office building. During the course of construction, the partly finished building collapsed, resulting in considerable damage to Creative's property. As well, there was a substantial delay in the completion of the office building. Creative conducted an investigation as to the cause of the collapse, and they obtained the opinion of another consulting engineering firm. The second firm thought that the structural design, as supplied by Jason Biggar, was inadequate in the circumstances.

The investigation also revealed that Sharp & Associates had retained Subsurface Wizards Inc., soils experts, to carry out soils tests, prior to Abel's preparation of the structural design. Creative subsequently obtained an opinion from another firm specializing in soil tests; the second firm concluded that many more tests should have been performed by Subsurface Wizards Inc. As well, the second firm thought, the results of the tests that were performed were "borderline": the employee of Subsurface Wizards Inc., who prepared the original report, had very seriously erred in concluding that the test results were satisfactory. The second soils experts also concluded that the subsurface conditions resulted in serious settlement on one side of the building during construction; that settlement contributed to the collapse.

Explain the potential liabilities arising from the preceding set of facts *in tort law*. Discuss, with reasons, a likely outcome of the matter.

2   Jason Smith is a twenty-five per cent shareholder and director of Skylift Inc., a company engaged in commercial helicopter services in Ontario.

James Johnson, a friend of Smith's, sought Smith's technical and financial support in forming another commercial helicopter business in British Columbia. Smith agreed to participate, and acquired a fifty-per-cent shareholder interest in the second company, known as Johnson's Skyhooks Limited.

Eventually, Skylift Inc. became interested in purchasing all of the assets of Johnson's Skyhooks Limited. Jason Smith was in no way involved in promoting the purchase of Johnson's Skyhooks Limited until the proposed purchase was presented to the five-man board of directors of Skylift Inc. for approval. At that meeting, Smith did not disclose his shareholder interest in Johnson's Skyhooks Limited. But

Smith cast the deciding vote in passing the directors' resolution to authorize the asset purchase. Shortly after the asset purchase had been finalized, the board of directors of Skylift Inc. became aware of Jason Smith's shareholder interest in Johnson's Skyhooks Limited. On further investigation, the board concluded that the price paid for the assets of Johnson's Skyhooks Limited was unreasonably high.

What action might the board of directors and shareholders of Skylift Inc. take in the circumstances? State, with reasons, the likely outcome of the action.

3   Acme Ltd., a manufacturing company, wished to expand its business by purchasing the business of one of its competitors, Jones Brothers Limited. The president of Acme met with the president of Jones Brothers to discuss the possibility of the purchase. At the conclusion of the meeting, both presidents felt that the matter was worth pursuing. The president of Acme presented a letter to the president of Jones Brothers:

Jones Brothers Limited,   December 28, 1979.
Toronto, Ontario.

Attention: Harold Jones, Esq., President

Dear Sirs:

This letter will confirm our interest in purchasing, and your interest in selling, all of the assets, undertaking and business of Jones Brothers Limited for a total price of approximately $1,000,000, subject to the preparation of audited financial statements of Jones Brothers Limited and subject to our further negotiation of terms and conditions to apply to such sale, pending the finalization of which we agree to enter into a mutually satisfactory agreement to so acquire the business of Jones Brothers Limited.

If you are in agreement with the contents of this letter, would you please execute the duplicate enclosed copy and return.

Yours very truly,
Acme Ltd.
Per: James, Finnigan, President   313

As requested, the president of Jones Brothers signed and returned, by personal delivery, the enclosed copy of the letter.

Several weeks went by and the auditors of Jones Brothers Limited completed an audit of the company's books. In addition, there was a second meeting between Mr. Jones and Mr. Finnigan. At the meeting, Mr. Jones strongly recommended that, if Acme Ltd. did, in fact, purchase Jones Brothers Limited, Acme ought to seriously consider entering into a lease of desirable warehouse space located next door to Jones Brothers in order to accommodate Jones Brothers' expanding inventories. Mr. Jones emphasized that he had discussed the lease with the landlord; the landlord had informed him that, if a lease were to be signed, it must be signed not later than 29 January 1980. Eventually, the president of Jones Brothers Limited wrote the following letter to Acme Ltd.:

> Acme Ltd.,   January 25, 1980
> Toronto, Ontario.
>
> Attention: James Finnigan, Esq.,
>
> Dear Sirs:
>
> Jones Brothers Ltd. hereby agrees to sell to Acme Ltd. all of the assets, undertaking and business of Jones Brothers Limited for a total purchase price of $1,000,000, subject to the terms and conditions of the attached form of agreement, to which is attached a current audited financial statement of Jones Brothers Limited.
>
> This offer shall be firm and irrevocable for a period of twenty days from the date of this letter and your agreement to purchase our business in accordance with these terms and conditions will be sufficiently evidenced by your signing the enclosed copy of this letter. Upon receipt of your acknowledgement we can then arrange a meeting for the purpose of executing the attached agreement.
>
> Yours very truly,
> Jones Brothers Limited

Mr. Jones personally delivered the letter to Mr. Finnigan on 25 January 1980.

On 28 January 1980, Mr. Jones mailed a letter to Mr.

Finnigan revoking the offer to sell the business to Acme.

On 29 January 1980, Mr. Finnigan, as president of Acme Ltd., executed a two-year lease of warehouse space next door to Jones Brothers Limited. The warehouse was the building that Mr. Jones and Mr. Finnigan had previously discussed. Had it not been for Acme's interest in purchasing Jones Brothers Limited, Mr. Finnigan would not have executed the lease.

Mr. Finnigan received Jones's revocation on 31 January 1980. Immediately after receiving the revocation, Mr. Finnigan signed the duplicate of the letter dated 25 January 1980, and personally delivered it to Mr. Jones. Mr. Finnigan adamantly insisted that, in the circumstances of all of the correspondence and the meetings that had taken place between them, Jones Brothers Limited was obligated to either sell its business to Acme Ltd., or to assume the lease obligations and make all payments to the landlord.

a. Explain the nature of the legal relationships between Acme Ltd. and Jones Brothers Limited when:
i. the letter of 28 December 1979 had been signed and returned by Mr. Jones;
ii. the letter of 25 January 1980 had been signed and returned by Mr. Finnigan.
b. Discuss the merits of Mr. Finnigan's claim that Jones Brothers Limited was obligated to sell its business or assume the warehouse-lease obligations.

4   A professional engineer entered into a written employment contract with a Toronto-based civil-engineering design firm. His contract of employment stated that, for a period of five years after the termination of his employment, he would not practise professional engineering either alone, or in conjunction with, or as an employee, agent, principal, or shareholder of an engineering firm anywhere within the City of Toronto.

During his employment with the design firm, the employee engineer dealt directly with many of the firm's clients. He became extremely skilled in preparing cost estimates, and he established a good reputation for himself within the City of Toronto.

The engineer terminated his employment with the consulting firm after three years, and immediately set up his own engineering firm in another part of the City of Toronto. His previous employers then commenced a court action for an injunction, claiming that he had breached his contract and *should not* be permitted to practise within the City limits.

Do you think the engineer's former employers should succeed in an action against him? In answering, state the principles a court would apply in arriving at a decision.

5 Clearwater Limited, a process-design and manufacturing company, entered into an equipment-supply contract with Pulverized Pulp Limited. Clearwater agreed to design, supply, and install a cleaning system at Pulverized Pulp's Ontario mill for a contract price of $200,000. The specifications for the cleaning system stated that the equipment was to remove ninety-five per cent of prescribed chemicals from the mill's liquid effluent in order to comply with the requirements of the environmental control authorities in the area in which the mill was located.

In addition, the signed contract between Clearwater and Pulverized Pulp contained a warranty provision whereby Clearwater stated it would, for a period of one year from the date of installation, repair defects in the process and equipment arising from faulty design or parts or workmanship. But Clearwater accepted no responsibility whatsoever for any indirect or consequential damage arising as a result of the contract.

The cleaning system installed by Clearwater did not meet the specifications. In fact, only seventy per cent of the prescribed chemicals were removed from the effluent. As a result, Pulverized Pulp Limited was fined $10,000, and was shut down by the environmental control authorities. Clearwater made several attempts to remedy the situation by altering the process and cleaning equipment, but without success.

Pulverized Pulp eventually contacted another equipment supplier. For an additional cost of $250,000, the second supplier successfully redesigned and installed remedial process equipment, that cleaned the effluent to the satisfaction of the environmental authorities, in accordance with the original contract specifications between Clearwater and Pulverized Pulp.

Explain and discuss what claim Pulverized Pulp Limited can make against Clearwater Limited in the circumstances.

INDEX

Acceptance 61-65
Agency 119, 120
Appellant 9
Arbitration 153-155
Assignment 60
Assignment of copyright 198
Assignment of industrial
    designs 199
Assignment of patent rights 194
Associated corporations 15

Battle of the forms 64
Benefits 59-60
Bid-rigging 78, 171, 172, 173
Bonds 149-151
Breach of contract 105-112
Bribes 131, 132
Building permits 125

Capacity 75, 76
Certifier 133-134, 162
Certificate of authorization 183
Civil Code of Quebec 8
Civil litigation 9
Client-engineer agreement
    119-123
Code of Ethics 187-189
Codes (building) 124, 125
Combines Investigation Act 24,
    77, 171-175
Common law 2
Common-law notice of
    termination 207
Competition 78
Compliance with the law 123
Concurrent tortfeasors 34, 39,
    127-130
Condition 105
Consideration 69-74
Conspiracy 173
Constitution 3-7
Contract elements 59

Construction contracts 133-151
Copyright 197, 198
Copyright in engineering
    plans 198
Corporate veil 13, 16
Corporation 11-25, 76
Cost-plus contracts 144, 145
Court system 7, 8
Credibility of witnesses 57, 97
Creditor 9

Damages 105-108
Debtor 9
Defamation 53, 54
Defendant 9
Delay claims 149
Design-build contracts 146
Directors 21-25
Discharge of contracts 101-104
Disciplinary hearings 180, 181
Disclosure of conflicts 25
Discrimination in employ-
    ment 209
Drawings 140
Drunks 75
Duress 87
Duty of confidence (trade
    secrets) 202
Duty of honesty 131, 132

Economic loss 45-47
Effect of lien claim 160
Emergency 134
Engineer as contract adminis-
    trator 136-149
Engineer's remuneration 120
Engineer's standard of care
    (tort) 28-36
Engineer's standard of care
    (contract) 127
Equitable estoppel 70-74
Essential term 105

Estimated fee   120-122
Exemption clauses   100-102,
   109, 113-117, 123
Expert witness   57, 58

Fast-track   148
Force majeure   102-104
Form of contracts   81-83
Financial-guarantee bond   166
Fraud   131
Fraudulent misrepresentation   84
Frustration   102-104
Fundamental breach   113-117

Gifts to government employees
   132
Governing law   63, 64
Guarantee   9, 82
Guaranteed maximum price
   145, 146

Historical basis of common
   law   1
Holdback   158-164

Implied terms   98-100
Incorporation   19, 20
Indemnification   9
Industrial designs   198, 199
Industrial property   191
Infringement of patents   193
Infringement of trade-mark   197
Injunction   111, 112
Inspection services   136-138
Intent   67, 68
Interference claims   149
Interpretation   97, 98
Intervention with contractor   138
Irrevocable offers   61, 62

Joint venture   25
Judge-made law   2

Kickbacks   131, 132

Labour laws   205-211
Legality   77-80
Legislation   2, 3
Letters of credit   151
Letters of intent   67, 68
Liability insurance   39, 119,
   183
Liability of directors   23-25
Libel   53
Licensing requirements   78, 79
Lien claims by engineers
   167-169
Limitation periods   48-53, 127
Litigation   9
Lump-sum contracts   144
Lunatics   75

Mechanics' lien legislation
   157-170
Minors   75
Misleading advertising   171,
   172
Misrepresentation   85, 86
Mistake   89-95
Mitigation of damages   109

Negligent misrepresentation   31,
   86
Negligent design   32
Non-competition agreement   80
Nuisance   54, 55

Objects of incorporation   20
Obligations   59
Occupiers' liability   54
Offer   61
Officers   21
Option contract   62
Overlap with architectural
   services   184-187

Parol evidence rule 97, 98
Partnership 11, 14, 17, 18
Patents 191-195
Penalty clauses 109
Plaintiff 9
Planning Act 124-126
Prime contract 147, 148
Private (closely-held) corporations 20, 21
Private law 8
Privity of contract 9, 27
Products liability 30, 40-45
Project management 146
Proof 57
Public file 74
Public law 8
Public offering companies 20, 21
Public policy 79, 112

Quantum meruit 109, 110
Question of concurrent liability in tort and contract 127-130

Records 140
Rectification 89
Registered-user agreements 197
Release of holdback 157-159
Reliance on corporate official 76
Remedies 107-112
Repudiation 107
Respondent 9
Restraint of trade 79, 80

Safety laws 124, 125
Seal (of consideration) 69, 70
Seal (engineer's) 179
Secret commissions 131, 132
Shareholder 21
Slander 53

Sole proprietorship 11
Specific performance 111, 112
Specifications 140
Standard-form engineering agreements 122
Statute law 2, 3
Statute of Frauds 81-83
Statutes governing engineering 177-189
Stipulated price 144
Strict liability 36
Subcontracts 147
Subdivision control 125
Substantial compliance 110, 111
Substantial performance 162

Tax considerations 15, 16
Tendering (mistake) 89-95
Tendering process 142, 143
Termination of contract 101
Theory of precedent 2
Tort principles 28
Trade associations 174, 175
Trade-marks 196, 197
Trade secrets 200-202
Trust fund 167
Types of construction contracts 143-146

Undue influence 87
Unilateral mistake 89
Unit-price contract 144

Vicarious Liability 37-39

Waiver of lien rights 164
Warranty 105
Workers' compensation 45, 208